M000118694

Contents

www.britainonview.com

2003-2004 YHA ACCOMMODATION GUIDE
Published for the Youth Hostels Association (England & Wales) by Emap Active Create
© Youth Hostels Association (England & Wales)   Registered Charity Number: 301657   ISBN 0-904530-25-6

CREDITS
Printed on chlorine-free paper from a sustainable source by **Pindar plc** (Scarborough). Colour origination by **G&E 2000** (Peterborough)

For YHA
Editorial co-ordinator: **Liz Evans**
email: domking@yha.org.uk

Emap Active Create
Emap Active Ltd
Homenene House
Orton Centre
Peterborough
PE2 5UW
email: active.create@emap.com

Map illustrations: **Jeremy Ashcroft** (except p173-5)

Pictures: **www.britainonview.com** & courtesy of **YHA**

Public transport information provided by **Barry Doe, travel consultant**

For all the latest YHA news visit www.yha.org.uk

Welcome to the new YHA Guide, full of ideas, information and inspiration about how you can get the best from YHA.

This Guide will help you find hostels which suit your needs, whoever you are. You'll also find details of other ways in which you can get more out of your membership. If you're stuck for ideas for a different holiday or short break, look for details of activity breaks. If you're bringing a party to a hostel, you'll find information on group facilities and the educational support we can offer. For those who would like to play a more active part in the Association's work, volunteering may be the answer and you'll find out how you can get involved.

YHA is not just about accommodation: it's about people. The unique, friendly atmosphere of a Youth Hostel is part of your experience, and information from other travellers and hostel managers helps make a holiday more enjoyable. You'll find members' stories inside for inspiration and you'll receive even more free advice when you stay with us.

There is something for everyone in YHA. We hope you will be moved to learn about the countryside, that you'll share our enthusiasm for the world around us and care for its future. But above all, we hope this Guide will help you to enjoy yourself and get more from the experience of staying with YHA.

Happy hostelling,

Chris Boulton
Chairman

YHA (England and Wales) Ltd.
Registered Office: Trevelyan House, Dimple Road, Matlock, Derbyshire, DE4 3YH
Tel: 01629 592600 Fax: 01629 592702 web: www.yha.org.uk
Company No. 282555 A Company limited by guarantee
Registered Charity No: 306122

HOSTELLING
INTERNATIONAL

100% Recycled Paper

The Youth Hostels of England & Wales by region

1. Northumberland & North Pennines
2. Lake District
3. Yorkshire & South Pennines
4. North West cities & Peak District
5. Wales
6. Heart of England
7. East of England
8. South West England
9. South East England
10. London

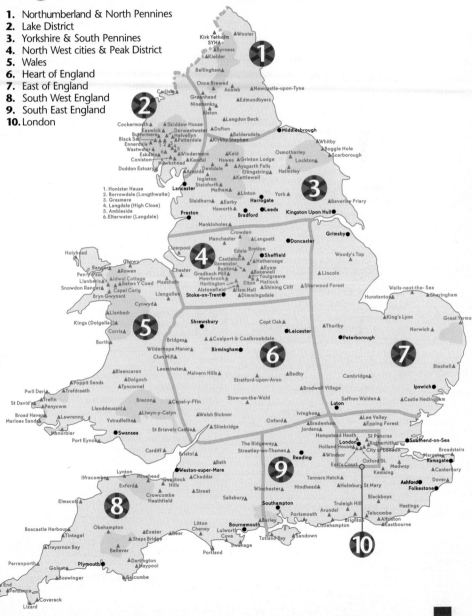

5

Welcome to YHA

Now that you are a YHA member, you are entitled to a wide range of benefits, not least a very warm welcome whenever you stay at a Youth Hostel. Read on to discover how to make the most of your membership and what you can expect from YHA.

Your membership

You already enjoy the benefits of individual YHA membership, but are you aware of all we have to offer, including...

Family membership: Joining as a family makes sound economic sense – when one or both parents join, children between five and 17 are enrolled free. Turn to page 14 to see how your family can enjoy a holiday with the YHA and its child-friendly facilities.

Life membership: Invest in YHA membership for life and choose to pay in a single sum or five annual instalments.

Group membership: This enables formally constituted groups and organisations to stay at Youth Hostels worldwide. Your membership card can be used for groups of five or more (10 or more outside England and Wales). To learn more about what YHA can offer, turn to page 16.

International membership: The International Youth Hostel Federation sets minimum standards for hostels. YHA members are welcome at these hostels (see panel) plus those in other affiliated countries. For more details see page 32. If you are visiting England and Wales from abroad, either buy membership at home or International Membership on arrival.

Australia
Australian Youth Hostel Association
Tel: (61) (2) 9565 1699 Fax: (61) (2) 9565 1325
Email: yha@yha.org.au Web: www.yha.com.au

Canada
Hostelling International
Tel: (1) (613) 237 7884 Fax: (1) (613) 237 7868
Email: info@hihostels.ca Web: www.hihostels.ca

France
Fédération Unie des Auberges de Jeunesse (FUAJ)
Tel: (33) (0) 1 44 89 87 27 Fax: (33) (0) 1 44 89 87 10
Email: fuaj@fuaj.org Web: www.fuaj.org

Germany
Deutsches Jugendherbergswerk (DJH)
Tel: (49) (5231) 99 360 Fax: (49) (5231) 99 3666
Email: hauptverband@djh.org Web: www.djh.de

Republic of Ireland
Irish Youth Hostel Association (An Óige)
Tel: (353) (1) 830 4555 Fax: (353) (1) 830 5808
Email: mailbox@anoige.ie Web: www.irelandyha.org

Northern Ireland
Hostelling International Northern Ireland (HINI)
Tel: (44) (28) 9032 4733 Fax: (44) (28) 9043 9699
Email: info@hini.org.uk Web: www.hini.org.uk

Italy
Associazione Italiana Alberghi per la Gioventù (AIG)
Tel: (39) (06) 487 1152 Fax: (39) (06) 488 0492
Email: aig@uni.net Web: www.hostels-aig.org

Japan
Japan Youth Hostels (JYH)
Tel: (81) (3) 3288 1417 Fax: (81) (3) 3288 1248
Email: info@jyh.or.jp Web: www.jyh.or.jp

Netherlands
Dutch Youth Hostel Association (NJHC)
Tel: (31) (10) 264 6064 Fax: (31) (10) 264 6061
Email: info@njhc.org Web: www.njhc.org

New Zealand
Youth Hostels Association of New Zealand Inc (YHANZ)
Tel: (64) (3) 379 9970 Fax: (64) (3) 365 4476
Email: info@yha.org.nz Web: www.stayyha.com

Scotland
Scottish YHA (SYHA)
Tel: (44) 1786 891 400 Fax: (44) 1786 891 333
Email: info@syha.org.uk Web: www.syha.org.uk

South Africa
Hostelling International – South Africa (HISA)
Tel: (27) (21) 424 2511 Fax: (27) (21) 424 4119
Email: info@hisa.org.za Web: www.hisa.org.za

USA
Hostelling International – American Youth Hostels (HI-AYH)
Tel: (1) (202) 783 6161 Fax: (1) (202) 783 6171
Email: hiayhserv@hiayh.org Web: www.hiayh.org

For offers and discounts visit www.yha.org.uk

What do you get?

Individual YHA membership is valid for one year from the date of joining. It entitles you to:

- Stay in any of the varied Youth Hostels in England, Wales, Scotland and Ireland, as well as over 4,500 Youth Hostels worldwide.

- Take advantage of substantial discounts at local attractions, shops and other organisations to save yourself money (ask your chosen hostel about discounts available in the area).

- Receive Triangle magazine, which is packed with news and ideas to help you get the most from your stays.

- Information on a wide range of services, such as travel insurance, tailored to the needs of YHA members.

- Take part in hostel-based activities and make new friends (see page 30 for details).

- Make a difference by volunteering or contributing to the governance of YHA.

HOW DO YOU APPLY?

With a credit or debit card:
Call 0870 770 8868

By post:
YHA (England & Wales), Trevelyan House, Dimple Road, Matlock, Derbyshire DE4 3YH

At the hostel:
Simply join when you arrive at your chosen hostel

Via the web:
www.yha.org.uk
(you can also join at selected agents and tourist information centres)

The accommodation

Every time you stay in YHA accommodation, you will enjoy a different experience. From remote camping barns set in spectacular countryside to rambling Victorian mansions and modern, purpose-built venues, every hostel is unique. Our diverse range of accommodation falls into three groups:

Youth Hostels

You will stay in comfortable bunk-bedded rooms, shared with people of the same sex. Families may be able to book a room to themselves. You will be given laundered bed linen to make up your bed and pillows, duvets and blankets are provided. At most hostels, you will find a sitting area, self-catering kitchen, drying room and cycle store. Many offer a much wider range of facilities including a full meals service – check the individual hostel entries in the directory to see what each offers. The daytime access section also lists the minimum you can expect during the day and if you arrive without a reservation – more than this may be available, check when booking. Above all, we aim to make you very welcome.

Camping Barns

Converted farm buildings, camping barns offer simple self-catering accommodation. Facilities are generally basic but, as a minimum, you can expect one or more sleeping platforms, tables and benches for eating and preparing food, a supply of cold running water and a flush toilet. Many boast increased levels of comfort with hot water, showers and cooking facilities.

Bunkhouses

Similar to Youth Hostels, bunkhouses have bunks plus shared cooking and daytime facilities. They are mostly used by groups, although families and individuals are also welcome. Three bunkhouses are included in this guide: Blaencaron, Dolgoch and Tyncornel, all of which are in Wales.

For more information visit www.yha.org.uk

How to book

We have made our booking system as flexible as possible. Once you know your ideal Youth Hostel, simply get in touch. Here's how.

More than a week ahead: Call the Youth Hostel of your choice to check availability and your accommodation will be provisionally reserved. Although larger hostels can handle enquiries throughout the day, if you have chosen a smaller hostel, it's best to call before 10.00hrs or after 17.00hrs. You can also book via the secure server at **www.yha.org.uk** or write to, email or fax your chosen hostel. If your booking is less than £100, you will be asked to make full payment to secure your stay. If your booking is in excess of £100, you will be asked to pay a minimum £100 deposit. You can pay at most hostels by credit or debit card, or send a cheque made payable to YHA. For Youth Hostels in London, or other areas where there is a high demand for accommodation, you will be asked to pay in full for your stay, regardless of cost.

One week before: Call your chosen Youth Hostel. Reservations will be held until 18.00hrs on the day of your arrival unless an alternative time has been agreed or you can pay by credit card to secure your bed.

On the day: We strongly recommend you book your bed in advance. Although you can just turn up at

your chosen hostel on the day and present your membership card, you are advised to call ahead and check availability.

From one hostel to the next: Once you are on the hostelling trail, most hostels are able to book ahead for you using our booking system. Just ask at the reception desk about the Book A Bed Ahead scheme, giving details of your chosen hostel(s) and dates you wish to stay.

On a long-distance route: Let us help you book your trip. Simply call the Booking Bureau (tel: 0870 770 6113) with details of your itinerary and we will book your accommodation (and any other services you require, such as meals) on your behalf. For further details, see page 22.

As a group: Call our Group Reservations Department on 0870 770 6117 (see page 16).

A walking holiday: Call 0870 770 6113 (see page 22 for more details).

An activity holiday: YHA has two dedicated activity centres. Call Edale Youth Hostel (tel: 0870 770 5808) or Okehampton Youth Hostel

(tel: 0870 770 5978) (see page 28 for details). Activity breaks are also organised at other Youth Hostels. Triangle, the members' magazine, carries details or visit **www.yha.org.uk**

How to cancel your visit:
If you have to cancel your visit, please call the relevant Youth Hostel(s) as soon as possible. This is especially important in mountainous and remote areas – if you don't arrive at the hostel, police or rescue teams may be called out to look for you.

Getting a refund

Individual and families: As an individual or family member of YHA England and Wales, and other associations within the International Youth Hostel Federation, your booking is covered by the YHA's cancellation refund package. Under this scheme, the YHA will refund its members in respect of loss of charges paid to YHA for accommodation and meals not taken up, where you have been forced to cancel or curtail your journey, providing three day's notice has been given to the Youth Hostel(s) concerned. Every claim is subject to a small administrative fee. We recommend that you also hold a suitable travel insurance policy, including cancellation insurance, when you travel on a YHA holiday.

Activity holidays: Those run by the YHA are subject to

separate cancellation terms – you will find full details on the booking form and in information sent to participants before the holiday.

Group members: If you are making a group booking, we strongly recommend you take advantage of our cancellation refund package, available for a nominal charge. You will find full details on our group booking form or call our Group Reservations Department on 0870 770 6117.

Other breaks: Terms and conditions for Rent-a-Hostel, walking holidays, special interest holidays, packages and other products will vary – full details are always available on booking.

To apply: Request a refund application form from the hostel or Customer Services (tel: 0870 770 8868). Send this with supporting evidence (include copies of booking forms, invoices, receipts and medical certificates), to YHA National Accounts Office, YHA, PO Box 30, Trevelyan House, Dimple Road, Matlock, Derbyshire DE4 3JX.

Overnight prices

YHA aims to provide comfortable accommodation at an affordable cost. That's why, although overnight prices vary between hostels according to their facilities and location, you will always get great value for money. Some hostels provide private rooms and family rooms, for which you will be charged on a per room basis. Call your chosen hostel for the current charges and you will be quoted the price for a bed in a shared, single-sex room. Don't forget that you may be entitled to a concession (see page 19 for details). Prices change annually on March 1st and full details of prices and open dates for each hostel will be sent to you regularly, including current special offers.

Contact us

YHA would love to hear from you. If your stay in a Youth Hostel is perfect, let us know. If it isn't, tell us that too. Call, fax, write or email your comments.
Call: 0870 770 8868
Fax: 0870 770 6127
Write: YHA (England and Wales) Ltd, Trevelyan House, Dimple Road, Matlock, Derbyshire DE4 3YH
Email: customerservices@yha.org.uk
Visit: www.yha.org.uk

Our promise to you

YHA England and Wales has adopted the worldwide Hostelling International Assured Standards. This means that all hostels displaying the Hostelling International sign will provide the following standards:

Welcome: Above all, staff will be totally committed to welcoming and helping you. From the staff at our smallest hostels to YHA's chief executive, nearly everyone has participated in the tourism industry's Welcome Host training schemes in customer care. Hostel receptions will be open between 08.00hrs and 10.00hrs and 17.00hrs and 22.00hrs as a minimum. Your enquiries will be dealt with promptly and bookings can be made in advance.

Comfort: Your bed will be comfortable and linen provided. There will be sufficient hot showers, toilets and washbasins. The hostel will be well lit and noise levels both inside and outside of the hostel kept to an acceptable level.

Cleanliness: High standards of hygiene and cleanliness will be met throughout the hostel.

Security: YHA staff will do all they can to ensure your personal safety and the security of your belongings during your stay. Where appropriate, Youth Hostels provide secure lockers.

Privacy: Most accommodation is in rooms shared with others of the same sex, although some private and family rooms can be reserved. Proper levels of privacy will be provided in toilets, showers and washing areas.

Environmental standards: We are committed to improving our conservation of resources, particularly in the areas of purchasing, recycling and pollution, energy conservation, water conservation and transport.

For current prices visit www.yha.org.uk

How to use this guide

This guide has been specifically designed to help you choose the right hostel every time you book a stay. As well as a detailed entry for each Youth Hostel, bunkhouse and camping barn, the guide offers a wealth of information to ensure you get full value from your YHA membership.

Don't miss out!

To help you make the most of your membership, the guide includes details of the diverse range of opportunities available to you with YHA. How can you and your friends have a hostel all to yourselves? Which hostels offer facilities that cater for every member of your family? How can you volunteer to help YHA? What exciting activity breaks, special interest and educational school trips are on offer? The answers to all these questions, and plenty more, are detailed from page 12 onwards.

A star rating is also included to allow you to assess the standard of accommodation on offer at most hostels. Between one and five stars have been awarded according to the Hostel Standards set respectively by the English Tourism Council and Wales Tourist Board.

How to choose your ideal hostel

If you already know which hostel to stay in: Turn to the index on page 176 and then to the hostel's individual entry. An index of camping barns is on page 177.

If you know which region you want to visit: The directory is divided into regional sections. These are shown on the map on page 4 and indexed on page 35. At the start of each section, you will find a regional map showing the location of all the Youth Hostels and camping barns. On the subsequent pages you will find detailed descriptions of the hostels and barns listed alphabetically.

If you know the type of hostel you want: Youth Hostels are wonderful places to stay and you'll be welcome at any Youth Hostel, camping barn or bunkhouse. If you're travelling with your family or a group, your requirements may be more particular. To help you find your ideal hostel fast, each hostel entry has a colour-coded suitability rating. If you're looking for a hostel that's particularly suitable for families or groups, a Camping Barn, or you want a city, traditional, coastal or rural break, use this rating – a key at the top of every page shows you what colour represents each category. Then simply flick through the directory to find hostels that match your requirements.

If you know what facilities you require: The guide has been designed to give you as much information about the hostels' facilities as possible. Perhaps you require a family room, education package, classroom or hostel to rent. Or do you need to reach the hostel using public transport, prefer a non-smoking policy or want 24-hour access to the Youth Hostel? Simply decide which facilities are essential to your stay and look through the directory to discover which hostel fits the bill. You will also find a list of hostels that offer camping on page 21 and those with facilities for the less able on page 18.

To make a booking visit www.yha.org.uk

The individual Youth Hostel entries

Each Youth Hostel entry provides full details to help you decide whether the accommodation will suit your specific needs. Here's how to extract as much information as possible, using a sample directory entry:

1 BEST FOR RATING
The colour-coded boxes indicate the hostel's suitability for various types of stays. You will find the key at the top of every page.

2 STAR RATING
Most hostels have been awarded between one (lowest grading) and four (highest grading) ETC stars or up to five WTB stars. Camping barns and bunkhouses are not covered by this scheme.

3 CONTACT DETAILS
All the contact details you need to communicate with your chosen hostel are here.

4 DESCRIPTION
Read the description for a taste of the hostel, including attractions within easy visiting distance.

5 LOCATION
Find the exact location of the hostel with the Ordnance Survey (Landranger series) map number and six-figure grid reference.

6 GREAT FOR/YOU NEED TO KNOW
Is this hostel really the right one for you? Make up your mind here, where we tell you any other facts we feel you should know before you visit.

7 ACCOMMODATION
The number of beds will tell you how large or small the hostel is. The size of the rooms will also let you know what to expect of your sleeping accommodation.

8 SPECIAL FACILITIES
Some hostels boast family rooms, offering families a room to themselves that's accessible throughout the day once you've booked in (for details, turn to page 14). If you are planning a group stay, you may want to know if the hostel has a classroom and/or education packages (see page 16 for details). This section also tells you if the hostel is part of the Rent-a-Hostel scheme (see page 26).

9 FACILITIES
The hostel's facilities are listed, including the minimum you can expect to be available in the daytime or if you arrive without a reservation (additional facilities may be available during the day to those with reservations – call your chosen hostel to find out). Access to bedrooms is normally available after 17.00hrs (family rooms unrestricted). Rooms must be vacated by 10.00hrs. In the evenings, Youth Hostels are generally open until 23.00hrs with lights out at 23.30hrs, although larger hostels are more flexible.

10 NO SMOKING
Many Youth Hostels have areas set aside for members to smoke. If this is not the case at your chosen hostel, this symbol will be displayed in the entry. Please respect non-smoking policies during your stay for the comfort and safety of others.

11 MEALS
Discover whether the hostel offers a full menu of meals or self-catering accommodation only. Please book your meals in advance (ask the hostel staff for last ordering times). Self-catering kitchens will be equipped with a minimum of ring hobs, a grill, kettle and toaster, with pots, pans, crockery and cutlery provided.

(2)

(1) ●● BYRNESS ☆
(3) 7 Otterburn Green, Byrness, Newcastle-upon-Tyne, Northumberland NE19 1TS;
reservations@yha.org.uk
Tel: 0870 770 5740 Fax: 0870 770 5740
Advance booking: 0870 770 6113

(4) Two adjoining Forestry Commission houses have been converted to create a small, basic hostel that's ideal for exploring the northern part of the Northumberland National Park. Just five miles from the Scottish Border, it lies on the Pennine Way in the foothills of the Cheviot Hills. From its doorstep, you can walk in practically every direction but don't miss out on a well-earned rest in the garden where red squirrels and roe deer are often seen.

(5) Location: OS 80, GR 764027.

(6) Great for... keen walkers who don't mind basic facilities.
You need to know... bring plenty of provisions as only limited supplies are available 0.5 mile away.

(7) Accommodation: 22 beds: 2x2- and 3x6-bed rooms.

(8) Family Rooms: No. Rent-a-Hostel: Yes.
Classroom: No. Education packages: No.

(9) Facilities: Lounge/games room, self-catering kitchen, showers, cycle store and garden. Daytime access: Restricted. **(10)**

(11) Meals: Self-catering only. Packed lunches available if pre-booked.

(12) Reception open: 17.00hrs.

(13) Getting there: Turn off A68 at sign for Byrness.

(14) Parking: Yes.

(15) Nearest other hostels: Bellingham 15 miles, Kielder 15 (by part-surfaced toll road), Kirk Yetholm 27, Wooler 28 (all by Pennine Way).

(16) Public transport: BUS: McEwans bus Edinburgh–Newcastle, daily except Sunday, National Express Edinburgh–Newcastle (pass close to Newcastle and Edinburgh Stations). FERRY: Newcastle 40 miles. RAIL: Morpeth 34 miles, Newcastle 40.
NATIONAL EXPRESS Byrness lay-by 0.25 mile.

12 RECEPTION OPEN
As soon as reception is open, you can book in.

13 GETTING THERE
Concise directions are given here (there are maps at the back of the book for hostels that are difficult to find). These instructions are as clear as possible but maps of all Youth Hostels can be requested when you book and are available on our website.

14 PARKING
Please observe any parking limitations shown here.

15 NEAREST OTHER HOSTELS
Explore the area by staying in a number of hostels. And don't forget that you can use the Book a Bed Ahead scheme to book other hostels during your stay.

16 PUBLIC TRANSPORT
We encourage our members to use public transport and a guide to services that will help you reach the hostel is given here. Once you arrive at the hostel, you will find more detailed information about the range of public transport in the area.

Now turn the page to discover just how much YHA has to offer

Flexible Breaks

Go! *As you please*

A vast network of Youth Hostels gives you the freedom to explore
England, Wales and beyond, whatever your needs might be.

Explore
near or far
and unwind
in a
new hostel
each night

5 reasons why the choice is always yours

1 YHA is everywhere

Since its birth in 1930, the YHA has grown to become part of the largest budget accommodation network in the world. There are more than 220 hostels throughout England and Wales, many in such unusual locations that they offer the only accommodation for miles around. We also have a network of over 50 camping barns in stunning countryside locations if you would prefer more basic accommodation. There are separate associations in Scotland, Northern Ireland and the Irish Republic and your membership allows you to stay at some 4,500 places in more than 60 countries around the world (turn to page 32 for more details).

2 Youth Hostels are totally unique

We pride ourselves on the sheer variety of our Youth Hostels, from historic buildings full of character to modern, purpose-built venues. Some are simple stone cottages, others are impressive Victorian country houses. Whatever you are looking for, rest assured that you will be able to find a location that best suits your needs. Be it a

remote camping barn or a busy city-centre base, you'll enjoy a different experience every time.

3 Meals are flexible

Many of our Youth Hostels offer a full catering service so you and your family or travelling companions can forget about slaving over a hot stove. If you prefer the DIY option, most of our hostels provide well-equipped self-catering kitchens. Many of our hostels also stock basic foodstuffs and have alcohol licences. At all hostels you are welcome to bring your own wine and beer to consume with your evening meal.

4 Booking is easy

Simply call the hostel to check availability. It is advisable to book ahead but, once on the hostelling trail, you'll find that most hostels will be able to do this for you. Remember to bring your membership card with you. If you are not sure of your plans call Customer Services who can advise you. Or visit **www.yha.org.uk** for up-to-date news and bookings.

5 We offer a choice

It's a simple fact of life that as we grow, our needs change. By design, the YHA reflects this. When the freedom of youth allows you to explore, hostels provide an affordable base for your tours. For those seeking a family break, many of our hostels have been designated as family-friendly. And, when the kids have flown the nest, Youth Hostels offer a perfect base for a break in the city or the countryside. We also boast a host of special interest breaks to make your stay one to remember, including walking holidays and outdoor activity breaks.

Go! *with the family*

Whether you want a break in the country, a traditional seaside holiday or an overnight stay in the city, there is a family-friendly Youth Hostel that's ideally suited to your needs.

Fun
and dedicated
facilities at an
affordable price

10 reasons to bring the kids

1 You can book a family room

Many hostels have family rooms available at a sole use room rate. Expect a comfortable bunk-bedded room with a wash basin, storage space, bed linen and duvets. Some Youth Hostels offer en-suite facilities. You will also get your own key so you can come and go as you please.

2 Let us cook...

Choose a hostel with a meals service and forget about doing the cooking. Some hostels also offer a special menu for children under 10. We know that parents like to relax in the evening too, so feel free to bring your own wine or beer to drink with your meal.

3 ...or self-cater

We also understand how important it is to be flexible when travelling with children, which is why, at all bar a very few Youth Hostels, there is always the option of self-catering. If you need a night off, then book an evening meal.

4 All ages are welcome

Whatever the age range of your family, we have a hostel that will suit you. Over 80 hostels are suitable for children under three with dedicated facilities. Hostelling is also an ideal introduction for youngsters spending their first nights away from the family home in a secure and safe environment. Teenagers aged 14 or over are welcome to stay on their own or with friends.

5 You can travel light

Many hostels offer child-oriented equipment for hire, allowing you to travel that bit lighter. These include cots, highchairs, towels, baby baths and alarm clocks – just ask your chosen hostel for availability and don't forget to pre-book. There are laundry and clothes-drying facilities too.

6 There's plenty of entertainment

All Youth Hostels offer a selection of activities, from board games to kite making, keeping the children amused and giving you time to relax. For more organised entertainment, book an activity break at one of our activity centres where outdoor pursuits include climbing and watersports (see page 28) or choose a special interest holiday advertised in Triangle, the members' magazine.

7 You are in the great outdoors

With many Youth Hostels set in some of our finest countryside, you can give your kids freedom to explore. YHA Poppit Sands overlooks a Blue Flag sandy beach where dolphins often swim, while YHA Sherwood Forest is surrounded by acres of ancient woodland. Other hostels enjoy acres of grounds, allowing the children plenty of room for outdoor games.

8 It's relaxing!

Leave all the hard work to us. The only thing we ask is that you tidy up after yourselves.

9 We'll help you plan your break

Our staff know their local areas well and will help you find the best activities for your family, making sure you get the most out of your stay.

10 It's great value

Joining as a family makes sound economic sense. YHA offers reduced rates for one-parent families, while under-18s are enrolled free of charge.

For more information on all 118 family-friendly hostels, send for the free Family Breaks brochure, available from **www.yha.org.uk** or call the hotline: **0870 770 8868.**

For all the latest YHA news visit www.yha.org.uk

www.britainonview.com

Go! As a group

Many hostels are tailor-made for groups of every age, from school children upwards, while our special packages offer exceptional value.

Our activities are designed to **challenge** and **stimulate** your team

10 reasons to go as a group

www.britainonview.com

1 It's great value
A group card allows you and your group (of five or more) to stay at Youth Hostels. All we ask is that you are a formally constituted group and, if your group includes young people under 14, there is an adult leader of each sex.

2 You get exclusive use of a hostel
We will try to give your group exclusive use of the Youth Hostel of your choice, provided your group is a suitable size. Some hostels are exclusively available to organised groups on weekdays during term-time. To enqure call your chosen hostel or Group Reservations on 0870 770 6117.

3 Special packages
From personal development programmes to action-filled activity breaks, all group activities are designed to challenge and stimulate your team. We offer educational breaks plus enjoyable stays such as a look behind the scenes at Old Trafford while staying at YHA Manchester.

4 We adapt to you
Whether your group includes wheelchair users or those requiring special diets, rest assured we can meet your needs. We also run schemes tailored to help certain groups, such as young people at risk of offending.

5 Leaders stay for free
Leaders go free on a ratio of one leader for every 10 paying participants if the group takes full board. Leader rooms are usually available.

6 Help with planning
To help get the most out of the trip, group leaders are entitled to a free planning visit to the Youth Hostel after booking.

School trips

A Youth Hostel is the ideal base for a residential school trip – thanks to our stimulating National Curriculum-linked packages.

In partnership with key national attractions, countryside and heritage organisations, we have developed a range of National Curriculum-linked packages to maximise the educational and social value of school trips. Activities are linked to key stages 2,3 & 4, A level and GNVQ studies. Examples include:

'Roadwise' road safety course
Youngsters joining this two-day fun and educational programme run by the Heritage Motor Centre at YHA Stratford-upon-Avon will gain a deeper understanding of road safety.

A level geography field studies
With the assistance of the Peak District National Park Education Service, GCSE and A level students will benefit from four days of activities at YHA Edale Activity Centre.

Life skills
Three days of personal development and team building activities led by specialists in adventure education at YHA Alfriston.

History (key stages 2 & 3)
Understand how Victorians lived with a two-day trip to YHA Llangollen. Pupils experience a Victorian lesson and enjoy a steam train ride.

Leisure, Tourism & Land management
A three-day GNVQ-linked package based at YHA Langdon Beck in Northumberland including a study of rural tourism.

For more information visit www.yha.org.uk

www.britainonview.com

7 Costs can be shared

We are committed to providing accommodation for less privileged youngsters. The Give Us A Break scheme aims to help youngsters who, without financial help, would be unable to join friends on a hostel trip. If you feel your group might be eligible, call 01629 592638.

8 We value safety

At YHA we know how important it is for groups – particularly children – to feel safe and secure when away from home. We invest heavily to ensure all staff work to the most exacting standards in matters of health, safety and security. For example, all staff are trained to handle emergency situations and have emergency access to a telephone at all times. YHA is also registered with the Criminal Records Bureau to assist the assessment of staff's suitability.

9 We'll entertain you

Groups have access to free and low-cost activities designed to provide safe recreation, educational support or just to fill gaps in a programme.

10 We cover the world

Groups may stay at any of the 4,500 Youth Hostels in 60 countries around the world.

For more information on choosing the most appropriate hostel, call YHA's Group Reservation Office on **0870 770 6117**. To request your free Groups brochure, please call **0870 770 8868**.

Go! *With equal rights*

More than 20 Youth Hostels have specific facilities for wheelchair users, while most other hostels offer limited access but aim to be as flexible as possible. Please contact the Youth Hostel staff before booking to ensure the facilities are suitable. Here are just a few of the ways YHA aims to help:

• YHA is a registered user of Typetalk, enabling hostels and booking points to communicate with textphone users via a Typetalk operator.
• Although many hostels are in old buildings which can make access difficult, many offer ground floor rooms, access to bathrooms and convenient parking spaces.
• Arrangements can be made for registered assistance dogs at most hostels.
• Staff attend the English Tourism Council's Welcome All course.

Where to stay

Youth Hostels are inspected by a number of different organisations to assess their accessibility. A new single standard has been agreed at the time of going to press. The English Tourism Council and Wales Tourist Board will assess Youth Hostels against these standards. In the meantime the following Youth Hostels offer degrees of accessibility. You should check direct with each Youth Hostel to assess their suitability.

North Pennines: Wooler, Kielder
Lake District: Duddon Estuary
Yorkshire & South Pennines: Dentdale, Mankinholes
Peak District & North West: Hartington Hall, Ilam Hall, Liverpool, Manchester, Sherwood Forest
Heart of England: Coalport, Leominster, Oxford
South East England: Medway, Littlehampton

East of England: Blaxhall, Wells-next-the-Sea, Sheringham
London: Rotherhithe, St Pancras
Wales: Broad Haven, Conwy, Manorbier, Trefdraeth, Idwal Cottage

For current prices visit www.yha.org.uk

Go! For less

Youth Hostels represent an affordable option for all. But with key local attractions offering discounts and concessions on overnight prices, you could get even better value for money.

www.britainonview.com

5 ways to save money

1 Adapt to suit your budget
Youth Hostels offer incredible flexibility. Choose full or half board, self-cater or mix and match for a range of inexpensive but hearty meals. Opt for a bed in a shared dormitory or occupy a private room at a higher charge. Whatever your needs and budget, you'll find an affordable solution with YHA. And with no single supplements in sight, Youth Hostels are one of the few places where you won't be penalised for travelling on your own.

2 Save money as a student
If you are a student, not travelling as part of a group, you will receive a reduction on the Youth Hostel's overnight charge on production of a valid ISIC, EURO 26 or NUS card at reception.

3 Take advantage of concessions
Adult members of YHA not travelling as part of a group who can show they receive means tested benefits related to low income will be charged the under-18 overnight rate for their stay. This concession is not available in London Youth Hostels and only applies to accommodation in shared dormitories. Single parent families are offered a discount on all family rooms.

4 Ask about big discounts
Many organisations offer discretionary discounts to YHA members including local attractions, travel, entry to properties and deals on clothing and equipment.

5 Stay for free!
A new loyalty scheme is being introduced, entitling you to free nights at Youth Hostels. Just collect the FreeNite points, awarded every time you stay in a participating hostel, and redeem them against overnight stays or other hostel offers. For details, visit **www.freenites.com**

To make a booking visit www.yha.org.uk

Go! *In search of peace*

If you need a break from modern living, take time out at a hostel or camping barn miles away from the noise of the city.

Find peace and quiet in stunning locations miles from anywhere

5 reasons to go back to basics

Go!
Camping

1 It's a chance to escape modern life...

Imagine leaving civilisation behind and travelling to your chosen hostel on foot or by bicycle, surrounded by hills and without a street light in sight. A handful of hostels are inaccessible by car, including YHA Skiddaw House beneath Skiddaw's summit in the Lakes, England's highest Youth Hostel at 1,550 feet. But you don't need to venture high to guarantee a memorable experience. YHA Tanner's Hatch is in the Surrey Hills Area of Outstanding Natural Beauty with a mile's walk to its door – enough to ensure rural isolation without incurring any blisters.

2 ...and make the most of the outdoors

These homely hostels nestle in some of Britain's finest stretches of countryside and enjoy stunning views, making them perfect for walkers, cyclists and nature lovers. You could, for example, wake up to a vista of untamed seas in YHA Perranporth, a former coastguard station set on Cornish cliff-top. With miles of footpaths and bridlepaths in the area, some running right past the hostel's front door, you can immerse yourself in the outdoors for a healthy, relaxing break.

3 You'll love the challenge

If you never leave home without your mobile phone, a break in a remote hostel will allow you time to appreciate what's really important in your life. While some accommodation will exceed all your expectations of a small hostel, others, such as YHA Black Sail in Cumbria, have no mains electricity. Just remember to take a torch and a sense of adventure.

4 You'll meet like-minded friends

The real charm of these smaller hostels is their friendly, relaxed atmosphere. Many of the smaller hostels are without a television, so expect to spend your evenings chatting to new-found companions in front of open fires in cosy lounges and sharing stories over dinner.

5 Camping Barns offer even more variety

You don't need to be a YHA member to use Camping Barns – converted farm buildings offering simple, self-catering accommodation. You could find yourself staying in a former cornstore or cattle byre, with a choice of countryside on your doorstep. Facilities are generally basic with a shared sleeping area, food preparation area, cold running water and a toilet, although many offer hot water, heating and showers. It's like camping, except you will enjoy a weatherproof roof over your head. Just look for the Camping Barn colour-coded circle in the directory to find barns in North Yorkshire, the Forest of Bowland, Lake District, North Pennines, Peak District, Kent, Exmoor and Dartmoor.

YHA members who bring their own tents and bedding may camp in the grounds of the following Youth Hostels. The charge is half of the adult overnight price, per person, per night. No price concessions are available. You are welcome to use the hostel's washing, toilet, laundry, self-catering and recreational facilities, although campers must observe any restrictions imposed by managers. Please book ahead as there is a strict limit on the number of campers at each hostel.

Camping is available at the following hostels.

Northumberland & the North Pennines
Baldersdale (p37), Bellingham (p38), Edmundbyers (p40)

Wales Bryn Gwynant (p99), Capel-y-Ffin (p102), Cynwyd (p104), Idwal Cottage (p106), Llanddeusant (p108), Llwyn-y-Celyn (p109), Manorbier (p110), Poppit Sands (p112), Pwll Deri (p113), St Davids (p114)

Heart of England
Bridges Long Mynd (p118), Clun Mill (p119), Welsh Bicknor (p125)

East of England Thurlby (p132)

South East England
Arundel (p154), Blackboys (p155), Epping Forest (p158), Hastings (p159), Holmbury St Mary (p160), Jordans (p160), Kemsing (p161), The Ridgeway (p163), Tanners Hatch (p165)

South West England
Burley (p137) Coverack (p139), Crowcombe (p139), Exeter (p140), Land's End (p142), Okehampton (p145), Penzance (p146), Quantock Hills (p148), Street (p150)

For the ultimate remote hostelling break, head to the hostels below.

Black Sail (p48)	Blaencaron (p98)	Dolgoch (p105)	Ennerdale (p53)
Hindhead (p159)	Marloes Sands (p110)	Shining Cliff (p95)	Skiddaw House (p60)
St David's (p114)	Steps Bridge (p149)	Tanners Hatch (p165)	Tyncornel (p116)

For offers and discounts visit www.yha.org.uk

Go! On foot or by bike

Discover the best of Britain's countryside with a self-led or guided walking package, or stay at Youth Hostels on a long-distance route.

Inspiring walks and rides are right outside your door

6 reasons to walk or cycle with us

1 It's making the most of the countryside

Many Youth Hostels and Camping Barns enjoy to-die-for locations in incredible tracts of countryside, including Areas of Outstanding Natural Beauty and National Parks. With such scenery on your doorstep, you can't help but enjoy days of exploring the surrounding footpaths and bridleways on foot or by bike. Some Youth Hostels, such as YHA Edale, in the Peak District, and YHA Okehampton, on the edge of Dartmoor, offer spe cialised breaks. You can find details in the members' magazine, Triangle or at **www.yha.org.uk**

2 You can choose to be led by experienced, friendly guides...

To take all the hassle out of a walking break, book a YHA Walking Holiday. We offer a wide choice of routes, all selected to sample the finest landscapes in England and Wales. You will be guided by a qualified YHA leader in small groups of no more than 12. And, as you would expect from YHA, these exclusive breaks are fantastic value for money.

3 ...or guide yourself

Stay with YHA and it's easy to explore under your own steam too. The YHA Booking Bureau can book a number of single nights at various hostels on your behalf – all you have to do is provide the leg-power between overnight stays. There are many recognised inter-hostel routes – you can buy the guidebooks and maps from the Booking Bureau.

4 Take a trip of a lifetime

It's every serious walker's and cyclist's dream to complete a ▶

I've wanted to do this for years so, after months of planning, I set off with hopes held high. I've hostelled for over 25 years and knew I'd find helpful staff, comfortable beds and good food. Oh yes, and invaluable drying rooms. It also meant I didn't have to cart too much luggage around on my bike.

It took me 16 days to cycle the 975 miles. I'd pre-booked the hostels so I knew how many miles I had to achieve each day – there was no ducking out when it rained. The 74-mile ride to YHA Bridges was very hard. I called ahead to say I'd be late and, when I finally arrived, Sarah the manager had put my dinner in the oven to keep warm. I could have married her there and then!

The sight of the sea at John O'Groats was a scene to gladden the heart. It had been hard but I'd made it without a single puncture!

YHA and the National Cycle Network

Many Youth Hostels sit on or very close to some of the 7,000 miles of the National Cycle Network developed by Sustrans, the sustainable transport charity. Sustrans works on practical projects to encourage people to walk, cycle and use public transport to reduce traffic. By 2005, its aim is to have over 10,000 miles of traffic-free routes, quiet lanes and traffic-calmed streets forming a comprehensive cycling net-work across the country. Many Youth Hostels offer cycle hire so even if you don't have your own bike, you can explore some of these routes during your stay. Visit www.sustrans.org.uk for online mapping of routes or call 0117 929 0888 for more information.

www.britainonview.com

long-distance route at some stage in their lives. Whether you decide to embark on a National Trail, a classic route such as the Coast to Coast, or devise your own epic route, you will find conveniently-located hostels on the way. Long-distance routes are also available in the range of YHA Walking Holidays.

5 You travel light

If you're striding or pedalling between hostels, you will want to travel light. Stay in a camping barn and you don't need to pack a tent. Choose a youth hostel and leave your sleeping bag at home too. On a YHA Walking Holiday, we'll transport your luggage between hostels, leaving your days hindered by nothing more than a day pack.

6 You can expect a warm welcome

We know that, after a full day's walking or cycling, you want to relax. So choose a hostel offering a full meals service and you can enjoy a three-course breakfast, picnic lunch and evening meal. Self-catering facilities allow you to prepare flasks, cycle stores will keep your bike safe while drying rooms revive wet clothes. So you'll have plenty of time to swap experiences with fellow hostellers in a sociable atmosphere.

Selected walking breaks

YHA offers an exciting range of walking breaks to suit both seasoned hikers and newcomers. Here's just a taste of what's on offer.

Lakes & tarns of Lakeland

Suitable for... those wanting a self-led break in stunning surroundings.
Where you'll walk This 27-mile route explores the Lake District, passing through remote valleys and over some of the highest passes in the area. Walk at your own pace to two of Lakeland's largest lakes and a handful of its most beautiful tarns on this self-led holiday.
Where you'll stay Overnight stops at YHA Patterdale, Windermere and Grasmere. A booklet detailing the route is available from these hostels or via Customer Services (tel 0870 770 8868).

Byways of Borrowdale

Suitable for... all walkers seeking a relaxed break with a guide.
Where you'll walk Borrowdale is one of Lakeland's finest valleys with classic views of mountains and fells. But you don't have to climb high to appreciate this imposing landscape – this two-day break leads you along quiet valley byways to wonderful vistas.
Where you'll stay Stay in a tranquil, riverside location at YHA Borrowdale during this centre-based break.

The White Peak Way

Suitable for... reasonably fit walkers wanting guided hikes but no hard climbs in the ever-changing scenery of the Peak District National Park.
Where you'll walk The White Peak takes its name from the white limestone which has created a distinctive landscape of river valleys in the Peak District National Park. You will explore its picturesque dales and market towns on this 90-mile route.
Where you'll stay From the gothic splendour of YHA Ilam Hall to the 17th century style of YHA Hartington Hall, enjoy a range of unique accommodation on this circular walk.

For details of the full range of led breaks, send for the Walking Holidays brochure. To request your free copy, visit **www.yha.org.uk** or call **0870 770 8868**. For booking and information, please call **0870 770 6113**. Find details of other walking breaks at **www.yha.org.uk**

Go! *Easy on the environment*

By walking or cycling between hostels you are helping our planet. Rest assured that YHA takes a serious interest in protecting the environment too.

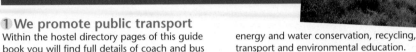

3 reasons to have a clear conscience

1 We promote public transport

Within the hostel directory pages of this guide book you will find full details of coach and bus services and nearby train stations for each hostel. You can then easily work out whether public transport is a feasible option for your hostelling trip. As a member organisation, the YHA has an unrivalled track record in promoting walking, cycling and public transport as a means of getting to and between our hostels. You are welcome to bring your own car but we're proud to say that more of our guests arrive without cars than in any comparable tourist operation.

2 We hold high values

YHA has always been a force for sustainable tourism. We are committed to the principles of the International Youth Hostels Federation Environmental Charter, which sets objectives for energy and water conservation, recycling, transport and environmental education.

3 We practise what we preach

Some of our hostels demonstrate environmental best practice. YHA Sherwood Forest has the latest energy conservation features, while renewable energy schemes have been recently installed at YHA Langdon Beck, YHA Ennerdale and YHA Ilfracombe. We also aim to contribute to worthwhile environmental initiatives. For example, Lakeland Youth Hostels have joined the Lake District Tourism and Conservation Partnership. This initiative is raising money to restore badly-eroded footpaths. Through action such as this, YHA aims to practise what we preach, which is to promote greater love, care and understanding of the countryside.

The Ramblers' Association

The YHA has for many generations worked alongside the Ramblers' Association to open up the countryside for the enjoyment of all sections of society. Were it not for the Ramblers' dedication to protecting our footpaths, encouraging walking and campaigning for greater access on foot to the country-side together with the YHA's provision of affordable places to stay, thousands of people would have been denied the opportunity to enjoy the hidden secrets of Britain.

It is thanks to over 60 years of Ramblers' campaigning that it will soon be possible for the public to walk through four million acres of unculti-vated, open country.

That is why, as a member of the YHA, we would also

encourage you to become a member of the Ramblers' Association*. Doing so enables you to participate in regular walks and a range of local activities, while helping to protect the places you love for future generations to enjoy.

*Benefits include a free Ramblers' Yearbook, quarterly magazine, discounts at outdoor clothing stores and membership of your local walking group which provides its own walks programme and social activities. Visit **www.ramblers.org.uk**, email **rebeccab@london.ramblers.org.uk** or call **020 7339 8573** and quote 'YHAG'

Go! With friends

Need a venue for a large
gathering? Ask about
Rent-a-Hostel, the scheme that
allows you to have an entire
building all to yourselves.

Book for a
family gathering,
meeting or
special party

MEMBER'S STORY

7 reasons to rent a hostel

1 The location will be totally unique

Rent-a-Hostel offers you the unique opportunity to stay in a wide range of buildings, each with their own character. Whether you would prefer sea views or mountain vistas, a central town location or a forest retreat, we have a hostel that's perfect for your needs. Our more unusual properties include a former chapel, a remote mountain hut, a 17th century water mill, a former lifeboat station and a spectacular shooting lodge. Use your imagination to add the finishing touch to that special occasion.

2 You will have exclusive use of the hostel

You will have sole occupancy of the hostel, although some hostels may have a YHA representative staying. With your own key, you can come and go as you please.

3 We can cater for any number of people

Whether your group consists of 10 old friends, 20 work colleagues or a formal club of 30, we have a hostel the right size for you. Our knowledgeable staff will be happy to help you make your choice to ensure you find the hostel that best meets your needs.

4 You will get great value for money

When you rent a Youth Hostel, you pay for the whole building and not for each bed, offering unbeatable value for your money.

5 You still travel light...

All bed linen, kitchen equipment and cleaning materials are provided and many hostels have a selection of board games and cots

and highchairs for toddlers. In fact, all you need to bring are towels and yourself!

6 ...and you don't have to cook

If you're celebrating something special then you won't want to worry about preparing meals. So let us do the cooking instead. At some Youth Hostels, a meals service is available for one-off celebratory meals or you can choose full catering during your break, with flexible meal times agreed in advance.

7 Making a booking is simple

Rent-a-Hostel is generally available between September and Easter but some locations can be rented for periods during the spring and summer months. The scheme is particularly popular at weekends, during school holidays and over the Christmas and New Year period so it's advisable to book early to avoid disappointment. And it really couldn't be simpler. Just decide the area in which you'd like to stay and how many people will be in your group. Then call the Rent-a-Hostel Booking Office on **0870 770 6113** or email **rentahostel@yha.org.uk** where staff will advise you of suitable Youth Hostels.

To discover which hostels are available to rent, refer to the individual hostel entries in the directory section of this guide or call **0870 770 8868** to request your free Rent-a-Hostel brochure. You can also book Youth Hostels in England, Wales, Scotland and Ireland via **www.rentahostel.com**

Liz Woznicki, 31, from London, rented a castle* on New Year's Eve for a very special office party.

I work for the Wildlife Trusts and wanted to organise a cheap but memorable holiday for staff to say thank you for all their hard work throughout the year. Through the Rent-a-Hostel scheme I was able to hire a castle surrounded by fantastic countryside at mimimal cost.

It was a fabulously grand setting and, when it snowed heavily on our first day, looked magical. The gothic castle had marble statues and an art gallery. The accommodation itself was more basic, but it was clean, warm and well-equipped.

I had booked a caterer, two bands, a disco and a storyteller. Over the four days we had enormous fun but New Year's Eve was the best: we danced until seven in the morning and had bacon sand-wiches for breakfast. Needless to say, we're going again this year.

*SYHA Carbisdale Castle

For offers and discounts visit www.yha.org.uk

Go!

For an active break

The YHA boasts two dedicated activity centres where you can try new sports, improve old skills or simply have great fun.

Try a
multi-activity
break or learn a
new skill
under expert tuition

8 reasons to join in the fun

1 You will be spoiled for choice

You could try caving or canoeing, watersports or winter mountaineering, archery or abseiling. Then there's orienteering, raft building, navigating, night hiking, climbing... and that's just the start. Join a course that concentrates on improving your talents in one particular area or opt for a break that combines a wide variety of activities. Some stays lead to recognised qualifications, others teach you universally useful skills such as first aid. Your only problem will be finding time to do everything you want to do.

2 We will work around you

Come by yourself, bring friends and colleagues or stay as a family and we will cater for your needs. Some multi-activity programmes are designed with families in mind, with a wide range of activities to appeal to all family members. Courses that improve specific skills will appeal to the individual, and you will meet new friends. Book as a group and our staff will work closely with you to design a break that targets your objectives.

3 You don't have to be Superman

With such a wide range of courses, we offer beginners a taste of a new sport as well as help already accomplished folk hone their skills. You don't need any previous experience and rest assured – our friendly, experienced instructors know how to help you achieve your potential without pushing you past your limit.

4 Fantastic locations

Both our activity centres are set in incredible locations. YHA Edale sits on the flanks of Kinder Scout in the heart of the Peak District while YHA Okehampton is on the edge of Dartmoor National Park, within easy walking distance of the most remote area in southern England.

5 You'll experience real challenges...

You won't just learn how to paddle a canoe on our activity breaks. Trying a new sport involves a leap of faith as you venture into new territory. As you conquer your fears and master a fresh skill, you will build your confidence, learn more about yourself and develop your teamworking and communication skills. All in all, it will be a highly rewarding adventure.

6 ...in a safe environment

All our instructional staff hold relevant National Governing Body qualifications, including first aid, and are subject to on-going training and monitoring procedures. All are trained to operate to written

health, safety and security standards and can deal with emergency situations at any hour. Equipment is continually inspected and maintained to ensure its safety and both centres are registered by The Adventure Activities Licensing Authority. Rely on us – you're in safe hands.

7 It's great value

The price you pay includes all expert instruction, food, specialist equipment, accommodation, transport and VAT during your stay.

8 Other hostels offer plenty of breaks too

Whether you want to learn to surf at YHA Treyarnon Bay, kayak at YHA Windermere or try a family paintballing break at YHA Poppit Sands, a wealth of individual hostels have tailored activity breaks too. Details of current courses on offer are in the members' magazine, Triangle, or visit www.yha.org.uk and follow the 'activities' link.

www.britainonview.com

For details of activity breaks contact YHA Edale (tel 0870 770 5808), YHA Okehampton (tel 0870 770 5978) or Customer Services (tel 0870 770 8868).

For offers and discounts visit www.yha.org.uk

Go!

And get involved

YHA is a charity that
has always depended
on its members'
support. Here's
how you can
make a
difference.

Help us and
**we'll help
you** make the most of
your talents

Victoria Clark, 25, of Lancaster, joined a trek to raise money for YHA's Give us a Break scheme.

"It all started with a phone call from a friend asking if I fancied going walking in Nepal – it was only later I realised it was a gruelling 75-mile, six-day trek at high altitude, and I had to raise £2,000 for the privilege of taking part!

The reward for months of fund-raising far exceeded all my expectations. Each day on the trek, we saw breathtaking scenery as our route took us via tiny hillside villages, through terraced fields and along narrow mountain ridges. The highlight came on the fifth day when we climbed our highest peak – 3,597 metres above sea level. We all felt on top of the world, literally.

Walking in the scorching sun followed hours later by snow all added to the fun. Exhausting and physically demanding – but easily the most unforgettable time I have ever experienced."

5 reasons to support YHA

1 The choice is yours
YHA offers you vast opportunities to make the most of your talents. You can volunteer to help with fundraising, publicity, hostel wardening, conservation and countryside work, professional advice, tour guiding... the list is endless. Call 0870 770 8868 and ask for an information pack.

2 YHA supports you too
In return for all your efforts, we will give you the level of supervision, training and support you need. As well as your efforts being invaluable to us, we promise they will be rewarding too.

3 You'll shape the future
YHA members can be considered for election to YHA's Board of Trustees, which takes overall responsibility for YHA. Board members need a wide range of experiences, professional expertise, and a broad understanding of hostelling activities and philosophy. If you feel you have the necessary skills and time to contribute to this important role, please write to the National Secretary at YHA National Office, Trevelyan House, Dimple Road, Matlock, Derbyshire, DE4 3YH. You can also become involved by attending a regional meeting – see our magazine, Triangle or visit the website www.yha.org.uk for details.

4 We value your opinions
Triangle is the YHA magazine issued to all member households twice a year. If you have a point to make or simply an entertaining hostelling tale to share, please get in touch.

5 YHA is a charity
Which means it needs your help to raise funds to continue with its work, whether it be upgrading premises or giving youngsters a chance for a holiday on the Give Us A Break scheme. Whether you donate from your own pocket or would like to raise funds on YHA's behalf, we will always be pleased to hear from you.

Volunteer to help YHA and meet like-minded friends.

For more information visit www.yha.org.uk

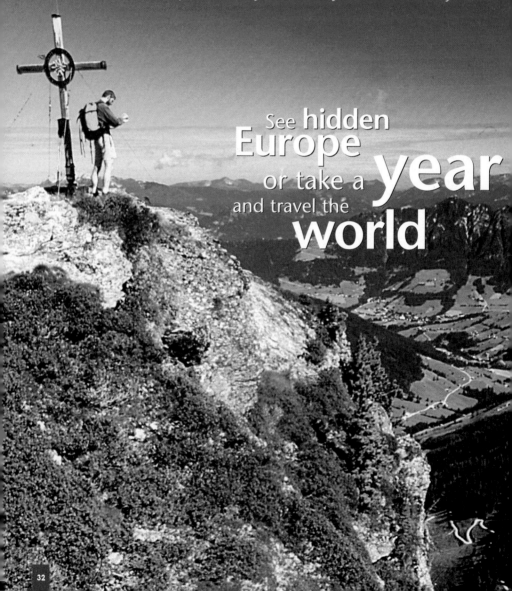

Go! *Worldwide*

An extensive network of Youth Hostels across the globe means a safe and comfortable place to stay wherever your travels take you.

See **hidden Europe**
or take a **year**
and travel the
world

Phil Wharmby, 50, from Manchester, travelled through central Europe with a friend.

"We took a car tour to Vienna, Brno, Prague, Krakow and Bratislava, armed with little more than a guidebook and the YHA International Booking Network. There are incredible places out there where Brits simply don't think of going.

The most impressive sight was Krakow. It's a gorgeous city and we went to the salt mines of Wieliczka and to Auschwitz. That was a real emotional experience, but worthwhile. And we saw caves in Brno in the Czech Republic that were many, many times the size of those in Cheddar Gorge – I stood and looked up a 400-foot airhole.

All the hostel managers said they rarely see British tourists here. The locals welcomed us, happy to see us travelling by our own steam now that the East has opened up. There's just too much to see – I'll be going back for more."

5 reasons to spread your wings with YHA

Jeremy Woodhouse, Getty Images

1 Youth Hostels are everywhere
With over 4,500 hostels in 60 countries, whether you're embarking on a month's trip to experience Europe or a year's odyssey around the world, you'll find a range of Youth Hostels in the locations you need. As you would expect, all the hostels have their own character. You could find yourself staying in a Swiss Youth Hostel that's situated inside a train or booking a skiing holiday in a hostel at the heart of the Andean mountains in Chile. To see the exciting range of hostels available, visit www.iyhf.org or buy the Hostelling International Guides (Volume One details Europe and the Mediterranean while Volume Two covers Africa, America and Asia) by calling 0870 770 8868.

2 It's easy to book
Simply book online at **www.hostelbooking.com** or call **0870 770 8868**.

3 You can depend on us
In a new country of different cultures and language, you can trust us to provide you with a good night's sleep. You always know what to expect when travelling the world as a YHA member because all Youth Hostels must meet the International Youth Hostel

Federation's safety and security standards. Just look for the Hostelling International logo, which assures you of comfortable, safe and clean and accommodation.

4 Free nights
A new loyalty programme called FreeNites has been introduced to reward members. Every time you stay in a participating hostel, you are awarded FreeNite points which can be redeemed against overnight stays, hostel services and promotions. It's just another way to make your international trip even better value for money. Visit **www.freenites.com**

5 Savings on calls home
When you're travelling the world, we know how important it is to stay in contact with family and friends back home. That's why we offer the YHA eKit, a global calling and messaging service that you can access both online and over the phone. With savings of up to 85% on calls, access to voicemail, faxmail and email and a travel assistance bureau open 24 hours a day, it will ensure you stay informed and in touch. For more details, visit **www.yha.ekit.com**

HOSTELLING INTERNATIONAL

For all the latest YHA news visit www.yha.org.uk

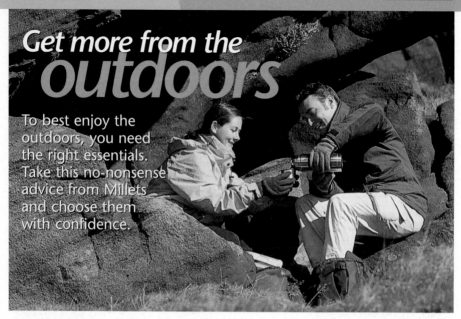

Get more from the outdoors

To best enjoy the outdoors, you need the right essentials. Take this no-nonsense advice from Millets and choose them with confidence.

Rucksack

What size? For general walking a day-sack with a capacity of 25-30 litres is ideal to hold waterproofs, lunch, drinks and a spare fleece.

Pack well The most important rule is to make sure that the heaviest items of gear are close to your back and therefore your own centre of gravity.

Keep the insides dry A rucksack can never be totally waterproof because it has so many seams. Use a waterproof ruck-sack liner or pack your kit in plastic bags to ensure it stays dry.

Wear and tear Your daysack can take a bashing over the years so check it regularly. Look out for frayed stitching, rips in the base and cracked buckles.

Longer trips For longer day trips, winter walking and weekends away a sack of around 35-40 litres will swallow the extra essentials you need.

Boots

Try them twice Try the boots on, then come back and try them again later in the day – feet can expand a full size between morning and late afternoon.

Bring your walking socks Always try the boots on with the type of socks you would normally walk in. If you have one foot bigger than the other, bring an extra sock for the smaller foot. If you usually wear a heavy rucksack, bring that too as it may affect the way you walk.

Try all sorts Some men have the same shaped feet as women and vice versa. Try on all pairs that look as if they will fit, even if it means those made for the opposite sex.

Wear them at home Try out your boots indoors to be sure they fit before using them outside.

Jacket

Which one? Your choice depends on the type of walking you do. More breathable fabrics deliver better performance and durability but they will cost you more.

Aim for a snug fit A jacket that's too loose will be draughty and may affect breathability if sweat condenses. But check it isn't too tight across your shoulders. Leave room for other layers for ultimate temperature control.

Look after it If your jacket is wet after a walk, let it dry naturally away from direct heat. And always store your jacket hanging up – leaving it creased can create weak spots in the fabric while dampness may cause rotting.

•hostel directory

In this section...

For offers and discounts visit www.yha.org.uk

The Youth Hostels of...

Northumberland & North Pennines

Nature's playground: Kielder Water is just one of the many attractions that brings outdoor adventurers flocking to Northumberland.

Hostel Index

For further information visit www.yha.org.uk

● FAMILY   ● CITY   ● GROUP   ● TRADITIONAL   ● CAMPING BARN   ● COASTAL   ● RURAL

www.britainonview.com

Hadrian's Wall: near YHA Acomb, Greenhead and Once Brewed.

● ACOMB ☆

Main Street, Acomb, Hexham, Northumberland NE46 4PL; Tel: 0870 770 5664

These converted stables offer simple accommodation close to the market town of Hexham with its fine abbey, museum and theatre. Better still is the hostel's proximity to breathtaking countryside. Follow winding lanes to pretty villages, enjoy the river and forest trails or take to the high moorlands of Northumberland and the North Pennines. Hadrian's Wall is also nearby.

Location: OS 87, GR 934666.
Great for... a simple, get-away-from-it-all active holiday.
You need to know... the facilities are basic.
Accommodation: 36 beds: 1x4- and 2x16-bed rooms.
Family rooms: No. **Rent-a-Hostel:** No.
Classroom: No. **Education packages:** No.
Facilities: Lounge/common/dining room.
Daytime access: Restricted. ⊗
Meals: Self-catering only.
Reception open: 17.00hrs.
Getting there: From the east/Newcastle take A69 to 1 mile past Bridge End roundabout, turn right on A6079, then first right at Acomb village sign. Follow Main Street uphill to hostel.
Parking: On-street only.
Nearest other hostels: Once Brewed 15 miles, Bellingham 15, Edmundbyers 16, Newcastle 20.
Public transport: BUS: Tyne Valley 880/2 from Hexham, otherwise Arriva 685 Carlisle–Newcastle-upon-Tyne, alight Hexham 2.5 miles. RAIL: Hexham 2 miles. FERRY: Newcastle 25 miles.

●● ALSTON ☆☆☆

The Firs, Alston, Cumbria CA9 3RW;
alston@yha.org.uk
Tel: 0870 770 5668 Fax: 0870 770 5669

Stay on top of the world in England's highest market town where steep, cobbled streets are surrounded by wild, solitary fells. Walkers and cyclists will love this modern hostel overlooking the South Tyne Valley, on the Pennine Way and Coast-to-Coast cycle route.

Location: OS 86, GR 717461.
Great for... cycling and walking.
Accommodation: 30 beds: 2x2-, 2x4- and 3x6-bed rooms.
Family rooms: No. **Rent-a-Hostel:** Yes.
Classroom: No. **Education packages:** No.
Facilities: Lounge, self-catering kitchen, dining room, showers, drying room and cycle store. **Daytime access:** All areas. ⊛
Meals: Breakfast, picnic lunch, evening meal.
Reception open: Staff available before 10.00hrs and after 17.00hrs.
Getting there: At the south end of Alston (opposite Hendersons Garage), turn onto The Firs and take first right at top of bank.
Parking: Yes.
Nearest other hostels: Ninebanks 8 miles, Langdon Beck 15, Greenhead 15 (17 by Pennine Way), Dufton 22 (by Pennine Way).
Public transport: BUS: Wrights 681 from Haltwhistle, 888 from Penrith, Highfield 680 from Carlisle. RAIL: Haltwhistle 15 miles, Langwathby 15, Penrith 19.

●● BALDERSDALE

Blackton, Baldersdale, Barnard Castle, County Durham DL12 9UP
Tel: 0870 770 5684 Fax: 0870 770 5685

If you're walking the Pennine Way, you'll be glad to rest your sore feet at Baldersdale, nestling in a green oasis with moorland all around. The hostel, an old stone farmhouse, has 10 acres of grounds where the only sounds you'll hear are the calls of curlews and lapwings. Home-grown, home-made food will restore your spirits to explore nearby Teesdale and Killhope Mining Museum. When you return, a well-earned pot of tea with cake awaits in the sheltered garden with views over Blackton Reservoir.

Location: OS 91, GR 931179.
Great for... traditional hostellers seeking rural isolation.
You need to know... it's difficult to access by public transport.
Accommodation: 40 beds: 1x3-, 1x4-, 3x6-, 1x7- and 1x8-bed rooms.
Family rooms: No. **Rent-a-Hostel:** Yes.
Classroom: Yes. **Education packages:** No.
Facilities: Dining room, pool table, quiet room, TV, showers, drying room, cycle store and self-catering kitchen. Limited shop. Camping.
Daytime access: All areas. ⊛
Meals: Breakfast, picnic lunch, evening meal.
Reception open: Staff available before 10.00hrs and after 17.00hrs.
Getting there: From Barnard Castle take the B6277 to Romaldkirk. Turn left at hostel sign to go through the hamlets of Hunderthwaite and Hury. Do not turn off to South Baldersdale. After 5 miles turn left

Northumberland & North Pennines

● FAMILY ● CITY ● GROUP ● TRADITIONAL ● CAMPING BARN ○ COASTAL ● RURAL

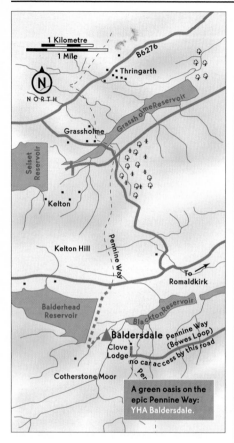

A green oasis on the epic Pennine Way: YHA Baldersdale.

at sign to Balderhead Reservoir gate, go across reservoir dam, and at the end turn left. The remaining stretch (0.25 miles) is not surfaced. No car access from Cotherstone village via Clove Lodge.
Parking: Yes.
Nearest other hostels: Keld 15 miles, Langdon Beck 15, Kirkby Stephen 18.
Public transport: BUS: Arriva North East 95/6 from Barnard Castle (connections from Darlington Station), alight Cotherstone or Romaldkirk 6 miles. RAIL: Darlington 27 miles.

● BANKSHEAD
campingbarns@yha.org.uk
Booking: 0870 770 6113
Arrival time: Mrs Ivinson, 01697 73198

This camping barn is a converted stone byre on a traditional family-run farm. It's an ideal stop-over while walking Hadrian's Wall and you'll enjoy outstanding views over the Irthing Valley.
Accommodation: Sleeps 10.

Facilities: Shower (coin-operated meter), toilet, hot water, cooking and recreation area with table and chairs, double burner gas stove, fridge, kettle, power points, crockery, cutlery, pans, oil-filled radiators on coin meter in recreation and sleeping areas, electric light.
Nearest pub: 2 miles. **Nearest shop:** 5 miles.
Location: OS 86, GR 586649.

Family picnic spots abound in Northumberland.

● BARRASFORD
campingbarns@yha.org.uk
Booking: 0870 770 6113
Arrival time: Mr Milburn, 01434 681237

This converted stone coach house, now a camping barn, overlooks the North Tyne River. Walkers and cyclists will find it allows easy access to the breathtaking scenery surrounding Hadrian's Wall. For a camping barn, the facilities are very good with light, heat, a nearby shop and even a drying room.
Accommodation: Sleeps 8x2 in bunkbeds.
Facilities: Drying room, heating, electric light, toilets in adjacent building, hot water, cooking area and metered electricity.
Nearest pub: Next door. **Nearest shop:** 200 metres.
Location: OS 87, GR 919733.

●● BELLINGHAM ☆☆
Woodburn Road, Bellingham, Hexham, Northumberland NE48 2ED
Tel: 0870 770 5694 Fax: 0870 770 5694

This red cedarwood, purpose-built hostel sits on the Pennine Way, high above the little border town of Bellingham. But don't just make this a one-night stop while walking the epic long-distance route. Stay a while longer and you'll discover quiet lanes offering excellent cycling, and there's good walking on the Northumberland Moors too. Kielder Water, Europe's largest man-made lake, has watersports and miles of forest trails, with Hadrian's Wall nearby.

For more information visit www.yha.org.uk

● FAMILY ● CITY ● GROUP ● TRADITIONAL ● CAMPING BARN ● COASTAL ● RURAL

Location: OS 80, GR 843834.
Great for... an active, outdoor break.
You need to know... it's self-catering accommodation only.
Accommodation: 28 beds: 1x6-, 1x10- and 1x12-bed rooms.
Family rooms: No. **Rent-a-Hostel:** Yes.
Classroom: No. **Education packages:** No.
Facilities: Lounge/dining room, self-catering kitchen, showers, cycle store and grounds. Credit cards not accepted.
Daytime access: All areas. ⊗
Meals: Self-catering only.
Reception open: Staff available before 10.00hrs and after 17.00hrs.
Getting there: Heading north, turn right off B6320 in town centre (signposted West Woodburn), continue straight up main road and hostel is 600 metres on left.
Parking: Yes.
Nearest other hostels: Acomb 15 miles, Byrness 15 (via Pennine Way), Kielder 18, Once Brewed 18 (14 via Pennine Way).
Public transport: BUS: Tyne Valley 880 from Hexham (passes Hexham Station), Postbus 815 from Hexham morning and afternoon. RAIL: Hexham 16 miles. FERRY: Newcastle.

●● BYRNESS ☆

7 Otterburn Green, Byrness, Newcastle-upon-Tyne, Northumberland NE19 1TS;
reservations@yha.org.uk
Tel: 0870 770 5740 Fax: 0870 770 5740
Bookings more than 7 days ahead: 0870 770 6113

Two adjoining Forestry Commission houses have been converted to create a small, basic hostel that's ideal for exploring the northern part of the Northumberland National Park. Just five miles from the Scottish border, it lies on the Pennine Way in the foothills of the Cheviot Hills. From its doorstep, you can walk in practically every direction but don't miss out on a well-earned rest in the garden where red squirrels and roe deer are often seen.
Location: OS 80, GR 764027.
Great for... keen walkers who don't mind basic facilities.
You need to know... you should bring plenty of provisions as only limited supplies are available half a mile away.
Accommodation: 22 beds: 2x2- and 3x6-bed rooms.
Family rooms: No. **Rent-a-Hostel:** Yes.
Classroom: No. **Education packages:** No.
Facilities: Lounge/games room, self-catering kitchen, showers, cycle store and garden. **Daytime access:** Restricted. ⊗
Meals: Self-catering only. Packed lunches available if pre-booked.
Reception open: 17.00hrs.
Getting there: Turn off A68 at sign for Byrness.
Parking: Yes.
Nearest other hostels: Bellingham 15 miles, Kielder 15 (by part-surfaced toll road), Kirk Yetholm 27, Wooler 28 (all by Pennine Way).
Public transport: BUS: McEwans bus Edinburgh–Newcastle, daily except Sunday, National Express Edinburgh–Newcastle (passes close to Newcastle and Edinburgh stations). FERRY: Newcastle 40 miles. RAIL: Morpeth 34 miles, Newcastle 40.
 NATIONALEXPRESS》 Byrness lay-by 0.25 miles.

Mountain biking on the Pennine Way bridleway near YHA Byrness.

●● DUFTON ☆

Dufton, Appleby, Cumbria CA16 6DB;
dufton@yha.org.uk
Tel: 0870 770 5800 Fax: 0870 770 5801

This large stone house stands on the green in a quiet, pretty village on both the Pennine Way and Cumbria Cycle Way. Approach Cross Fell or High Cup Nick from here, or take a ride from Appleby on the famous Settle to Carlisle Railway. It's perfectly situated for exploring the moorland of the North Pennines or the green valleys of the River Eden.
Location: OS 91, GR 688251.
Great for... walkers and cyclists.
You need to know... this hostel may close during 2003. Please enquire before planning your stay.
Accommodation: 36 beds: 1x4- and 4x8-bed rooms.
Family rooms: No. **Rent-a-Hostel:** Yes.
Classroom: No. **Education packages:** No.
Facilities: Lounge, two dining rooms, self-catering kitchen, showers, drying room, cycle store, shop and garden.
Daytime access: All areas. ⊗
Meals: Breakfast, picnic lunch, evening meal.
Reception open: Staff available before 10.00hrs and after 17.00hrs.
Getting there: Leave A66 at Appleby, follow signs for Long Marton and Dufton, 3.5 miles.
Parking: Yes.
Nearest other hostels: Langdon Beck 12 miles (by Pennine Way), Kirkby Stephen 15, Alston 22 (by Pennine Way).
Public transport: RAIL: Appleby 3.5 miles, Penrith 13.

● FAMILY　● CITY　● GROUP　● TRADITIONAL　● CAMPING BARN　● COASTAL　● RURAL

●● EDMUNDBYERS ☆☆☆

**Low House, Edmundbyers, Consett, Co Durham
DH8 9NL; edmundbyers@yha.org.uk
Tel: 0870 770 5810 Fax: 0870 770 5810**

This hostel is a former inn dating from 1600 with beamed ceilings and a cosy open fire, and has been refurbished to provide a comfortable and memorable place to stay. The village of Edmundbyers is surrounded by a 360-degree panorama of heather moorland. Active outdoor folk will be keen to explore the country lanes and moorland of this Area of Outstanding Natural Beauty. It's only quarter of a mile from Derwent Reservoir which is ideal for watersports and trout fishing. All types of walker will be happy here – visit the picturesque village of Blanchland for a lowland stroll, or head on to the rugged uplands or to Hadrian's Wall for a day's hike.
Location: OS 87, GR 017500.
Great for... walkers, cyclists and mountain bikers of all abilities.
You need to know... camping is available; there's no shop in the village.
Accommodation: 29 beds: 1x3-, 1x4-, 2x5- and 2x6-bed rooms.
Family rooms: Yes. **Rent-a-Hostel:** Yes.
Classroom: No. **Education packages:** No.
Facilities: Self-catering kitchen, showers, drying room, cycle store, disabled shower and toilet unit. Small but well-stocked shop.
Daytime access: Restricted. ⊗
Meals: Self-catering only.
Reception open: 17.00hrs.
Getting there: The hostel is just off the A68 Darlington–Corbridge

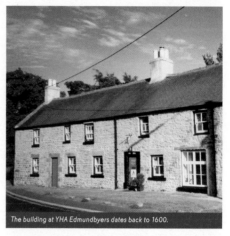
The building at YHA Edmundbyers dates back to 1600.

road, situated on the roadside just opposite the turning for the B6306 to Blanchland and Hexham.
Parking: Yes.
Nearest other hostels: Acomb 16 miles, Newcastle 20.
Public transport: BUS: Stanley Taxis 773 Consett–Townfield with connections on Go Northern 719, 765 Durham–Consett (passes close to Newcastle station); otherwise alight Consett 5 miles.
RAIL: Hexham 13 miles. FERRY: Newcastle 25 miles.

●● KIELDER

**Butteryhaugh, Kielder Village, Hexham,
Northumberland NE48 1HQ;
kielder@yha.org.uk
Tel: 0870 770 5898 Fax: 0870 770 5898**

Welcome to Britain's finest adventure playground for outdoor people. Kielder Forest has cycle trails, walking routes and birdwatching sites galore. Kielder Castle offers a dastardly dose of history, a tricky maze to complete and quiet woodland walks. And then there's Kielder Water, where you can try your hand at just about any watersport. After all that, you'll appreciate a rest at the hostel, which offers accommodation of a very high standard.
Location: OS 80, GR 632932.
Great for... fit and active folk wanting an energetic holiday.
Accommodation: 41 beds: 2x2-, 2x3-, 2x4-, 1x5- and 3x6-bed rooms.
Family rooms: Yes. **Rent-a-Hostel:** Yes.
Classroom: No. **Education packages:** No.
Facilities: Lounge, dining room, self-catering kitchen, cycle store, showers, drying room, shop.
Daytime access: Restricted. ⊗
Meals: Breakfast, picnic lunch, evening meal.
Reception open: 17.00hrs.

Getting there: The hostel is in the Butteryhaugh section of Kielder Village at the western end of Kielder Water.
Parking: Yes.
Nearest other hostels: Byrness 15 miles (toll), Bellingham 18.
Public transport: BUS: Snaith's 814, Postbus 815 (from Hexham station via Acomb and Bellingham morning and afternoon), also Arriva Northumbria 714 from Newcastle (Sun and Wed, June–Sept only). RAIL: Hexham 33 miles.

Take your pick from a wide range of watersports at YHA Kielder.

● FAMILY ● CITY ● GROUP ● TRADITIONAL ● CAMPING BARN ● COASTAL ● RURAL

●● GREENHEAD ☆☆☆

Greenhead, Brampton, Cumbria CA8 7HG;
greenhead@yha.org.uk
Tel: 0870 770 5842 Fax: 0870 770 5843

If you're planning on visiting the Hadrian's Wall Roman heritage sites, YHA Greenhead is very convenient. Mind you, the hostel has plenty of history of its own. It was built in 1886 as a Methodist Chapel, fuelled by the religious fervour of the village's mining population. The church gave its last service in 1972 and has been a hostel since 1978. Walkers of all levels will also find plenty of interest in the area and like-minded company in the lounge as YHA Greenhead is a popular stop on the Pennine Way.

Location: OS 86, GR 659655.
Great for... walkers with a head for history.
Accommodation: 40 beds: all 6–8-bed rooms.
Family rooms: No. **Rent-a-Hostel:** Yes.
Classroom: No. **Education packages:** No.
Facilities: Self-catering kitchen, showers, drying room, shop and cycle store. **Daytime access:** Restricted. 😣
Meals: Breakfast, picnic lunch, evening meal.
Reception open: 17.00hrs.
Getting there: From Carlisle take A69 to Newcastle. Turn off for Greenhead (34 miles), turn right at T-junction and hostel is on left opposite Greenhead Hotel. From Newcastle take A69 to Carlisle, turn right at Greenhead sign (45 miles), follow instructions above.

YHA Greenhead was an active Methodist chapel until 1972.

Parking: Roadside only.
Nearest other hostels: Once Brewed 7 miles, Ninebanks 16, Alston 17 (by Pennine Way), Carlisle 18.
Public transport: BUS: Arriva Northumbria 685 Carlisle–Newcastle-upon-Tyne (passes Haltwhistle station). RAIL: Haltwhistle 3 miles.

HOSTEL MANAGERS CHOOSE...

THE REGION'S BEST CYCLE TRAILS

North Pennines Cycle Web YHA Baldersdale: "You can visit all nine of the North Pennines Youth Hostels on this trail, suitable for anyone who is moderately fit. Contact 0870 770 8868 or any of the hostels on the route for a leaflet."

Hamsterley Forest YHA Baldersdale: "On summer Sundays and Bank Holidays, the Black Grouse Bike Bus travels between Newcastle and Barnard Castle with a loop to Hamsterley Forest, where you'll find bike hire and great mountain bike trails."

Pennine Cycleway YHA Wooler: "There's no better way to get off the beaten track. This new route runs from Cumbria to Berwick-upon-Tweed in north Northumberland through spectacular countryside."

Hadrian's Way Cycle Route YHA Once Brewed: "A great route for exploring Hadrian's Wall and the countryside between Lemington and Tynemouth. We're on the cycleway and have secure storage for bicycles."

The National Cycle Network YHA Baldersdale: "Route 68 goes from Berwick to Appleby, Route 1 from Middlesborough to Berwick. Then there's the C2C and the Reivers Way. Phew!"

● HOLWICK

campingbarns@yha.org.uk
Booking: 0870 770 6113
Arrival time: Mr & Mrs Scott, 01833 640506

If you've never stayed in a camping barn before, let Holwick be your first experience. After making the most of the walking all around, your return to the barn will be a pleasant surprise. The two field barns on Low Way Farm have heaters, gas cooking facilities and hot water, while there's a butcher's shop and café on the farm. For a camping barn, it's luxury indeed!

Accommodation: Sleeps 28 in bunkbeds in two areas.
Facilities: Sitting area, heaters, shower, gas cooking facilities (no oven), hot water, electric light and fridge (both on meter). Farmhouse café where meals can be ordered and butcher's shop.
Nearest pub: 0.5 miles. **Nearest shop:** 3 miles.
Location: OS 92, GR 914270.

● KIRK YETHOLM ☆☆

Kirk Yetholm, Kelso, Roxburghshire TD5 8PG;
reservations@syha.org.uk
Tel: 08701 553255

An excellent centre for hill walking, this Scottish hostel is close to the Cheviots and St Cuthbert's Way and at the northern end of the Pennine Way. Situated in beautiful surroundings, it's also within easy visiting distance of many historical sites including the Border castles and abbeys.

Location: OS 74, GR 082802.
Great for... those starting or finishing the Pennine Way and walking St Cuthbert's Way.
Accommodation: 22 beds: 2x2-, 1x4-, 1x6- and 1x8-bed rooms.
Family rooms: No. **Rent-a-Hostel:** No.

● FAMILY ● CITY ● GROUP ● TRADITIONAL ● CAMPING BARN ● COASTAL ● RURAL

Classroom: No. Education packages: No.
Facilities: Lounge, self-catering kitchen, showers, drying room, shop and cycle store. Daytime access: Restricted. Ⓢ
Meals: Self-catering only.
Reception open: 17.00hrs.
Getting there: The hostel lies 150 metres down the lane at the western corner of the village green.
Parking: Limited.
Nearest other hostels: Wooler 14 miles, Melrose (SYHA) 24, Byrness 27 (via Pennine Way), Coldingham (SYHA) 28.
Public transport: BUS: First Edinburgh/Swan/Northumbria 23 Berwick-upon-Tweed station, through on Sundays, but changing at Kelso on other days between 23 and First Edinburgh.
RAIL: Berwick-upon-Tweed 21 miles.

Facilities: Lounge/dining room, self-catering kitchen, showers, drying room, cycle store, laundry facilities and grounds.
Daytime access: Restricted. Ⓢ
Meals: Breakfast, picnic lunch, evening meal.
Reception open: 17.00hrs.
Getting there: The hostel is on the B6277, 7 miles northwest of Middleton-in-Teesdale.
Parking: Yes.
Nearest other hostels: Alston 15, Baldersdale 15 miles (by Pennine Way), Dufton 35 (12 by Pennine Way).
Public transport: BUS: Arriva North East 95/6 from Middleton-in-Teesdale (connections from Darlington station), alight High Force 2 miles. RAIL: Darlington 33 miles.

●● LANGDON BECK ☆☆

Forest-in-Teesdale, Barnard Castle, Co Durham
DL12 0XN; langdonbeck@yha.org.uk
Tel: 0870 770 5910 Fax: 0870 770 5911

Those of you who have 'gone green' will appreciate the environmental efforts made in this hostel. There are recycling and alternative energy breaks, as well as weekend courses on the outdoors and the environment. And you'll certainly appreciate the environment while you're here – in the centre of one of Britain's largest Areas of Outstanding Natural Beauty, this is one of the highest hostels in England with magnificent views across the North Pennines landscape from the lounge.

Location: OS 91, GR 860304.
Great for... active families with an environmental conscience.
Accommodation: 34 beds: 3x2-, 4x4- and 2x6-bed rooms.
Family rooms: Yes. Rent-a-Hostel: Yes.
Classroom: No. Education packages: Yes.

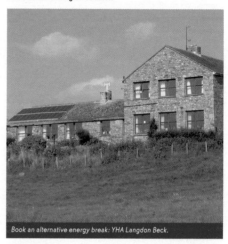

Book an alternative energy break: YHA Langdon Beck.

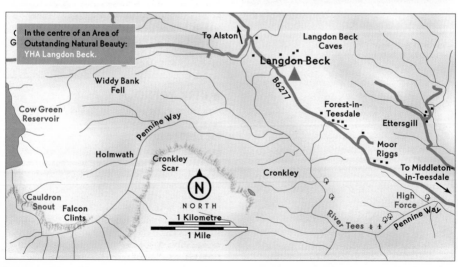

In the centre of an Area of Outstanding Natural Beauty: YHA Langdon Beck.

For offers and discounts visit www.yha.org.uk

● FAMILY ● CITY ● GROUP ● TRADITIONAL ● CAMPING BARN ● COASTAL ● RURAL

Shopping in Newcastle city centre.

● NEWCASTLE ☆

107 Jesmond Road, Newcastle-upon-Tyne,
Tyne & Wear NE2 1NJ; newcastle@yha.org.uk
Tel: 0870 770 5972 Fax: 0870 770 5973

Newcastle is the friendly, distinctive and undisputed capital of England's northeast. Located on the city fringe, this hostel is ideally placed for exploring the area's attractions on foot, by car or using public transport. Enjoy the modern attractions of Newcastle and the age-old splendour of Northumberland's coast and countryside.
Location: OS 88, GR 257656.
Great for... a busy city break.
You need to know... there are no drying or laundry facilities.
Accommodation: 58 beds: 5x2-, 2x4-, 4x6- and 2x8-bed rooms.
Family rooms: No. **Rent-a-Hostel:** No.
Classroom: No. **Education packages:** Yes.
Facilities: TV lounge, games room, self-catering kitchen, dining room, showers and cycle store. **Daytime access:** All areas.
Meals: Breakfast, picnic lunch, evening meal.
Reception open: From 7.00hrs to 23.00hrs.
Getting there: From the metro (underground) by foot – under 5 minutes' walking on left side of Jesmond Road East (A1058). By car, access the A1058 (Jesmond Road) from central motorway (A167M), which is left from the northwest or right from the south (see map on page 174).
Parking: Yes.
Nearest other hostels: Acomb 20 miles, Edmundbyers 20, Osmotherley 50, Wooler 50.
Public transport: BUS: Frequent from surrounding areas.
RAIL: Jesmond (Tyne & Wear Metro) 0.25 mile, Newcastle 1.5.
FERRY: 7 miles, services to Gothenburg via Kristiansand, Bergen–Stavanger and Amsterdam (all year).
NATIONALEXPRESS» Gallowgate coach station 1.5 miles.

●● NINEBANKS ☆

Orchard House, Mohope, Ninebanks, Hexham,
Northumberland NE47 8DQ;
ninebanks@yha.org.uk
Tel: 0870 770 5974 Fax: 0870 770 6109

This small hostel offers a quiet retreat. Originally a 17th century lead miner's cottage, it stands in the peaceful valley of Mohope Burn in the North Pennines Area of Outstanding Natural Beauty. Walkers can explore secluded countryside and wild moorland, both of which are rich in wildlife, flora, fauna and industrial archaeology. The hostel is also near the C2C cycle route and close to Killhope lead mining centre, the A686 (England's most scenic road) and Isaac's Tea Trail.
Location: OS 86, GR 771514.
Great for... walkers, cyclists and those seeking peace and quiet.
You need to know... it's a 5-mile trip to the nearest pub.
Accommodation: 24 beds: 1x4-, 2x6- and 1x8-bed rooms.
Family rooms: Yes. **Rent-a-Hostel:** Yes.
Classroom: No. **Education packages:** No.
Facilities: Common room, self-catering kitchen, showers, drying room, laundry, shop and cycle store. **Daytime access:** Restricted.
Meals: Self-catering only. Group catering by prior arrangement.
Reception open: 17.00hrs.
Getting there: Signposted from A686 south of Whitfield. The hostel is at Mohope, signposted from Ninebanks hamlet (see map on page 175).
Parking: Yes.
Nearest other hostels: Alston 8 miles, Greenhead 16, Edmundbyers 26.
Public transport: BUS: Wrights (tel: 01434 381200) Hexham Alston, Tues and Fri only (passes close to Hexham and Haydon Bridge stations), otherwise 888 Keswick–Newcastle-upon-Tyne (passes Penrith, Hexham and Haydon Bridge stations), alight Ouston 1 mile. RAIL: Haydon Bridge 11 miles. FERRY: Newcastle 38 miles.

YHA Ninebanks offers a quiet retreat for walkers.

See how the Romans lived at Vindolanda near YHA Once Brewed.

●● ONCE BREWED ☆

**Military Road, Bardon Mill, Northumberland
NE47 7AN; oncebrewed@yha.org.uk
Tel: 0870 770 5980 Fax: 0870 770 5981**

Few folk venture to Northumberland without walking a part of Hadrian's Wall and this purpose-built hostel is just half a mile from its most spectacular section. Being two miles north of Bardon Mill, it's also within easy walking distance of Vindolanda, where you can see how the Romans lived, and Housesteads Fort, the most complete Roman fort in Britain. Once you've had your fill of history, the hills of the Northumberland National Park await.

Location: OS 86, GR 752668.
Great for... visiting Hadrian's Wall.
Accommodation: 77 beds: mostly 4-, 1x5-, some 6- and 1x8-bed rooms.
Family rooms: Yes. **Rent-a-Hostel:** No.
Classroom: No. **Education packages:** Yes.
Facilities: Lounge, small self-catering kitchen, dining room, showers, toilets, dormitories, games room, laundry, drying room, garden and cycle store. **Daytime access:** All areas. ☺
Meals: Breakfast, picnic lunch, evening meal.
Reception open: 14.00hrs.
Getting there: Hostel is on B6318 above Bardon Mill.
Parking: Yes.
Nearest other hostels: Greenhead 7 miles, Acomb 15, Bellingham 15, Ninebanks 16 (12 by path), Alston 23.
Public transport: BUS: White Star 185 from Carlisle, Stagecoach in Cumbria AD122 (passes Hexham and Haltwhistle stations) June–Sept, otherwise Northumbria 685 Carlisle–Newcastle, alight Henshaw 2 miles. RAIL: Bardon Mill 2.5 miles.

● WEARHEAD

**campingbarns@yha.org.uk
Booking: 0870 770 6113
Arrival time: Mr Walton, 01388 537395**

This farmhouse is a listed building and has been carefully converted to a camping barn. Just half a mile away from the Weardale Way,

there are plenty of local walks in the area. Make sure you're a dab hand at lighting fires – coal is available at cost price for the open fire, which also heats the water.
You need to know... there's no electricity.
Accommodation: Sleeps 12 on the first floor.
Facilities: Cooking, eating and sitting area, toilet, open fire (coal available to buy).
Nearest pub: 1 mile. **Nearest shop:** 1 mile.
Location: OS 91, GR 851397.

● WITTON

**campingbarns@yha.org.uk
Booking: 0870 770 6113
Arrival time: Witton Estate, 01388 488322**

A former barn and dairy, this camping barn is on the Witton Castle estate. You'll find plenty to do. The facilities include an outdoor swimming pool, public bars, games and television rooms, a shop and café in the grounds of the 15th century castle. For more rural entertainment, the Weardale Way is just half a mile away.
Accommodation: Sleeps 15.
Facilities: Cooking and eating area with cooker, toilets, electric light, wood-burning stove and shower.
Nearest pub: 0.5 miles. **Nearest shop:** 0.5 miles.
Location: OS 92, GR 155298.

HOSTEL MANAGERS CHOOSE...

THE BEST LOCAL SPOTS FOR WILDLIFE

St Mary's Island (seals) YHA Newcastle: "A fascinating marine reserve across a tidal causeway from the mainland. Don't forget to look out for the porpoises too."
North Pennines (black grouse) YHA Baldersdale: "The North Pennines is the last stronghold of the black grouse in England. I've even seen these fascinating birds performing elaborate mating displays in the hostel grounds."
Teeside (wild flowers) YHA Langdon Beck: "Teesdale is home to the blue gentian and the famous Teesdale Assemblage with some of the country's rarest plants. We'll tell you where to see them."
Kielder (red squirrels) YHA Kielder: "Guests are always pleased to see our red squirrels. They're few and far between in England today, but they still have a stronghold at Kielder where you can watch the nut-hoarders in their natural environment."
Langdon Beck (breeding waders) YHA Langdon Beck: "We offer regular birdwatching weekends, perfect for viewing breeding waders such as golden plover, lapwing, curlew and snipe."

For current prices visit www.yha.org.uk

● FAMILY ● CITY ● GROUP ● TRADITIONAL ● CAMPING BARN ● COASTAL ● RURAL

Ride part of the 200-mile Steel Bonnet cycle route from YHA Wooler.

●● WOOLER (CHEVIOT) ☆

**30 Cheviot St, Wooler, Northumberland
NE71 6LW; wooler@yha.org.uk
Tel: 0870 770 6100 Fax: 0870 770 6101**

Wooler makes an ideal base from which to explore the foothills of the Cheviots, Dunstanburgh Castle and Holy Island. Keen walkers will want to sample St Cuthbert's Way and the Ravenber long-distance walks that pass through the town, while cyclists can ride part of the 200-mile Steel Bonnet cycle route. Weather permitting, a boat trip to the Farne Islands will keep birdwatchers smiling.

Location: OS 75, GR 991278.
Great for... walkers, cyclists and birdwatchers.
Accommodation: 46 beds: 4x2-, 8x4- and 1x6-bed rooms.
Family rooms: No. **Rent-a-Hostel:** Yes.
Classroom: No. **Education packages:** No.
Facilities: Common room, self-catering kitchen, showers, drying room, laundry facilities and cycle store.
Daytime access: All areas. ♿
Meals: Breakfast, picnic lunch, evening meal.
Reception open: Staff available before 10.00hrs and after 17.00hrs.
Getting there: Heading towards Coldstream on the A697, turn left for the town centre and then first left at the top of the hill up Cheviot Street. Go up road past Anchor Pub for 400 metres and then down drive on right-hand side marked YHA. If coming from Scotland, follow the signs for Wooler and, at the end of the High Street, turn right after the Bank of Scotland in Cheviot Street.
Parking: Yes.
Nearest other hostels: Kirk Yetholm (SYHA) 14 miles, Byrness 28 (by path), Newcastle 50.
Public transport: BUS: IDM Travelsure 464, Border Village 267 from Berwick-upon-Tweed (passes close to Berwick-upon-Tweed station), IDM Travelsure 470/3 from Alnwick, with connections from Newcastle. RAIL: Berwick-upon-Tweed 16 miles.

Views of Holy Island after a day's riding near YHA Wooler.

TRY RENT-A-HOSTEL

Many of the hostels in Northumberland and the North Pennines can be booked through the Rent-a-Hostel scheme. For full details, turn to page 26.

To make a booking visit www.yha.org.uk

The Youth Hostels of…
The Lake District

Stunning landscapes: few regions of the country can match the views on offer in the Lake District.

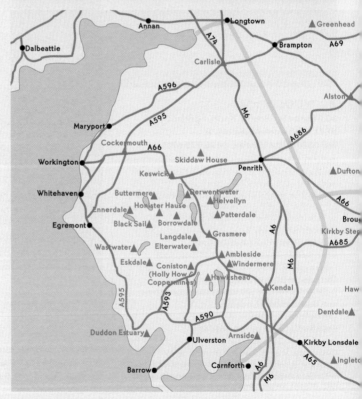

For further information visit www.yha.org.uk

● FAMILY ● CITY ● GROUP ● TRADITIONAL ● CAMPING BARN ● COASTAL ● RURAL

● ● AMBLESIDE ☆☆☆

Waterhead, Ambleside, Cumbria LA22 OEU;
ambleside@yha.org.uk
Tel: 0870 770 5672 Fax: 0870 770 5673

Ambleside is in the very heart of the Lake District and a popular base for watersports, walking and climbing enthusiasts. This large hostel is just outside a busy village on the shores of Lake Windermere. The views from the hostel lounge and many of the waterfront bedrooms are outstanding and, should you feel the need for an extra degree of comfort, premium rooms are available.
Location: OS 90, GR 377031.
Great for... outdoor people wanting a range of activities nearby.
Accommodation: 245 beds: 43x2–5- and 16x6–8-bed rooms.
Family rooms: Yes. **Rent-a-Hostel:** No.
Classroom: No. **Education packages:** Yes.
Facilities: Reception, lounges, games room, residential licence, TV room, coffee shop, luggage store, laundry, drying room, self-catering kitchen, showers, internet access and cycle store.
Daytime access: All areas.
Meals: Breakfast, picnic lunch, evening meal. Hot buffet lunch by arrangement.
Reception open: 7.15hrs to 23.45hrs (24hr access March–Oct).
Getting there: The hostel is 1 mile south of Ambleside village at Waterhead on the A591 Windermere Road by Steamer Pier.
Parking: Yes.

YHA Ambleside offers watersports for all abilities nearby.

Nearest other hostels: Windermere 3 miles, Langdale 4, Grasmere Butterlip How 5.
Public transport: BUS: During spring, summer and autumn, the YHA Shuttlebus meets most trains at Windermere station until the early evening, offering a free transfer to the Youth Hostel. Stagecoach services from surrounding areas (many pass Windermere station). RAIL: Windermere 4 miles.
NATIONALEXPRESS» King Street 1 mile.

● ● ARNSIDE ☆

Redhills Road, Arnside, Cumbria LA5 0AT;
arnside@yha.org.uk
Tel: 0870 770 5674 Fax: 0870 770 5675

If you love the Lake District but not its summer crowds, try YHA Arnside. This mellow Edwardian-Tudor house is positioned above the waters of Morecambe Bay and boasts great views of the Lake District mountains. It's a good touring base both for the Lakes and the western Yorkshire Dales and you'll find a variety of walks in the area. Birdwatchers will enjoy the RSPB reserve nearby and wildlife lovers shouldn't miss Arnside Knott, famous for its butterflies.
Location: OS 97, GR 452783.
Great for... a quiet base for wildlife wanders.
Accommodation: 72 beds: all 2–9-bed rooms.
Family rooms: Yes. **Rent-a-Hostel:** No.
Classroom: Yes. **Education packages:** Yes.
Facilities: Lounge with TV, sitting room, self-catering kitchen, drying room, games room, map room, showers, cycle store and garden. **Daytime access:** All areas.
Meals: Breakfast, picnic lunch, evening meal.
Reception open: Staff available before 10.00hrs and after 17.00hrs.
Getting there: From south, leave M6 at J35 and take A6 to Milnthorpe. From north, leave M6 at J36, turn left and immediately left again onto A65 (Crooklands), then left on B6385 to Milnthorpe. Take B5282 to Arnside.

Parking: Yes.
Nearest other hostels: Kendal 12 miles, Hawkshead 18, Ingleton 19, Slaidburn 32.
Public transport: BUS: Stagecoach 552 from Kendal.
RAIL: Arnside 1 mile. FERRY: Heysham to Isle of Man 15 miles (rail link) and Belfast (summer only).

● BENTS

Booking: 017687 72645
Arrival time: Dorothy Ousby, 017683 71760 (home) or 015396 23681 (farm)

The building of this camping barn dates back to the 17th century. Walkers will find plenty to do here as the barn is close to the Howgill Fells, Sunbiggin Tarn and Smardale Gill Nature Reserve and on the Coast-to-Coast long-distance path.
Great for... the Coast-to-Coast, walking and enjoying the countryside.
You need to know... it's one mile from the village; there's parking at the farm and accommodation for tents nearby.
Accommodation: Sleeps 12 in bunk beds on first floor, foam mattresses are provided.
Facilities: Electric lighting, heating, power points (£1 meter), cooking facilities with cutlery and crockery.
Nearest pub: 2 miles. **Nearest shop:** 6 miles.
Location: OS 91, GR 708065.

The Lake District

● FAMILY   ● CITY   ● GROUP   ● TRADITIONAL   ● CAMPING BARN   ● COASTAL   ● RURAL

● BLAKE BECK

Booking: 017687 72645

This 18th century camping barn is on the edge of the northern fells, close to Blencathra. The landscape up here is dramatic and you will no doubt be tempted to explore. Just as well, then, that Ullswater and Aira Force are only five miles away and Carrock Fell is nearby.

Great for... exploring the northern fells.

You need to know... there's an adjoining farmhouse and self-catering complex.

Accommodation: Sleeps 12 on first floor. Access is via external stone steps and mattresses are provided.

Facilities: Cooking/eating area, metered showers, toilets, washbasins, wash-up area, electric light, hot water, radiators and cooking hob available for hire, metered electricity. Locked cycle shed and drying room.

Nearest pub: 2 miles. **Nearest shop:** 5 miles.

Location: OS 90, GR 367278.

●● BORROWDALE ☆☆☆

Longthwaite, Borrowdale, Keswick, Cumbria CA12 5XE; borrowdale@yha.org.uk
Tel: 0870 770 5706 Fax: 0870 770 5707

Surrounded by mountains, Borrowdale offers all the comfort and facilities of a large Lakeland hostel while retaining a relaxed, informal atmosphere. Derwentwater is ideal for watersports, Whinlatter Forest Park offers orienteering courses and Keswick has mountain bikes for hire. There are many local walking routes too and the hostel lies on the long-distance Coast-to-Coast path and the Cumbria Way.

Location: OS 90, GR 254142.

Great for... families wanting a varied outdoor holiday.

Accommodation: 88 beds: mostly 2-, 4- and 6- plus 1x8-bed rooms (2 rooms converted for disabled access with shower and toilet opposite).

Family rooms: Yes. **Rent-a-Hostel:** No.

Classroom: Yes. **Education packages:** Yes.

●● BLACK SAIL ☆

Black Sail Hut, Ennerdale, Cleator, Cumbria CA23 3AY
Tel: 07711 108450 Fax: 07711 159472

Black Sail is a legend, famous for being a remote and isolated shepherd's bothy at the head of Ennerdale, accessible only on foot. This location provides great access to the surrounding fells: Great Gable, Pillar, Red Pike and Steeple to name a few. It's on the Coast-to-Coast walking route and is renowned as a base for enjoying the mountains of the Lake District.

Location: OS 89, GR 194124.

Great for... hardcore walkers with a sense of adventure.

You need to know... there's no access to the hostel by car; YHA Black Sail now has electrical supply (but no electrical sockets).

Accommodation: 16 beds: 2x4- and 1x8-bed rooms.

Family rooms: Yes. **Rent-a-Hostel:** Yes.

Classroom: No. **Education packages:** No.

Facilities: Sitting/dining room, self-catering kitchen, shower, shop, drying room and table licence.

Daytime access: All areas. ⊗

Meals: Breakfast, picnic lunch, evening meal.

Reception open: Staff are available before 10.00hrs and after 17.00hrs.

Getting there: The nearest roads are the summit of Honister Pass or Gatesgarth in the Buttermere Valley. From either, it is a 2.5-mile mountain walk to the hostel. Alternatively, walk or cycle along the forest track in the Ennerdale Valley or take the mountain walk over Black Sail Pass from Wastwater.

Parking: No.

Nearest other hostels: Honister 2.5 miles, Buttermere 3.5, Ennerdale 4.

Public transport: BUS: Stagecoach 77/A from Keswick, alight Honister 3 miles, Apr–Oct only; otherwise 79 Keswick–Seatoller, then 3.5 miles (for train connections see YHA Keswick). RAIL: Whitehaven 19 miles.

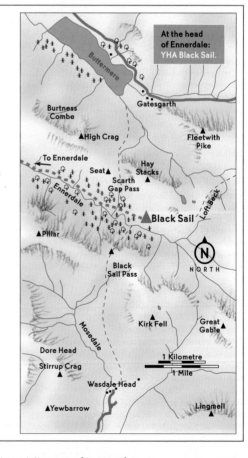

At the head of Ennerdale: YHA Black Sail.

FAMILY CITY ⬤ GROUP ⬤ TRADITIONAL ⬤ CAMPING BARN ⬤ COASTAL ⬤ RURAL

Facilities: Lounge, self-catering kitchen (with disabled access), dining room, drying room, showers, laundry, shop, cycle store and grounds.
Daytime access: All areas. 🚭
Meals: Breakfast, picnic lunch, evening meal.
Reception open: 13.00hrs.
Getting there: Follow Borrowdale signs and take B5289 from Keswick. Turn second right after Rosthwaite village. Follow YHA signs to lane end.
Parking: Yes.
Nearest other hostels: Honister 2 miles, Derwentwater 5, Buttermere 7.
Public transport: BUS: Stagecoach 79 from Keswick (for train connections see YHA Keswick).
RAIL: Workington 25 miles, Penrith 26.

A classic Lakeland view of Derwentwater, near YHA Borrowdale.

www.britainonview.com

⬤⬤ BUTTERMERE ☆☆☆

Buttermere, Cockermouth, Cumbria CA13 9XA;
buttermere@yha.org.uk
Tel: 0870 770 5736 Fax: 0870 770 5737

If you're visiting the Lakes in high summer, Buttermere offers a quieter corner where many tourists never venture. Crummock Water and Buttermere are within a stone's throw of the hostel and Loweswater and the Vale of Lorton are within easy reach. Walks for all levels of experience start from the doorstep. Afterwards, relax in the lounge and enjoy views of Red Pike and along to High Stile.
Location: OS 89, GR 178168.
Great for... families and walkers looking for a quieter break.
Accommodation: 70 beds: 1x2- but mostly 4–6-bed rooms.
Family rooms: Yes. **Rent-a-Hostel:** No.
Classroom: No. **Education packages:** Yes.
Facilities: Lounges, dining room, self-catering kitchen, table licence, showers, drying room and cycle store.
Daytime access: All areas. 🚭

Meals: Breakfast, picnic lunch, evening meal.
Reception open: Staff available before 10.00hrs and after 17.00hrs.
Getting there: The hostel is 0.5 miles south of Buttermere village on B5289 road to Honister Pass and Borrowdale.
Parking: Yes.
Nearest other hostels: Black Sail by mountain path 3.5 miles, Honister 4, Borrowdale 7.
Public transport: BUS: Stagecoach 77/A from Keswick (Apr–Oct only). RAIL: Workington 18 miles.

⬤ CARLISLE

Old Brewery Residences, Bridge Lane,
Caldewgate, Carlisle CA2 5SR;
dee.carruthers@unn.ac.uk
Tel: 0870 770 5752 Fax: 0870 770 5752

Stay in an award-winning conversion of the former Theakston's Brewery. These university halls of residence offer comfortable rooms just a few minutes' walk from Carlisle's city centre and historic castle. Also within easy reach are Hadrian's Wall and the Lake District.
Location: OS 85, GR 394560.
Great for... shopping, exploring Hadrian's Wall and a stop en-route to Scotland.
You need to know... this accommodation is only available during the university's summer holiday period.
Accommodation: 56 beds: single beds in flats for up to 7 people.
Family rooms: No. **Rent-a-Hostel:** No.
Classroom: No. **Education packages:** No.
Facilities: Self-catering kitchens, bathrooms, cycle store and laundry. **Daytime access:** Restricted. 🚭
Meals: Self-catering only.
Reception open: 17.00hrs.
Getting there: Head for Carlisle town centre and take A595 west. The Old Brewery Residences are on the right past the castle.
Parking: Yes.
Nearest other hostels: Greenhead 18 miles, Cockermouth 24.
Public transport: BUS: Local services to Wigton/West Cumbria and central Lakes. RAIL: Carlisle 1 mile.
NATIONAL EXPRESS Carlisle Bus Station 1 mile.

⬤ CATBELLS

Booking: 017687 72645

Part of a traditional set of farm buildings dating back to the 14th century, this camping barn is on the slopes of Catbells in the tranquil Newlands Valley. The Cumberland Way passes through the farmyard and both Borrowdale and Buttermere are within walking distance.
Great for... exploring the northern fells.
Accommodation: Sleeps 12, mattresses provided.
Facilities: Shower, electric light, electric point, cooking area and toilet in adjacent building, hot water, gas heaters. Breakfast may be booked in advance.
Nearest pub: 1 mile. **Nearest shop:** 2 miles.
Location: OS 90, GR 243208.

● FAMILY ● CITY ● GROUP ● TRADITIONAL ● CAMPING BARN ● COASTAL ● RURAL

●● COCKERMOUTH ☆

Double Mills, Cockermouth, Cumbria CA13 0DS;
reservations@yha.org.uk
Tel: 0870 770 5768 Fax: 0870 770 5768
Bookings more than 7 days ahead: 0870 770 6113

This 17th century watermill on the banks of the River Cocker is just a 10-minute walk from the centre of busy Cockermouth where you'll find William Wordsworth's birthplace and Jenning's Brewery. Crummock Water and Loweswater are both within easy reach, as is excellent walking on the quiet western edge of the Lake District. It's also popular with cyclists riding the Coast-to-Coast route.
Location: OS 89, GR 118298.
Great for... those combining touring with walking.
You need to know... parking is limited.
Accommodation: 26 beds: 1x4-, 1x10- and 1x12-bed rooms.
Family rooms: No. **Rent-a-Hostel:** Yes.
Classroom: No. **Education packages:** No.
Facilities: Lounge, self-catering kitchen, showers, drying room, large cycle store and grounds. **Daytime access:** Restricted. ⊗
Meals: Self-catering only.
Reception open: 17.00hrs.
Getting there: From Main Street follow Station Street, then left into Fern Bank and at the end take the track. From A66, take A5086 to Cockermouth then first right into Park Avenue. At the end turn right down track.
Parking: Yes, but limited.
Nearest other hostels: Buttermere 10 miles, Skiddaw House 12, Keswick 13, Derwentwater 15.
Public transport: BUS: Stagecoach X4/5 Penrith Station–Workington (passes close to Workington and Penrith stations). RAIL: Workington 8 miles.
NATIONALEXPRESS» Monument, Main Street 0.5 miles.

●● CONISTON COPPERMINES ☆☆

Coniston, Cumbria LA21 8HP;
coppermines@yha.org.uk
Tel: 0870 770 5772 Fax: 0870 770 5772

If you're planning to scale the slopes of the Old Man of Coniston, give yourself a head start by staying at Coniston Coppermines. Almost halfway up a mountain with a view to match, this hostel is surrounded by fells, allowing hillwalkers easy access onto Wetherlam and the Old Man of Coniston itself.
Location: OS 96, GR 289986.
Great for... walkers who want to stay in the hills.
You need to know... the track leading to the hostel is unsurfaced; the hostel is 1.25 miles from the village.
Accommodation: 26 beds: 3x4-, 1x6- and 1x8-bed rooms.
Family rooms: No. **Rent-a-Hostel:** Yes.
Classroom: No. **Education packages:** No.
Facilities: Common room, self-catering kitchen, dining room, showers, drying room, residential licence and cycle store.
Daytime access: All areas.
Meals: Breakfast, picnic lunch, evening meal.

Reception open: Staff available before 10.00hrs and after 17.00hrs.
Getting there: From Coniston, take road between Black Bull pub and Co-op supermarket, and opposite post office, signposted to hostel, which becomes a mile-long track. Pass several waterfalls on left and, as the track levels, the hostel can be seen at head of valley.
Parking: Yes.
Nearest other hostels: Coniston Holly How 1.25 miles, Elterwater 6, Hawkshead 6.
Public transport: BUS: Stagecoach 505/6 from Ambleside (with connections from Windermere station), then 1 mile. RAIL: Ulverston 14 miles.

Have the hills on your doorstep, stay at YHA Coniston Coppermines.

●● CONISTON HOLLY HOW ☆☆

Far End, Coniston, Cumbria LA21 8DD;
conistonhh@yha.org.uk
Tel: 0870 770 5770 Fax: 0870 770 5771

Leave your car at home and enjoy a wide range of activities from this hostel. All levels of walking routes, including the Old Man of Coniston, lead from the hostel's door, as do some of Britain's finest mountain biking trails. Sail, canoe or cruise on the lake, climb a classic Lake District crag or try pony trekking. John Ruskin's home and museum and lots of Arthur Ransome connections are nearby.
Location: OS 96, GR 302980.
Great for... a family holiday to please all tastes.
Accommodation: 60 beds: 4x4-, 4x8- and 1x12-bed rooms.
Family rooms: Yes. **Rent-a-Hostel:** No.
Classroom: No. **Education packages:** Yes.
Facilities: Lounge, games/TV room, drying room, self-catering

To make a booking visit www.yha.org.uk

● FAMILY ● CITY ● GROUP ● TRADITIONAL ● CAMPING BARN ● COASTAL ● RURAL

Lake Coniston is near YHAs Coniston Coppermines and Holly How.

kitchen, showers, cycle store, laundry facilities and garden.
Daytime access: All areas. ⊗
Meals: Breakfast, picnic lunch, evening meal.
Reception open: Staff available before 10.00hrs and after 17.00hrs.
Getting there: From Coniston village take A593 towards Ambleside. After 200 metres look for hostel sign on old-fashioned finger post, pointing the way to hostel up a short lane on left.
Parking: Yes.
Nearest other hostels: Coniston Coppermines 1.25 miles, Hawkshead 5, Elterwater 5.
Public transport: BUS: Stagecoach in Cumbria 505/6 from Ambleside (with connections from Windermere station) and X12/512 from Ulverston. RAIL: Ulverston 13 miles, Windermere 13.

● CRAGG
Booking: 017687 72645

This camping barn is among traditional buildings on a typical hill farm with hardy Herdwick sheep. In one of the least developed (and quietest) valleys in the Lake District, between Buttermere and Crummock Water, it provides a good base for walking, climbing and fishing. Book your break here for peace and a plethora of outdoor activities.
Great for... exploring the northwest Lakes.
Accommodation: Sleeps 8 on the first floor.
Facilities: Cooking slab, eating area, electric light, toilet and shower.
Nearest pub: 0.5 miles. **Nearest shop:** 6 miles.
Location: OS 90, GR 174172.

●● DERWENTWATER ☆☆☆
Barrow House, Borrowdale, Keswick, Cumbria
CA12 5UR; derwentwater@yha.org.uk
Tel: 0870 770 5792 Fax: 0870 770 5793

This 200-year-old mansion is ideally suited for a relaxing family or group break. Boasting extensive grounds with a large play area and woodlands, children will find plenty of space in which to vent excess energy. It's also right on the shore of Derwentwater, which many say is the most picturesque lake in Britain, and has a waterfall in the grounds. The lake itself will keep you occupied for days – children can paddle while the more adventurous take part in a wide variety of watersports. Or catch the launch nearby and stop off at any of the six jetties to explore the shoreline. There is also a selection of spectacular walks to suit all levels.
Location: OS 89, GR 268200.
Great for... a relaxing family holiday.
Accommodation: 88 beds: mostly 4–8-, 1x10- and 1x22-bed rooms.
Family rooms: Yes. **Rent-a-Hostel:** No.
Classroom: No. **Education packages:** Yes.
Facilities: Common rooms, games room, self-catering kitchen, TV room, cycle store, table licence, drying room, laundry, showers and toilets. **Daytime access:** All areas.
Meals: Breakfast, picnic lunch, evening meal.
Reception open: All day.
Getting there: From Keswick, follow the signs to Borrowdale. The hostel is 2 miles south on the Borrowdale road (B5289), 100 metres on the left past the turn off to Watendlath. Walkers should follow the lakeside path from Keswick.
Parking: Yes.
Nearest other hostels: Keswick 2 miles, Borrowdale 5.
Public transport: BUS: Stagecoach 79 Keswick–Seatoller (for rail connections see YHA Keswick). RAIL: Penrith 20 miles, Windermere 24. FERRY: Boat from Keswick.
NATIONAL EXPRESS» Keswick 2.25 miles.

YHA Derwentwater: on the shore of the most picturesque lake in Britain.

● FAMILY ● CITY ● GROUP ● TRADITIONAL ● CAMPING BARN ● COASTAL ● RURAL

● DINAH HOGGUS

Booking: 017687 72645

This traditional Lakeland field barn of Hogg-house is now a camping barn. Near the hamlet of Rosthwaite in the Borrowdale Valley and beside the old packhorse route to Watendlath, it is convenient for the Coast-to-Coast walk.

Great for... exploring the Borrowdale Valley.

You need to know... access to the first-floor sleeping is via external stone steps.

Accommodation: Sleeps 12 on the first floor.

Facilities: Cooking and eating area, electric kettle, washbasin, toilet, radiator available for hire and metered electricity.

Nearest pub: 300 metres. **Nearest shop:** 200 metres.

Location: OS 90, GR 259151.

Walk the packhorse trail to Watendlath near Dinah Hoggus.

●● DUDDON ESTUARY ☆☆☆

Borwick Rails, Millom, Cumbria LA18 4JU;
duddon@yha.org.uk
Tel: 0870 770 6107 Fax: 0870 770 6108

This purpose-built hostel sits on the banks of the Duddon Estuary with a stunning panorama of the Lake District fells. It's the ideal location for walkers, cyclists, birdwatchers and botanists and is on the Cumbria Cycle Way and Cumbria Coastal Way. Hodbarrow RSPB Reserve is a mile away and it's a short walk to a long sandy beach. Available primarily as Rent-a-Hostel, it can be booked by individuals.

Location: OS 96, GR 188798.

Great for... a holiday with a group of active friends.

You need to know... individuals should check availability 14 days ahead of your stay.

Accommodation: 18 beds: 1x2- and 2x8-bed rooms.

Family rooms: No. **Rent-a-Hostel:** Yes.

Classroom: No. **Education packages:** No.

Facilities: Lounge/dining room, kitchen, showers, laundry facilities, grounds and cycle store. **Daytime access:** Restricted. ◒

Meals: Self-catering only.

Reception open: 17.00hrs.

Getting there: Turn off A5093 over the railway bridge into Millom town centre. Go through market place and continue on Devonshire

Road for 1 mile, passing rugby club and Duddon Pilot Hotel. At end of the road there is a YHA sign and hostel is down lane on left.

Parking: Yes.

Nearest other hostels: Coniston Holly How 16 miles, Coniston Coppermines 17, Eskdale 20, Arnside 40.

Public transport: BUS: Stagecoach 511 from Ulverston and Broughton, X6 from Whitehaven station and St Bees, X7 from Barrow. Alight Millom 1 mile. RAIL: Millom (not Sun) 1.25 miles.

●● ELTERWATER ☆☆

Elterwater, Ambleside, Cumbria LA22 9HX;
elterwater@yha.org.uk
Tel: 0870 770 5816 Fax: 0870 770 5817

Converted from Elterwater's oldest farm, this hostel is superbly located for the Langdale fells in a popular, but peaceful village. Accommodation is comfortable, warm and friendly, the food is good and the pub and village shop are close to hand. There are outdoor

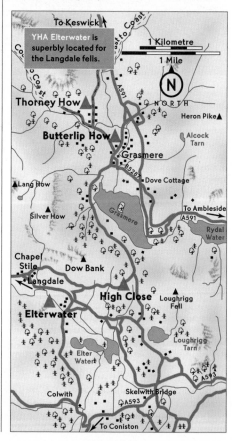

YHA Elterwater is superbly located for the Langdale fells.

● FAMILY ● CITY ● GROUP ● TRADITIONAL ● CAMPING BARN ● COASTAL ● RURAL

activities for all levels, with easy access to the Cumbria Way, road and mountain biking trails and crags for rock climbing.
Location: OS 90, GR 327046.
Great for... peace, quiet and walks for all abilities.
You need to know... parking is very limited at the hostel.
Accommodation: 43 beds: 6x2-, 1x3-, 1x4- and 4x6-bed rooms.
Family rooms: No. **Rent-a-Hostel:** No.
Classroom: No. **Education packages:** No.
Facilities: Self-catering kitchen, lounge/dining room, showers, drying room, cycle store, garden and internet access.
Daytime access: All areas. ⊗
Meals: Breakfast, picnic lunch, evening meal.
Reception open: Staff available before 10.00hrs and after 17.00hrs.
Getting there: Take A593 from Ambleside in Coniston direction. After 2 miles (Skelwith Bridge) turn right onto B5343, signposted Elterwater. After 2 miles cross a cattle grid and take next left signposted Elterwater 0.25 miles. Go through village and cross bridge. Hostel is 100 metres on right.
Parking: Free parking for National Trust Members, otherwise pay and display.

The Lake District has miles and miles of great cycling.

www.britainonview.com

Nearest other hostels: Langdale 1 mile, Ambleside 4, Grasmere 4.
Public transport: BUS: Stagecoach 516 from Ambleside (connections from Windermere station), YHA Shuttlebus.
RAIL: Windermere 8 miles.
NATIONALEXPRESS Ambleside, King Street 3.5 miles.

●● ENNERDALE ☆

Cat Crag, Ennerdale, Cleator, Cumbria
CA23 3AX; ennerdale@yha.org.uk
Tel: 0870 770 5820 Fax: 0870 770 5821

Two forestry cottages form this hostel in a remote wooded valley surrounded by fells, ridges and many famous peaks. Forest tracks offer sheltered, low-level walks and cycle rides while upland routes will challenge the more adventurous. It's also on the Coast-to-Coast walk, Sculpture Trail and the Ennerdale to Whitehaven cycle path.
Location: OS 89, GR 142141.
Great for... keen walkers who enjoy a remote location.
You need to know... Ennerdale now has electricity.
Accommodation: 24 beds comprised of 3x4- and 2x6-bed rooms.
Family rooms: No. **Rent-a-Hostel:** Yes.
Classroom: No. **Education packages:** No.
Facilities: Self-catering kitchen, common room, drying room, showers, alcohol licence and grounds. Limited shop.
Daytime access: All areas. ⊗
Meals: Breakfast, picnic lunch, evening meal.
Reception open: Staff available before 10.00hrs and after 17.00hrs.
Getting there: The hostel is 2.5 miles from Bowness Knott car park along Forest Road, 5 miles from Ennerdale Bridge.
Parking: Limited.
Nearest other hostels: Buttermere 3 miles (by path), Black Sail 4, Honister 7.
Public transport: BUS: Stagecoach 77/A from Keswick (Apr–Oct only), alight Buttermere 3 miles by path, and 263 from Buttermere

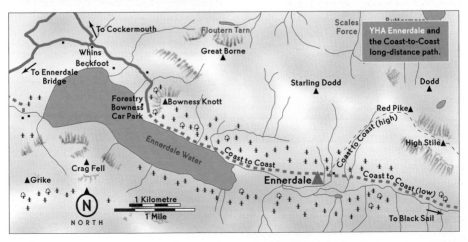

To Cockermouth
Floutern Tarn
Scales Force
Buttermere
YHA Ennerdale and the Coast-to-Coast long-distance path.
Whins
Beckfoot
Great Borne
To Ennerdale Bridge
Forestry Bowness Car Park
Bowness Knott
Starling Dodd
Dodd
Red Pike
Ennerdale Water
Coast to Coast
Coast to Coast (high)
High Stile
Crag Fell
Grike
Coast to Coast
Ennerdale
Coast to Coast (low)
1 Kilometre
1 Mile
N
NORTH
To Black Sail

● FAMILY　● CITY　● GROUP　● TRADITIONAL　● CAMPING BARN　● COASTAL　● RURAL

(Sat, Sun, July/August only), alight Bowness Knott, then 2 miles (for rail connections see YHA Keswick). RAIL: Whitehaven 15 miles.

●● ESKDALE ☆☆

Boot, Holmrook, Cumbria CA19 1TH;
eskdale@yha.org.uk
Tel: 0870 770 5824 Fax: 0870 770 5825

Nestling among the fells and set in its own extensive grounds, this purpose-built, child-friendly Youth Hostel is a good base for those seeking to explore a quieter corner of the Lake District. There are walking routes suitable for all abilities including an idyllic trail along the River Esk. Visit Upper Eskdale, home to Hardknott Roman Fort and Muncaster Castle. If you want to arrive in style, book a ticket on the Ravenglass & Eskdale Miniature Gauge Steam Railway.

Location: OS 89, GR 195010.
Great for... families whose children enjoy walking.
You need to know... public transport is limited.
Accommodation: 50 beds: 8x2–6- and 2x8-bed rooms.
Family rooms: Yes. **Rent-a-Hostel:** Yes.
Classroom: Yes. **Education packages:** Yes.
Facilities: Classroom/games room, self-catering kitchen, common room, dining room, drying room, laundry, showers, cycle store and grounds. **Daytime access:** All areas. ⊗
Meals: Breakfast, picnic lunch, evening meal.
Reception open: Staff available before 10.00hrs and after 17.00hrs.
Getting there: Via the Hardknott Pass, a steep and narrow approach. An alternative is via the A595.

HOSTEL MANAGERS CHOOSE...

THE BEST LAKELAND VIEWS

Helvellyn from Ullswater YHA Patterdale: "Wainwright considered Ullswater the most beautiful lake of all, and the shore path from Howtown to Patterdale was his favourite low-level walk."

From Scafell Pike YHA Wastwater: "I always think the views from England's highest mountain are well worth the climb. Walk from Wastwater for the quickest route to the summit, just over two miles."

Ullswater YHA Patterdale: "Scale the Eastern Fells for a marvellous panoramic view over Ullswater and the Eden Valley. On a clear day the view even stretches to the North Pennines."

Langdale Pikes YHA Elterwater: "The view from Elterwater Common over the Langdale Pikes is a classic. To see it at its best, set your alarm clock early to watch the winter sun rise over the misty lake and its frosty shore."

Windermere YHA Windermere: "Don't worry if you're not much of a walker – you don't have to miss out. Just take a seat on the terrace of the hostel and watch the sun set over the lake and mountains."

Parking: Yes.
Nearest other hostels: Wastwater 7 miles, Coniston Coppermines 10, Elterwater 9 (all by mountain path).
Public transport: RAIL: Eskdale (Ravenglass & Eskdale) 1.5 miles, Ravenglass (not Sun) 10, Drigg (not Sun) 10.

● FELL END

Booking: 017687 72645

This camping barn, 400 metres from the working farm, now overlooks superb scenery in southwest Lakeland and is within easy distance of Coniston and the Duddon Valley.

Great for... getting away from it all.
You need to know... there is no electricity so bring a torch.
Accommodation: Sleeps 12 on a platform on the ground floor.
Facilities: Cooking slab, eating area and heaters available for hire.
Nearest pub: 2 miles. **Nearest shop:** 3 miles.
Location: OS 96, GR 239881.

●● GRASMERE BUTTERLIP HOW ☆☆☆☆

Easedale Road, Grasmere, Cumbria LA22 9QG;
grasmere@yha.org.uk
Tel: 0870 770 5836 Fax: 0870 770 5837

Take your children to Butterlip How and test their energy levels. The hostel, a traditional Lakeland Victorian house, has extensive grounds with a safe play area for children and plenty of outdoor games equipment. Staff at the hostel can help you book a wide range of outdoor activities including watersports, climbing, orienteering, cycling and fishing. It goes without saying that there's walking galore, including high-level ridge and fell routes.

Location: OS 90, GR 336077.
Great for... families who enjoy a range of outdoor activities.
Accommodation: 80 beds: 5x2-, 8x4-, 2x5-, 2x6-, 1x8- and 1x10-bed rooms.
Family rooms: Yes. **Rent-a-Hostel:** No.
Classroom: Yes. **Education packages:** Yes.
Facilities: Lounge with open fire, games room and pool table, TV room, self-catering kitchen, dining room, table licence, showers, drying room, laundry, cycle store and grounds.

www.britainonview.com

Ancient routes abound: walking in the Lake District.

For current prices visit www.yha.org.uk

● FAMILY ● CITY ● GROUP ● TRADITIONAL ● CAMPING BARN ● COASTAL ● RURAL

Daytime access: All areas. ⊗
Meals: Breakfast, picnic lunch, evening meal.
Reception open: All day.
Getting there: From Grasmere centre bus stop (opposite Sam Reeds bookshop) take Easedale Road. In approx 200 metres, drive to YHA Grasmere Butterlip How is on right, well signed. Cars may be driven up to house to unload but must be returned to the car park.
Parking: Yes.
Nearest other hostels: Grasmere Thorney How 0.75 miles, Ambleside 5, Borrowdale 9 (by path), Patterdale 9 (by path).
Public transport: BUS: Stagecoach 555/6/9 Lancaster–Keswick, 599 from Windermere, alight Grasmere, 0.25 miles. RAIL: Windermere 8.5 miles.
NATIONALEXPRESS>> Prince of Wales Hotel 1 mile.

The Lake District: not just for hardcore hillwalkers.

www.britainonview.com

●● GRASMERE THORNEY HOW ☆

Easedale Road, Grasmere, Cumbria LA22 9QG; grasmere@yha.org.uk. Bookings handled by YHA Grasmere Butterlip How.
Tel: 0870 770 5836 Fax: 0870 770 5837

This was the first hostel bought by the YHA in 1931 and, while the original farmhouse retains its character, it has been extended and modernised. It's a 15-minute walk to Grasmere's town centre, making this a secluded spot for walkers with virtually no passing traffic. There are routes to suit all levels of abilities – hikers will want to head into the hills but there are nine lakes and tarns within reach for those wanting shorter expeditions. Wainwright's Coast-to-Coast long-distance path also passes the front door.

Location: OS 90, GR 332084.
Great for... walkers wanting varied terrain.
Accommodation: 53 beds: 3x4-, 1x5-, 2x6- and 2x12-bed rooms.
Family rooms: No. **Rent-a-Hostel:** Yes.
Classroom: No. **Education packages:** Yes.
Facilities: Lounge with open fire, dining room and common room, self-catering kitchen, drying room, showers and cycle store.
Daytime access: Restricted. ⊗
Meals: Breakfast, picnic lunch, evening meal.
Reception open: 17.00 hrs.
Getting there: From Grasmere centre bus stop, follow Easedale Road past the entrance to Grasmere Butterlip How on your right and continue for another 0.5 miles. After crossing the river at the sign turn right. Thorney How is approximately 0.75 miles on your left and is signed. Access for cars and minibuses but not coaches.
Parking: Yes.
Nearest other hostels: Grasmere Butterlip How 0.75 miles, Langdale 2.5, Elterwater 4, Ambleside 5, Borrowdale 9 (via footpath), Patterdale 9.
Public transport: BUS: Stagecoach 555/6/9 Lancaster–Keswick, 599 from Windermere, alight Grasmere, 0.5 miles (all pass Windermere station). RAIL: Windermere 8.5 miles.
NATIONALEXPRESS>> Prince of Wales Hotel 1 mile.

●● HAWKSHEAD ☆☆☆

Hawkshead, Ambleside, Cumbria LA22 0QD; hawkshead@yha.org.uk
Tel: 0870 770 5856 Fax: 0870 770 5857

This listed Regency mansion retains many of its original features including lavish plasterwork and a magnificently decorated cupola over the grand staircase. Overlooking the tranquil Esthwaite Water in the southern Lakes, it's a gorgeous spot from which to explore the surrounding Beatrix Potter country. Hawkshead village, known as the prettiest village in the Lake District with clusters of whitewashed houses, is just a mile from the hostel.
Location: OS 96, GR 354966.
Great for... an elegant base to explore Beatrix Potter country.
You need to know... there is a separate family annexe.
Accommodation: 109 beds: 14x3–4- and 8x6–8-bed rooms.
Family rooms: Yes. **Rent-a-Hostel:** Yes.
Classroom: Yes. **Education packages:** Yes.
Facilities: Lounge, TV and games room, self-catering kitchen, toilet, two drying rooms, laundry, showers, shop, cycle store and grounds.
Daytime access: All areas.
Meals: Breakfast, picnic lunch, evening meal.
Reception open: 13.00hrs.
Getting there: From M6 J36 follow A590 toward Barrow in Furness. At Newby Bridge go straight on at the roundabout then take next right following signs to Lakeside and Hawkshead. The hostel is approximately 1 mile before Hawkshead village on left (with Esthwaite Water on right). From Hawkshead village, follow signs to Newby Bridge and then hostel. Hostel is 1 mile along road on right.
Nearest other hostels: Coniston Holly How 5.5 miles, Ambleside 6, Windermere 9 (via ferry).

● FAMILY ● CITY ● GROUP ● TRADITIONAL ● CAMPING BARN ● COASTAL ● RURAL

Public transport: BUS: Stagecoach 505/6 from Ambleside (Windermere station), alight Hawkshead 1 mile. RAIL: Windermere 7 miles. FERRY: Across Windermere (except in high winds).

●● HELVELLYN ☆
Greenside, Glenridding, Penrith, Cumbria CA11 0QR; helvellyn@yha.org.uk
Tel: 0870 770 6110 Fax: 0870 770 5863

Approached by a 0.75-mile track from the village of Glenridding, this hostel is in an isolated and peaceful spot, 900 feet above sea level. Enjoy a hike up Helvellyn or the surrounding peaks or, for less strenuous walking, try the scenic lakeshore paths around Ullswater. Steam boat trips on the lake are also popular.
Location: OS 90, GR 366173.
Great for... high level and lakeside walking.
You need to know... the hostel is 1.5 miles from the village.
Accommodation: 60 beds: mostly 2–4- and 2x6-bed rooms.
Family rooms: No. **Rent-a-Hostel:** No.
Classroom: No. **Education packages:** Yes.
Facilities: Common rooms, self-catering kitchen, dining room, games room, showers, drying room, cycle store and grounds.
Daytime access: All areas. ⊗
Meals: Breakfast, picnic lunch, evening meal.

You'll have instant access to the hills staying at YHA Helvellyn.

Reception open: Staff available before 10.00hrs and after 17.00hrs.
Getting there: The hostel is signposted from Glenridding village, 1 mile past the Travellers Rest. The lane which leads to the hostel is unsurfaced but suitable for most vehicles.
Parking: Yes.
Nearest other hostels: Patterdale 2.5 miles, Grasmere 8 (both by mountain path).
Public transport: BUS: Stagecoach 108 from Penrith station, alight Glenridding 1.5 miles. RAIL: Penrith 14 miles, Windermere 15.

● HIGH GILLERTHWAITE (ENNERDALE)
Booking: 017687 72645

This camping barn is in the most remote of the Lakeland valleys with outstanding views of Pillar and the adjacent fells. It's a traditional barn dating back to the 16th century, which makes it an excellent base for fell walking and rock climbing plus cycling along the Coast-to-Coast long-distance route.
Great for... mountain scenery, peace and quiet.
You need to know... mattresses are provided; there are no electrical sockets.
Accommodation: Sleeps 12 in three sleeping areas on first and second floors.
Facilities: Sitting room with wood-burning stove, cooking area with hot water, bathroom, toilet, basin, shower and heaters. Electricity is supplied by generator for lighting only. Evening meals and breakfasts can be booked in advance by arrangement with YHA Ennerdale.
Nearest pub: 5 miles. **Nearest shop:** 5 miles.
Location: OS 89, GR 142141.

●● HONISTER HAUSE ☆
Seatoller, Keswick, Cumbria CA12 5XN; honister@yha.org.uk
Tel: 0870 770 5870 Fax: 0870 770 5870

This former quarry workers' building is in a spectacular setting at the summit of Honister Pass, a high-level route connecting the valleys of Borrowdale and Buttermere. This true mountain hostel provides easy access to the famous high peaks of Central Lakeland – Scafell, Great Gable, Pillar, Red Pike and Dale Head, as well as many other classic walking routes.
Location: OS 89, GR 226135.
Great for... dedicated walkers who are at home on the hills.
Accommodation: 26 beds: all 2–4-bed rooms.
Family rooms: No. **Rent-a-Hostel:** No.
Classroom: No. **Education packages:** No.
Facilities: Lounge/dining room, self-catering kitchen, showers, drying room and table licence. **Daytime access:** Restricted. ⊗
Meals: Breakfast, picnic lunch, evening meal.
Reception open: 17.00hrs.
Getting there: From Keswick follow the B5289 (signed Borrowdale) for approx 9 miles. The hostel is on left at top of pass.
Parking: Limited. Car park next to hostel. Also pay and display Lake

For all the latest YHA news visit www.yha.org.uk

● FAMILY ● CITY ● GROUP ● TRADITIONAL ● CAMPING BARN ● COASTAL ● RURAL

Scafell, near YHA Honister Hause, is among Lakeland's highest peaks.

District National Park car park to rear.
Nearest other hostels: Borrowdale 2 miles, Black Sail 3 (by mountain path), Buttermere 4.
Public transport: BUS: Stagecoach 771A from Keswick, March–Oct only; otherwise 79 Keswick–Seatoller, then 1.5 miles (for rail connections see YHA Keswick).
RAIL: Workington 23 miles, Penrith 27, Windermere 32.

● HUDSCALES
Booking: 017687 72645

This barn is part of a group of traditional farm buildings and lies at 1,000 feet on the northernmost flank of the Lakeland fells. With views over Caldbeck and Hesket Newmarket, it is an ideal base for exploring the northern fells and is on the Cumbria Way. And, with breakfast available, you can start your days in style.
Great for... exploring the quieter fells.
Accommodation: Sleeps 12 on the ground floor.
Facilities: Shower, power points, heaters (all on meter), cooking slab, eating area, toilet, washing facilities and electric light. Breakfast must be booked in advance.
Nearest pub: 2 miles. **Nearest shop:** 2 miles.
Location: OS 90, GR 332375.

●● KENDAL ☆
118 Highgate, Kendal, Cumbria LA9 4HE;
kendal@yha.org.uk
Tel: 0870 770 5892 Fax: 0870 770 5893

An attractive Georgian townhouse at the centre of an historic market town, this hostel forms part of the Brewery Arts complex. It's a convenient base from which to explore the southern Lakes and the Yorkshire Dales. Kendal itself has many attractions to keep all the family entertained, including the castle ruins. Explore further afield and you'll find the National Trust's Sizergh Castle and Levens Hall with its famous topiary gardens.
Location: OS 97, GR 515924.

Great for... a base for exploring southern Lakeland.
You need to know... cars must be left in a nearby pay and display car park (free between 18.00hrs and 9.00hrs); breakfast is included in the overnight price.

The famous topiary gardens of Levens Hall, near YHA Kendal.

Accommodation: 54 beds: 4x2-, 1x3-, 2x4-, 4x6-, 1x11-bed rooms.
Family rooms: Yes. **Rent-a-Hostel:** No.
Classroom: No. **Education packages:** Yes.
Facilities: Lounge, TV, self-catering kitchen, dining rooms, meeting room, showers, drying room and cycle store.
Daytime access: All areas. ⊗
Meals: Evening meals and packed lunches are available when pre-booked.
Reception open: 13.00hrs.
Getting there: The hostel is on the main street in Kendal (part of the one-way system).
Parking: No. Nearby pay and display car park.
Nearest other hostels: Windermere 11 miles, Arnside 12, Ambleside 13.5.
Public transport: BUS: Frequent from surrounding areas.
RAIL: Kendal 0.75 miles, Oxenholme 1.75.
NATIONAL EXPRESS ▶ Bus station 0.25 miles.

The Lake District

○ FAMILY ● CITY ● GROUP ● TRADITIONAL ● CAMPING BARN ○ COASTAL ○ RURAL

●● KESWICK ☆

Station Road, Keswick, Cumbria CA12 5LH;
keswick@yha.org.uk
Tel: 0870 770 5894 Fax: 0870 770 5895

Combine extensive walking with a wealth of evening entertainment at this hostel, which sits on the banks of the River Greta. There's plenty of walking here in the northern Lakes – if you need tempting then Skiddaw, one of the highest mountains in the Lake District, forms an impressive backdrop to the view from the hostel. It's just a few minutes' walk into the town centre, where you'll find plenty of pubs, a cinema and a theatre.

Location: OS 89, GR 267235.
Great for... those wanting to combine varied walking with nearby attractions.
You need to know... daytime parking is restricted.
Accommodation: 91 beds: mostly 3–4- plus 1x5-, 2x6- and 1x10-bed rooms.
Family rooms: No, but sole-use rooms are available.
Rent-a-Hostel: No.
Classroom: No, but large multi-functional rooms are available.
Education packages: No.
Facilities: Reception, lounge, TV and games room, dining room, self-catering kitchen, showers, drying room, laundry, educational resources, shop, map and towel hire and cycle store.
Daytime access: All areas.
Meals: Breakfast, picnic lunch, evening meal.
Reception open: All day.
Getting there: Approaching Keswick from Ambleside/Penrith, hostel is signposted on right turn into Station Road. After 50 metres turn left following hostel sign along the walkway by the River Greta.
Parking: Restricted daytime parking on roadside.
Nearest other hostels: Derwentwater 2 miles, Skiddaw House 6, Borrowdale 7.
Public transport: BUS: Stagecoach X4/5 Penrith–Workington (pass close to Workington and Penrith stations), 555/6 Lancaster–Carlisle (pass Windermere station and close to Carlisle station). RAIL: Penrith 17 miles, Windermere 22.
NATIONALEXPRESS Bus terminal, Lakes supermarket 0.5 miles.

●● LANGDALE ☆

High Close, Loughrigg, Ambleside, Cumbria LA22 9HJ; langdale@yha.org.uk
Tel: 0870 770 5908 Fax: 0870 770 5909

This rambling Victorian mansion with open fires is owned by the National Trust and stands in its own grounds between Elterwater and Grasmere. Close to the Langdale Pikes, it's an ideal base for walkers wanting to explore the Langdale valleys.

Location: OS 90, GR 338052.
Great for... getting away from it all.
You need to know... although the facilities are basic, this hostel's charm more than compensates.
Accommodation: 96 beds: 2x3–4-, 8x5–8- and 4x11-bed rooms.
Family rooms: No. **Rent-a-Hostel:** Yes.

YHA Langdale is a stylish Victorian mansion in its own grounds.

Classroom: Yes. **Education packages:** Yes.
Facilities: Lounges, TV, dining room, games room, self-catering kitchen, showers, cycle store and grounds.
Daytime access: All areas.
Meals: Breakfast, picnic lunch, evening meal.
Reception open: Staff available before 10.00hrs and after 17.00hrs.
Getting there: From Ambleside take the A593 (Coniston and Langdale). After 1.5 miles, turn right and follow a minor road uphill for 1.75 miles. At the summit of Red Bank, turn left and the hostel is 0.25 miles on left.
Parking: Yes.
Nearest other hostels: Elterwater 1 mile, Grasmere Butterlip How 2, Ambleside 4.
Public transport: BUS: Stagecoach 516 from Ambleside, alight 0.75 miles southeast of Elterwater or any service to Grasmere, then 1.5 miles. RAIL: Windermere 10 miles.
NATIONALEXPRESS Ambleside, King Street 3.5 miles.

● MILL HOUSE

Booking: 017687 72645

You'll find this camping barn on a large working farm in a secluded valley 1 mile from the thriving village of Gosforth. It makes a good base to explore the western fells close to Wastwater and Scafell Pike.
Accommodation: Sleeps 12 on the ground floor.
Facilities: Cooking slab, electric light, metered power point, gas heater available for hire, metered electricity. Toilet and hot water are in adjacent building. Breakfast can be booked in advance.
Nearest pub: 0.5 miles. **Nearest shop:** 0.25 miles.
Location: OS 91, GR 800044.

● FAMILY   ● CITY   ● GROUP   ● TRADITIONAL   ● CAMPING BARN   ● COASTAL   ● RURAL

The Lake District: expansive mountain views.

● MURT BARN

Booking: 017687 72645
Arrival time: Mr & Mrs Grant, 019467 26044

Murt is a traditional Lakeland farm, dating back to 1728, and is situated in the Wasdale Valley. The camping barn is a converted stone hayloft and byre and enjoys stunning views to the Scafell Massif, Great Gable and the surrounding fells. Situated less than a mile from Wastwater, it's an ideal base for high fell, lake and valley walking with direct access to footpaths and bridleways.

Accommodation: Sleeps 8 on the first floor, mattresses provided.
Facilities: Cooking area, toilet, washing-up facilities, metered electric light, water heater, shower and power point, electric heater available to hire. No dogs. Car parking next to barn.
Nearest pub: 10-minute walk. **Nearest shop:** 4 miles.
Location: OS 91, GR 131040.

●● PATTERDALE ☆

Patterdale, Penrith, Cumbria CA11 0NW;
patterdale@yha.org.uk
Tel: 0870 770 5986 Fax: 0870 770 5987

Situated on the Coast-to-Coast route, this Scandinavian-style building was designed to blend in with the glorious scenery just south of Ullswater. It makes the ideal base to explore the ridges and fells around Ullswater. The energetic who stay at this unique hostel will want to climb Helvellyn while those seeking more gentle pursuits can enjoy a cruise on the Ullswater steamer.

Location: OS 90, GR 399156.
Great for... outdoor enthusiasts.
Accommodation: 82 beds: 3x2-, 7x8- and 2x10-bed rooms.
Family rooms: No. **Rent-a-Hostel:** No.
Classroom: No. **Education packages:** Yes.
Facilities: Reception, lounge, self-catering kitchen, dining room, table licence, showers, drying room, cycle store, laundry facilities, internet access and grounds. **Daytime access:** All areas. 🐕
Meals: Breakfast, picnic lunch, evening meal.
Reception open: Staff available before 10.00hrs and after 17.00hrs.
Getting there: The hostel is 0.25 miles south of Patterdale village on the A592 to Kirkstone Pass.
Parking: Yes. Coaches by arrangement.
Nearest other hostels: Helvellyn 2.5 miles, Grasmere 9 (by path), Ambleside 10.
Public transport: BUS: Stagecoach Cumberland/Postbus 108 from Penrith Station, YHA Shuttlebus from YHA Ambleside (summer only). RAIL: Penrith 15 miles. FERRY: Ullswater steamer (March–Oct) 1 mile.

HOSTEL MANAGERS CHOOSE...

THE BEST THRILLS IN THE HILLS

Helvellyn (for mountaineering) YHA Patterdale: "I always consider the eastern fells the best for hillwalking and winter mountaineering. They also provide excellent mountain bike routes."

Pinnacle Ridge (scrambling) YHA Patterdale: "The area around Patterdale is great for scrambling and climbing in both summer and winter. Pinnacle Ridge is perhaps the best of the lot, while Swirral and Striding Edges on Helvellyn are an easier but no less spectacular alternative."

Bowfell Buttress (climbing) YHA Elterwater: "Bowfell Buttress and Middlefell Buttress are simply classic climbs."

Wastwater Screes (hiking) YHA Wastwater: "The scree slopes rising from the shore of Wastwater are very impressive. A circular route around these slopes makes for a truly spectacular hike."

Pillar Rock (mixed activities) YHA Black Sail: "For a great outdoor mix, I tell guests to bike along the rough track to YHA Black Sail. A walk to Pillar's summit is a tough but not technical hike, while climbers will want to try the classic slab-and-notch route up Pillar Rock."

The Lake District

●● SKIDDAW HOUSE

Bassenthwaite, Keswick, Cumbria CA12 4QX;
skiddaw@fouracretrust.org.uk
Tel: 07801 207401 Fax: 01981 580015

This is England's highest Youth Hostel, sheltering beneath the summit of Skiddaw at 1,550 feet. On the Cumbria Way with many footpaths from Keswick, Carrock Fell, Bassenthwaite and Threlkeld, it's remote and only accessible on foot. But those who stay here will be well rewarded — draught beer from the local brewery is available.
Location: OS 89, GR 288291.
Great for... walkers who don't mind basic facilities.
You need to know... there's no mains electricity supply and only limited heating; you must book in advance.
Accommodation: 20 beds: all 4-, 5- and 6-bed rooms. No-one will be turned away when hostel is open.
Family rooms: No. **Rent-a-Hostel:** No.
Classroom: No. **Education packages:** No.

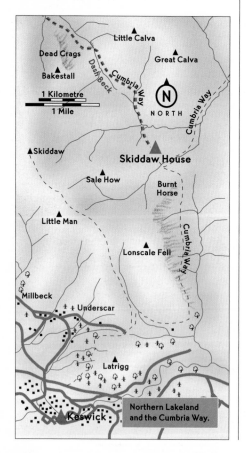

Northern Lakeland and the Cumbria Way.

Facilities: Games room, self-catering kitchen, drying room, hot water and shower, cycle store and grounds. 24v lighting only. Credit cards not accepted. **Daytime access:** All areas. ☺
Meals: Continental breakfast and local 'tatty pot'.
Reception open: Staff available before 10.00hrs and after 13.00hrs.
Getting there: From Keswick via Latrigg and Lonscale Fell. From Carrock Fell via Caldew Valley. From Threlkeld via Glenderaterra Valley. From Bassenthwaite via Dash Beck path.
Parking: Cars can be left at end of Blease Road via Threlkeld at Fell car park, or at Latrigg behind Keswick.
Nearest other hostels: Keswick 6 miles, Derwentwater 8, Cockermouth 12, Borrowdale 13, Carlisle 23.
Public transport: BUS: Stagecoach X4/5, Wrights 888 from Penrith Station, alight Threlkeld then 3.5 miles. RAIL: Penrith 24 miles.

● ST JOHN'S-IN-THE-VALE

Booking: 017687 72645
Arrival time: Mrs Chaplin-Brice, 01768 779242

This camping barn was once an 18th century stable and hayloft and stands in an idyllic setting overlooking St John's Beck on a peaceful hill farm. With stunning views to Blencathra, Helvellyn and Castle Rock, why not take advantage of sunny afternoons in the farm's tea-garden, where generous slices of home-made cake await.
Great for... walking, climbing, peace and quiet.
Accommodation: Sleeps 8.
Facilities: Sitting and dining area, toilet, shower (charge for hot water), cooking areas, barn lock-up space, wood-burning stove (fuel extra), BBQ and outside seating area. Use of washing machine and drier available. Breakfasts can be booked in advance.
Nearest pub: 2 miles. **Nearest shop:** 6 miles.
Location: OS 90, GR 316205.

● SWALLOW

Booking: 017687 72645

In the picturesque Loweswater Valley, this camping barn is part of a traditional set of farm buildings dating back to 1670. Permits for fishing and boat hire on Loweswater are available at the farm, or spend your days exploring the quiet western fells, nearby Crummock Water and Buttermere.
Accommodation: Sleeps 18 in four separate areas on ground floor.
Facilities: Eating area, cooking slab, electric light, cold water tap, toilets, showers (coin-operated) and hot-water heater.
Nearest pub: 1 mile. **Nearest shop:** 3 miles.
Location: OS 89, GR 116226.

● SWIRRAL

Booking: 017687 72645

One of a group of nine buildings, this remote camping barn is situated at 1,000 feet on the flank of the Helvellyn range. Popular routes to Striding Edge and Swirral Edge pass the door and there is quick access to Ullswater and the eastern fells.

To make a booking visit www.yha.org.uk

● FAMILY ● CITY ● GROUP ● TRADITIONAL ● CAMPING BARN ● COASTAL ● RURAL

●● WASTWATER ☆☆☆

Wasdale Hall, Wasdale, Seascale, Cumbria CA20 1ET; wastwater@yha.org.uk
Tel: 0870 770 6082 Fax: 0870 770 6083

A stunning half-timbered National Trust-owned house, this hostel dates from 1829 and still retains many original features. Enjoy beautiful mountain and lake views from its grounds, which extend to the shores of Wastwater, England's deepest lake. Within easy reach of England's highest mountain, walkers will be busy here.
Location: OS 89, GR 145045.
Great for... getting away from it all.
You need to know... public transport is limited; the nearest shop is 5 miles away.
Accommodation: 50 beds: 2x4-, 1x6-, 1x8- and 2x14-bed rooms.
Family rooms: Yes. **Rent-a-Hostel:** No.
Classroom: Yes. **Education packages:** Yes.
Facilities: Lounge, games room, dining room, showers, drying room, cycle store and shop. **Daytime access:** All areas. 🚭

www.britainonview.com

Feeding spring lambs at Garnett House Farm near YHA Kendal.

Great for... individual families or mixed groups; also walking the Helvellyn range and access to Ullswater lake.
You need to know... the showers take 50p coins.
Accommodation: Sleeps 8 on the first floor.
Facilities: Electric light and toilet in adjacent building.
Nearest pub: 1 mile. **Nearest shop:** 2 miles.
Location: OS 90, GR 364174.

● TARN FLATT

Booking: 017687 72645
Arrival time: Janice Telfer, 01946 692162

This camping barn is a traditional sandstone building on St Bees Head overlooking the Scottish coastline and the Isle of Man.
It's usually busy with walkers embarking on the Coast-to-Coast long-distance walk at St Bees. There's also easy access to the quieter western Lakeland fells and lakes. The Georgian town of Whitehaven is within easy reach.
Great for... rock climbing (at North Head St Bees), fishing, birdwatching (RSPB nature reserve).
You need to know... long- and short-stay car parking is available.
Accommodation: Sleeps 8 on ground floor.
Facilities: Electric light, cooking slab, open fire (wood available from farm), metered shower and toilets in adjacent building. Dinner, packed lunches and breakfast bookable in advance.
Nearest pub: 1 mile. **Nearest shop:** 2 miles.
Location: OS 89, GR 947146.

YHA Wastwater is on the shore of England's deepest lake.

Meals: Breakfast, picnic lunch, evening meal.
Reception open: Staff available before 10.00hrs and after 17.00hrs.
Getting there: From the south, follow A590 to Greenodd, then A595 Broughton-in-Furness to Nether Wasdale. From the north via Cockermouth, take A5086 to Egremont, then A595 to Gosforth and on to Nether Wasdale.
Parking: Yes.
Nearest other hostels: Black Sail 7 miles (by mountain path), Eskdale 10.
Public transport: BUS: Stagecoach 6, X6 Whitehaven–Seascale, alight Gosforth 5 miles. Taxibus service from Seascale and Gosforth on Thurs, Sat and Sun (book by 18.00hrs previous day on 019467 25308). RAIL: Seascale (not Sun) 9 miles, Irton Road (Ravenglass & Eskdale) 5.5.

The Lake District

FAMILY ● CITY ● GROUP ● TRADITIONAL ● CAMPING BARN ● COASTAL ● RURAL

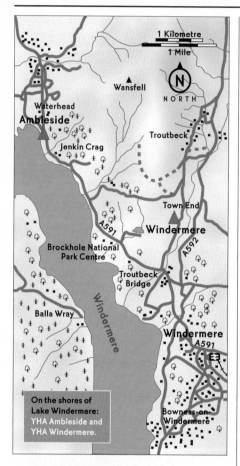

On the shores of Lake Windermere:
YHA Ambleside and YHA Windermere.

Family rooms: Yes. Rent-a-Hostel: No.
Classroom: No. Education packages: Yes.
Facilities: Lounge, TV, self-catering kitchen, showers, drying/laundry room, internet and cycle hire and store.
Daytime access: All areas.
Meals: Breakfast, picnic lunch and evening meal.
Reception open: All day except between 12.00hrs and 13.00hrs.
Getting there: From Windermere take A591 to Troutbeck Bridge. Turn right after filling station and hostel is 0.75 miles up Bridge Lane.
Parking: Yes.
Nearest other hostels: Ambleside 3 miles, Hawkshead 9 (by ferry), Kendal 11, Patterdale 11.
Public transport: BUS: Frequent, alight Troutbeck Bridge 0.75 miles, summer YHA Shuttlebus from Windermere station.
RAIL: Windermere 2 miles.
NATIONALEXPRESS» Windermere bus station 2 miles.

Soaking up the peace: Lake Windermere, near YHA Windermere.

●● WINDERMERE ☆☆☆

Bridge Lane, Troutbeck, Windermere, Cumbria
LA23 1LA; windermere@yha.org.uk
Tel: 0870 770 6094 Fax: 0870 770 6095

This hostel enjoys a spectacular site overlooking Lake Windermere with its own extensive grounds and panoramic views of the Lakeland mountains. Two miles outside the busy town of Windermere, it's ideal for those looking for a peaceful countryside setting close to local attractions. The quiet Troutbeck Valley offers a variety of good low and high level walking routes or, for a more sedate day out, visit the nearby National Park visitor centre, World of Beatrix Potter or join a cruise on Lake Windermere.
Location: OS 90, GR 405013.
Great for... families wanting a range of attractions.
You need to know... the hostel is 2 miles outside Windermere town.
Accommodation: 69 beds: mostly 4-bed rooms, plus 1x2-, 1x3-, 1x6- and 1x8-bed options.

TRY A YHA WALKING HOLIDAY

Many of the hostels in the Lake District feature on YHA Guided Walks. For details on current packages turn to the feature on page 22.

For offers and discounts visit www.yha.org.uk

62

The Youth Hostels of...

Yorkshire & South Pennines

Great for walking: seeing the best of Yorkshire on foot.

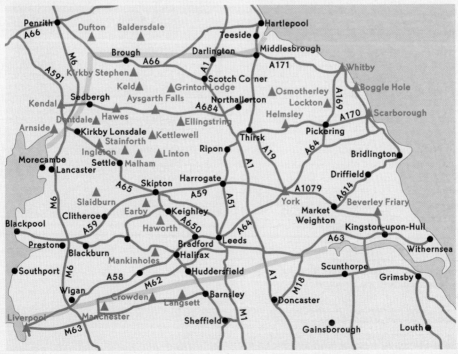

For further information visit www.yha.org.uk

● FAMILY ● CITY ● GROUP ● TRADITIONAL ● CAMPING BARN ● COASTAL ● RURAL

●● AYSGARTH FALLS ☆

Aysgarth, Leyburn, North Yorkshire DL8 3SR;
aysgarth@yha.org.uk
Tel: 0870 770 5678 Fax: 0870 770 5679

On the Herriot Way and a minute's walk from the famous falls, Aysgarth is a great base for exploring Wensleydale. It boasts a choice of circular walks and fine views of the valley, including Bolton Castle where Mary Queen of Scots was imprisoned.
Location: OS 98, GR 012884.
Great for... starting the Herriot Way and touring the Dales.
You need to know... this hostel may close during 2003. Please enquire before planning your stay.
Accommodation: 67 beds: 5x3-4- and 7x5-8-bed rooms.
Family rooms: Yes. **Rent-a-Hostel:** Yes.
Classroom: No. **Education packages:** Yes.
Facilities: Lounge, TV room, games room, self-catering kitchen, dining room, shop, showers, drying room and cycle store.
Daytime access: All areas.
Meals: Breakfast, picnic lunch, evening meal.
Reception open: Staff available before 10.00hrs and after 17.00hrs.
Getting there: The hostel is 0.5 miles east of Aysgarth on the A684.
Parking: Yes.
Nearest other hostels: Grinton Lodge 8 miles, Hawes 9, Kettlewell 13.
Public transport: BUS: Dales & District 156/7 Bedale–Hawes, with connections from Northallerton station, Dales Bus from West Yorkshire. RAIL: Garsdale 16 miles, Northallerton 24, Skipton 28.

●● BEVERLEY FRIARY ☆☆☆

Friar's Lane, Beverley, East Yorkshire HU17 0DF;
beverleyfriary@yha.org.uk
Tel: 0870 770 5696 Fax: 0870 770 5697

Beverley is one of northeast England's premier towns, its minster the superior of many an English cathedral. A beautiful old building in a quiet corner of the town, this hostel is close to the minster and ideally placed to explore the cobbled lanes and elegant Georgian and Victorian terraces. It also affords easy access to Hull, York and the Yorkshire Wolds, while the coast is just 15 minutes away. Whether you want to go cycling or shopping, birdwatching or sunbathing, this hostel makes a magical setting for your break.
Location: OS 107, GR 038393.
Great for... cycling, birdwatching and relaxing.
Accommodation: 34 beds: 1x5-, 1x13- and 1x16-bed rooms.
Family rooms: No. **Rent-a-Hostel:** No.
Classroom: Yes. **Education packages:** No.
Facilities: Common room, self-catering kitchen, shop, showers, cycle store and garden. **Daytime access:** Restricted.
Meals: Breakfast, picnic lunch and evening meal available if booked in advance.
Reception open: 17.00hrs.
Getting there: Follow signs to Minster and Friary. Turn down Friar's Lane next to Minster and follow to end of lane to car park (see map on page 173).
Parking: Hostel car park, limited parking in Friar's Lane.
Nearest other hostels: York 30 miles, Scarborough 36, Lincoln 50.
Public transport: BUS: Frequent from surrounding areas. RAIL: Beverley 0.25 miles. FERRY: Hull to Rotterdam and Zeebrugge 12 miles.
NATIONAL EXPRESS Beverley bus station 0.5 miles.

Perfect for a quiet family break: YHA Boggle Hole near Whitby.

●● BOGGLE HOLE ☆☆☆

Mill Beck, Fylingthorpe, Whitby, North Yorkshire YO22 4UQ; bogglehole@yha.org.uk
Tel: 0870 770 5704 Fax: 0870 770 5705

The bay in front of Boggle Hole Youth Hostel was once a notorious smugglers' haunt. Nowadays all ages will love beachcombing and searching for fossils and rockpool life on its shore. There's plenty to do nearby – the fishing village of Robin Hood's Bay is just a mile to the north. Walk part of the Cleveland Way to Whitby where you can take a boat ride to catch your own dinner. Or hire a bike to cycle the

Close to the coast and the Yorkshire Wolds: YHA Beverley Friary.

● FAMILY ● CITY ● GROUP ● TRADITIONAL ● CAMPING BARN ● COASTAL ● RURAL

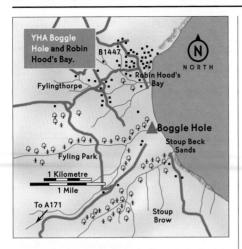

old Whitby to Scarborough railway line, which is safe, traffic-free and boasts stunning views.

Location: OS 94, GR 954040.

Great for... families looking for a quiet break.

You need to know... parking is quarter of a mile away down a very steep road with access over a narrow footbridge; some rooms are in an annexe accessed via 45 steps.

Accommodation: 80 beds: 4x2-, 14x4-, 1x6-, 1x10-beds.

Family rooms: Yes. **Rent-a-Hostel:** No.

Classroom: Yes. **Education packages:** Yes.

Facilities: Lounge, TV, self-catering kitchen, dining room, showers, toilets, drying room and cycle store. **Daytime access:** All areas.

Meals: Breakfast, picnic lunch, evening meal.

Reception open: 13.00hrs.

Getting there: From A171, take road signed to Boggle Hole. After 2.5 miles, the car park is on right. Road to the hostel is

The peaceful harbour of Boggle Hole, near YHA Boggle Hole.

unsuitable for vehicles. Park in National Park car park and walk.

Parking: Yes, 0.25 miles.

Nearest other hostels: Whitby 7 miles, Scarborough 13.

Public transport: BUS: Arriva North East 93A Scarborough–Whitby (passes Whitby and Scarborough Stations), alight Robin Hood's Bay 1 mile. RAIL: Whitby (not Sun, except June to Sept) 7 miles, Scarborough 15. FERRY: Hull 50 miles.

● BROMPTON-ON-SWALE

campingbarns@yha.org.uk

Booking: 0870 770 6113

Arrival time: Mr & Mrs Wilkin, 01748 818326

This former byre, now a camping barn, is in the farmyard of Village Farm in the village of Brompton-on-Swale. It is an excellent stopping-off point for the Coast-to-Coast walk which is just half a mile away at Catterick Bridge. The historic town of Richmond is three miles away.

Accommodation: Sleeps 12 on the first floor.

Facilities: Washing and drying facilities, toilet, shower, electric light, heater, cooking area with pans, crockery and cutlery, metered electricity. Dogs welcome.

Nearest pub: 100 metres. **Nearest shop:** 100 metres.

Location: OS 99, GR 216997.

● CHIPPING

campingbarns@yha.org.uk

Booking: 0870 770 6113

Arrival time: Mrs Stott, 01995 61209

A former stable and hayloft opposite the farmhouse, this camping barn is just half a mile from the village of Chipping and is an ideal base for group activities. You'll find orienteering, horse riding and a wild boar park nearby.

Accommodation: Sleeps 15 on the first floor.

Facilities: Dining area, separate kitchen with two hot plates, microwave, cutlery and pans, toilets, shower, metered electricity, recreation area, childrens' play area, BBQ, electric light, fridge, woodburner (wood available to buy). Dogs and tents by arrangement. Breakfast can be booked in advance.

Nearest pub: 0.5 miles. **Nearest shop:** 0.5 miles.

Location: OS 102, GR 616435.

●● DENTDALE ☆☆☆

Cowgill, Dent, Sedbergh, Cumbria LA10 5RN;

dentdale@yha.org.uk

Tel: 0870 770 5790 Fax: 0870 770 5791

This recently refurbished hostel is a haven for walkers and cyclists, situated in the upper reaches of Dentdale. The valley offers riverside walks as well as higher-level hikes to Whernside or adjacent dales. The picturesque village of Dent with its cobbled streets and old world atmosphere is just five miles away. And don't worry if it rains – White Scar Cave, the Dales Countryside Museum and Wensleydale

Creamery are all within 10 miles of this former shooting lodge.
Location: OS 98, GR 773850.
Great for... walkers and cyclists of all abilities.
You need to know... this hostel has good facilities for those with mobility problems.
Accommodation: 41 beds: 1x4-, 2x4–5- and 3x7–10-bed rooms. 1x4-bed wheelchair accessible room on ground floor with adjacent toilet and shower facilities.
Family rooms: Yes. **Rent-a-Hostel:** Yes.
Classroom: No. **Education packages:** Yes.
Facilities: Lounge, self-catering kitchen, dining room (can be used as classroom outside meal times), showers, drying room and cycle store. TV, video and overhead projector. **Daytime access:** All areas.
Meals: Breakfast (packed breakfast also available), picnic lunch, evening meal.
Reception open: Staff available before 10.00hrs and after 17.00hrs.
Getting there: Hostel is on Dentdale road northeast of Whernside, 2 miles from junction with Hawes–Ingleton road and 5 miles east of Dent.
Parking: Nearby, accessible by a short, level track.
Nearest other hostels: Hawes 8 miles, Ingleton 11, Stainforth 15, Kendal 20.
Public transport: BUS: Buses between Sedburgh and Dent stations on Weds and Sat, alight Cowgill 1.5 mile.
RAIL: Dent 2 miles, Oxenholme (Lake District) 20.

HOSTEL MANAGERS CHOOSE...

THE BEST
YORKSHIRE SCENERY

Spurn Point (sand dunes) YHA Beverley Friary: "My favourite! Don't miss this amazing three-mile-long sand dune. There are rare plants, migrating birds and a 120-foot lighthouse."

Haworth (heather) YHA Haworth: "To walk in a sea of purple, visit in late July or August when the heather is in full flower. Or follow the Railway Children on a trail around Haworth to see all the sights from the film."

North Yorkshire Moors Railway (moorland) YHA Scarborough: "As seen in the TV series, Heartbeat and the Harry Potter film. The line takes you through incredible moorland scenery. Book a one-way ticket and walk back."

Cod Beck Reservoir (dale views) YHA Osmotherley: "Enjoy an easy, scenic stroll around Cod Beck Reservoir or head to Black Hambleton for hillwalking with panoramic views towards the moors and dales on clear days."

Flamborough Head (cliffs) YHA Beverley Friary: "One of our most spectacular sections of coastline with limestone stacks and arches. Try a clifftop walk on Bempton Cliffs to watch the seabirds."

● **DOWNHAM** (NEW HAY)
campingbarns@yha.org.uk
Booking: 0870 770 6113
Arrival time: Mr Taylor, 01200 441242

This field barn is on the Downham Estate, near the foot of Pendle Hill and the picturesque village of Downham. Close to the Witches Way, Pendle Way, Ribble Way and the Lancashire Cycleway, walkers and cyclists will find plenty to do here.
Great for... stunning views of Pendle Hill.
You need to know... cars should be parked in the former quarry on the opposite side of the road from the barn.
Accommodation: Sleeps 12.
Facilities: Metered gas lighting, cooking rings, shower, hot water and wall-mounted heater. External BBQ. Dogs welcome.
Nearest pub: 0.5 miles. **Nearest shop:** 0.5 miles.
Location: OS 103, GR 795445.

YHA Earby is a quiet base for exploring the Yorkshire Dales.

● **EARBY** ☆☆
9-11 Birch Hall Lane, Earby, Lancashire BB18 6JX;
earby@yha.org.uk
Tel: 0870 770 5802 **Fax:** 0870 770 5802

A cottage on the outskirts of Earby village with a large and attractive garden, this hostel is close to the Yorkshire Dales. Visit historic Skipton, the Forest of Bowland and Pendle Hill, home of Lancashire's witches. As well as a rich array of industrial heritage, you'll find plenty of walking and cycle routes with the Pennine Way, Pendle Way and Lancashire Cycleway all nearby.
Location: OS 103, GR 915468.
Great for... those who want busy days and peaceful nights.
You need to know... it's self-catering accommodation only.
Accommodation: 22 beds: 1x2-, 2x6- and 1x8-bed rooms.
Family rooms: No. **Rent-a-Hostel:** Yes.
Classroom: No. **Education packages:** No.
Facilities: Two lounges, self-catering kitchen, dining room, showers, drying room and cycle store. **Daytime access:** Restricted. ⊗
Meals: Self-catering only.
Reception open: 17.00hrs.

● FAMILY ● CITY ● GROUP ● TRADITIONAL ● CAMPING BARN ● COASTAL ● RURAL

Getting there: The hostel is 300 metres beyond the Red Lion Pub.
Parking: At rear of hostel.
Nearest other hostels: Haworth 15 miles (via Pennine Way), Linton 15, Malham 16 (via Pennine Way), Slaidburn 19.
Public transport: BUS: Various services from Burnley, Skipton (passes close to Colne and Skipton stations), alight Earby 0.5 miles. RAIL: Colne 5 miles, Skipton (Settle to Carlisle line) 8.
NATIONALEXPRESS >> Barnoldswick, Station Road 3.5 miles.

●● ELLINGSTRING ☆
Ellingstring, Masham, nr Ripon, North Yorkshire HG4 4PW; ellingstring@yha.org.uk
Tel: 0870 770 5812 Fax: 0870 770 5812

Ellingstring is on the edge of the Yorkshire Dales in an Area of Outstanding Natural Beauty. Walkers and cyclists can enjoy the simple life while exploring the footpaths and quiet lanes of Nidderdale and the eastern part of the National Park. This stone cottage is set in a tiny hamlet on the North of England Way and close

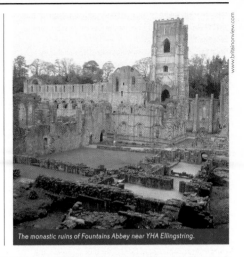
The monastic ruins of Fountains Abbey near YHA Ellingstring.

●● GRINTON LODGE ☆☆☆☆
Grinton, Richmond, North Yorkshire DL11 6HS; grinton@yha.org.uk
Tel: 0870 770 5844 Fax: 0870 770 5845

This impressive former shooting lodge in the Yorkshire Dales National Park stands high on heather-clad grouse moors and commands spectacular views of Swaledale and Arkengarthdale. Whatever your ability, you'll find excellent walking and cycling which will lead you to splendid natural features such as Kisdon and Wainwath Falls, the Buttertubs, Aysgarth Falls and Hardraw Force in Wensleydale. The historic town of Richmond, with cobbled alleys and castles, is just 10 miles away.
Location: OS 98, GR 048975.
Great for... walkers and cyclists keen on exploring natural wonders and spectacular countryside.
You need to know... the Salthouse can be hired under the Rent-a-Hostel scheme.
Accommodation: 69 beds: 2x2-, 1x3-, 7x4-, 3x6- and 2x8-bed rooms.
Family rooms: Yes. **Rent-a-Hostel:** Yes.

You can walk to Aysgarth Falls from YHA Grinton Lodge.

Classroom: Yes. **Education packages:** No.
Facilities: Self-catering kitchen, TV lounge, drying room, laundry, games room, showers, quiet room, cycle store, bike hire and grounds. **Daytime access:** All areas.
Meals: Breakfast, picnic lunch, evening meal.
Reception open: Staff available before 10.00hrs and after 17.00hrs.
Getting there: The hostel is 0.75 mile up hill from Grinton, due south on the Reeth to Leyburn road.
Parking: Yes.
Nearest other hostels: Aysgarth 8 miles, Keld 14, Ellingstring 14, Osmotherley 31.
Public transport: BUS: Arriva 30/6 Richmond–Keld (infrequent but passes Darlington station), alight Grinton 0.75 mile, Dales Bus from West Yorkshire. RAIL: Kirkby Stephen 24 miles, Darlington 25.

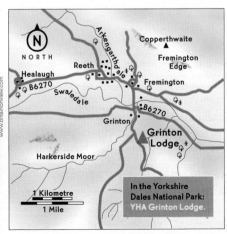

● FAMILY ● CITY ● GROUP ● TRADITIONAL ● CAMPING BARN ● COASTAL ● RURAL

to the monastic ruins of Fountains Abbey and Jervaulx Abbey. The Black Sheep Brewery and James Herriot Centre are also nearby.
Location: OS 99, GR 176835.
Great for... walkers and those with a love of Herriot country.
Accommodation: 18 beds: 1x4-, 1x6- and 1x8-bed rooms.
Family rooms: No. **Rent-a-Hostel:** Yes.
Classroom: No. **Education packages:** No.
Facilities: Common room, dining room, self-catering kitchen with microwave, fridge and freezer, showers, drying room, shop, garden, BBQ and picnic benches. **Daytime access:** Restricted. ⊗
Meals: Self-catering only.
Reception open: 17.00hrs.
Getting there: From A1 trunk road, look for signs to Masham, and turn onto B6267. At Masham, take A6108 to Leyburn. About 2.5 miles out of Masham, take road signposted Ellingstring through High Ellington. At crossroads turn right. The hostel is on your left.
Parking: Yes.
Nearest other hostels: Grinton 12 miles, Aysgarth 14, Osmotherley 25.
Public transport: BUS: Dales & District 159 Richmond–Ripon to within 1 mile (connections from Darlington, Harrogate and York stations), Ellingstring to Northallerton in termtime, Masham to Northallerton daily 93, 98, 144 and B78, Dales Bus from West Yorkshire. RAIL: Thirsk 16 miles, Northallerton 17.

● FARNDALE
campingbarns@yha.org.uk
Booking: 0870 770 6113
Arrival time: Mr & Mrs Mead, 01751 433053

Located in the farmyard of Oak House in the North York Moors National Park, this camping barn boasts excellent views over High Farndale. It is 1.5 miles from the Coast-to-Coast walk, two miles from the Lyke Wake Walk and three miles from the Cleveland Way.
Great for... getting off the beaten track.
You need to know... parking is limited to four vehicles; no dogs please.
Accommodation: Sleeps 12 on a wooden platform in barn loft.
Facilities: Electric light, wood-burning stove (one bag of logs provided per night), small cooker, toilet and shower in adjacent building. £1 charge per person per night for gas, electricity and logs. Breakfast is available but must be booked in advance.
Nearest pub: 0.75 miles. **Nearest shop:** 8 miles.
Location: OS 94, GR 659986.

●● HAWES ☆☆
Lancaster Terrace, Hawes, North Yorkshire DL8 3LQ; hawes@yha.org.uk
Tel: 0870 770 5854 **Fax:** 0870 770 5855

This modern hostel makes a great base for families, individuals and groups looking to explore the beautiful Yorkshire Dales. Ideally situated on the edge of the traditional market town of Hawes, home of the famous Wensleydale Cheese Factory, it is within easy distance of a range of tourist attractions and activities and on key

walking and cycling routes including the Pennine Way.
Location: OS 98, GR 867897.
Great for... views of Upper Wensleydale.
You need to know... the car park is a short walk away.
Accommodation: 54 beds: 2x2-, 3x3-, 2x4-, 1x5-, 2x6- and 2x8-bed rooms, some en-suite in autumn/winter.
Family rooms: Yes. **Rent-a-Hostel:** No.
Classroom: No. **Education packages:** Yes.
Facilities: Lounge, TV room, games room, self-catering kitchen, showers, drying room, cycle store and laundry facilities.
Daytime access: All areas. ⊗
Meals: Breakfast, picnic lunch, evening meal.
Reception open: Staff available before 10.00hrs and after 17.00hrs.
Getting there: The hostel is at the top of the steep rise on the B6255 (signposted to Ingleton), just off the junction with the A684.
Parking: Nearby.
Nearest other hostels: Dentdale 8 miles, Aysgarth 9, Keld 9.
Public transport: BUS: R Harrington from Garsdale Station, Dales & District 156/7 from Bedale with connections from Northallerton station, Dales Bus from West Yorkshire. RAIL: Garsdale 6 miles.

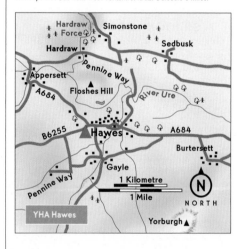

●● HAWORTH ☆
Longlands Drive, Lees Lane, Haworth, Keighley, West Yorkshire BD22 8RT; haworth@yha.org.uk
Tel: 0870 770 5858 **Fax:** 0870 770 5859

Revisit the tempestuous world of the Brontë classics, Wuthering Heights and Jane Eyre. This large Victorian mansion is built in a grand style and overlooks the village of Haworth. Brontë fans will enjoy the museum and leisurely walks to spots that inspired the famous books. There's also plenty of entertainment for children with Eureka!, Britain's first childrens' interactive museum at Halifax, and bowling, swimming and ice-skating facilities within a 10-mile radius.
Location: OS 104, GR 038378.

For more information visit www.yha.org.uk

● FAMILY ● CITY ● GROUP ● TRADITIONAL ● CAMPING BARN ● COASTAL ● RURAL

Great for... families; combining attractions with a variety of walks.
Accommodation: 94 beds: mostly 2–8- plus 1x10- and 1x12-bed rooms.
Family rooms: Yes. **Rent-a-Hostel:** No.
Classroom: Yes. **Education packages:** No.
Facilities: Lounge, games room, self-catering kitchen, showers, toilets, drying room, cycle store, laundry facilities and garden.
Daytime access: All areas. ⊗
Meals: Breakfast, picnic lunch, evening meal.
Reception open: All day.
Getting there: From Haworth centre, take B6142 towards Keighley for 0.75 miles. From Keighley, travel 3 miles south on A629 then take A6033 and B6142. Longlands Drive is almost opposite the Brontë Hotel.
Parking: Yes.
Nearest other hostels: Mankinholes 12 miles (18 via Pennine Way), Earby 18 (15 via Pennine Way), York 45.
Public transport: BUS: Keighley & District 663, 664, 665, M2–4 from Keighley. RAIL: Keighley 4 miles, Haworth (Worth Valley Rly) 0.5.
NATIONAL EXPRESS Keighley Bus Station 3.25 miles.

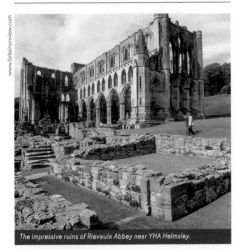

www.britainonview.com

The impressive ruins of Rievaulx Abbey near YHA Helmsley.

●● HELMSLEY ☆☆
Carlton Lane, Helmsley, North Yorkshire YO62 5HB; helmsley@yha.org.uk
Tel: 0870 770 5860 Fax: 0870 770 5860

This popular hostel is in one of the prettiest country towns in North Yorkshire. It's a cosy stone-walled building with comfortable, modern facilities on the edge of the National Park just a few minutes' walk from the shops and pubs of Helmsley. A favourite choice for groups, families and outdoor clubs, it's close to a host of attractions and activities including Rievaulx Abbey and is at the start of the Cleveland Way.
Location: OS 100, GR 616840.
Great for... those who want top attractions on their doorstep.

Accommodation: 38 beds: mainly 4- and 6-bed rooms.
Family rooms: Yes. **Rent-a-Hostel:** Yes.
Classroom: No. **Education packages:** Yes.
Facilities: Lounge, dining room, self-catering kitchen, showers, laundry facilities and grounds. **Daytime access:** Restricted. ⊗
Meals: Breakfast, picnic lunch, evening meal.
Reception open: 17.00hrs.
Getting there: The hostel is a few minutes from Helmsley market square at junction of Carlton Road and Carlton Lane (just off A170).
Parking: At hostel.
Nearest other hostels: Osmotherley 15 miles (20 by Cleveland Way), Lockton 19, York 23.
Public transport: BUS: Stephensons from York station, Scarborough & District 128 from Scarborough, regular local buses.
RAIL: Thirsk 15 miles, Malton 16, York 24.
FERRY: Hull to Rotterdam and Zeebrugge 60 miles.

● HURST GREEN
campingbarns@yha.org.uk
Booking: 0870 770 6113
Arrival time: Mrs Kay, 01254 826304

This camping barn, converted from a byre, is adjacent to a former hunting lodge where Henry VII is reputed to have stayed. This is an ideal base to enjoy walking, on- and off-road cycling routes, horseriding, coarse fishing, orienteering at Beacon Fell, canoeing, wall climbing, ghost walks and heritage trails. Hurst Green village, the Ribble Way and Longridge Fell are all nearby.
Great for... walking, cycling and much more.
Accommodation: Sleeps 12 on first floor.
Facilities: Electric light, cooking rings (electricity metered), wood-burning stove (wood available), hot water heater, BBQ, toilets in adjacent building.
Nearest pub: 1.25 miles. **Nearest shop:** 1.25 miles.
Location: OS 103, GR 674389.

●● INGLETON ☆☆☆☆
Sammy Lane, Ingleton, Carnforth, Lancashire LA6 3EG; ingleton@yha.org.uk
Tel: 0870 770 5880 Fax: 0870 770 5881

This renovated Victorian house is in the village of Ingleton and offers excellent accommodation for individuals and families alike. Within easy access of the M6, it's ideally located for exploring the Dales and just a short distance from the Lakes. Walks range from the gentle Waterfalls Walk to Thornton Force to the demanding Three Peaks Walk. There's also excellent limestone climbing for the adventurous. Children will love White Scar Cave, the largest show cave in Europe, and the open-air swimming pool and park next door.
Location: OS 98, GR 695733.
Great for... a family holiday with easy access.
Accommodation: 66 beds: 2x2-, the rest 4- and 6-bed rooms.
Family rooms: Yes. **Rent-a-Hostel:** No.
Classroom: No. **Education packages:** No.

○ FAMILY ● CITY ● GROUP ● TRADITIONAL ● CAMPING BARN ○ COASTAL ● RURAL

Enjoy a stroll to Ingleton Waterfalls: near YHA Ingleton.

Facilities: Dining room, lounge, showers, toilets, drying room, self-catering kitchen, cycle store and grounds.
Daytime access: All areas. ⊗
Meals: Breakfast, picnic lunch, evening meal.
Reception open: Staff available before 10.00hrs and after 17.00hrs.
Getting there: From High Street, take the lane between Barclays Bank and the newsagents down to the park.
Parking: At hostel.
Nearest other hostels: Stainforth 10 miles, Dentdale 11, Kendal 17.
Public transport: BUS: Stagecoach in Lancashire 80 from Lancaster (Lancaster and Bentham stations). RAIL: Bentham 3 miles, Clapham 4.

●● KELD ☆☆☆
Upper Swaledale, Richmond, North Yorkshire DL11 6LL; keld@yha.org.uk
Tel: 0870 770 5888 Fax: 0870 770 5889

Amid hills at the head of Swaledale sits the small village of Keld, its cottages clustered around a tiny square. The hostel, formerly a shooting lodge, stands overlooking the village and is a welcome resting place for walkers and cyclists at the cross-over point of the Pennine Way and Coast-to-Coast path. A variety of walking is on offer, ranging from gentle riverside rambles to hikes over the open fells. Birdwatchers should keep a keen eye out for a glimpse of the rare black grouse.
Location: OS 91, GR 892009.
Great for... keen walkers of all abilities.

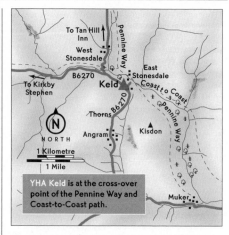

YHA Keld is at the cross-over point of the Pennine Way and Coast-to-Coast path.

You need to know... there are no shops or pubs in the village.
Accommodation: 38 beds: 1x2-, 5x4-, 1x6- and 1x10-bed rooms.
Family rooms: Yes. **Rent-a-Hostel:** Yes.
Classroom: No. **Education packages:** No.
Facilities: Lounge, self-catering kitchen, dining room, showers, drying room and cycle store. **Daytime access:** Restricted. ⊗
Meals: Breakfast, picnic lunch, evening meal.
Reception open: 17.00hrs.

Small fields encased by dry stone walls in Swaledale: near YHA Keld.

○ FAMILY   ● CITY   ● GROUP   ● TRADITIONAL   ● CAMPING BARN   ● COASTAL   ● RURAL

Getting there: The village of Keld lies just off B6270 Reeth to Kirkby Stephen road. Hostel sits on roadside southwest of village.
Parking: Roadside only.
Nearest other hostels: Hawes 9 miles, Kirkby Stephen 11, Grinton 13, Baldersdale 15.
Public transport: BUS: Arriva North East 30/6 from Richmond (infrequent but connections from Darlington station), daily Coast-to-Coast Packhorse bus. RAIL: Kirkby Stephen 11 miles.

●● KETTLEWELL ☆☆☆
Kettlewell, Skipton, North Yorkshire BD23 5QU;
kettlewell@yha.org.uk
Tel: 0870 770 5896 Fax: 0870 770 5897

For a relaxing holiday in the heart of the Dales, choose Kettlewell in the upper reaches of Wharfedale. Local walks take in some of the finest scenery in Yorkshire and are suitable for all abilities and age ranges. There are many local attractions nearby and children and adults alike will enjoy a ride on the Embsay Steam Railway and a visit to Bolton Abbey. If you're planning a visit in August, don't miss the bizarre Scarecrow Festival held in the village.
Location: OS 98, GR 970724.
Great for... an attraction-packed family holiday.
You need to know... parking is limited.
Accommodation: 43 beds: 2x2-, 1x4-, 1x5- and 5x6-bed rooms.
Family rooms: Yes. **Rent-a-Hostel:** No.
Classroom: No. **Education packages:** No.
Facilities: Dining room, TV, drying room, common room, showers, self-catering kitchen, cycle store, lockers and grounds.
Daytime access: All areas. ⊗
Meals: Breakfast, picnic lunch, evening meal.
Reception open: Staff available before 10.00hrs and after 17.00hrs.
Getting there: From Skipton, take B6160 towards Grassington. Follow road for 15 miles to Kettlewell. Go over bridge and turn first right in front of the Bluebell Inn. At the village shop, follow the hostel sign to the left.
Parking: Limited. Additional parking in village.
Nearest other hostels: Linton 8 miles, Aysgarth 13, Malham 14 (10 by path).
Public transport: BUS: Limited from Skipton bus station and from Ilkley, Dalesbus from West Yorkshire. RAIL: Skipton 16 miles.

● KILDALE
campingbarns@yha.org.uk
Booking: 0870 770 6113
Arrival time: Mr & Mrs Cook, 01642 722135

Now a camping barn, this former barn and wheelhouse is a listed building in the farmyard at Park Farm in the North York Moors National Park. The Cleveland Way is on the doorstep as are many good local walks.
Great for... exploring Captain Cook country and the Esk Valley Railway Line.
You need to know... the toilets are in an adjacent building.

Accommodation: Sleeps 18 in the first floor loft.
Facilities: Electric light, heat and cooking facilities (all on meter), toilets, showers, crockery, cutlery, drying facilities, hot water and fridge. Dogs welcome. Ample parking.
Nearest pub: 2 miles. **Nearest shop:** 1 mile.
Location: OS 94, GR 602085.

● KIRKBY STEPHEN ☆☆☆
Market St, Kirkby Stephen, Cumbria CA17 4QQ;
kirkbystephen@yha.org.uk
Tel: 0870 770 5904 Fax: 0870 770 5905

Kirkby Stephen is a converted methodist chapel with the original pews now in the dining room. Situated on Kirkby Stephen's main street in the upper Eden Valley and on Wainwright's Coast-to-Coast path, it offers easy access to Lady Anne's Walk, the peaceful Eden Valley and the Settle to Carlisle railway.
Location: OS 91, GR 774085.
Great for... walkers keen to explore the area.
Accommodation: 40 beds, 1x2-, 3x4-, 3x6- 1x8-bed rooms.

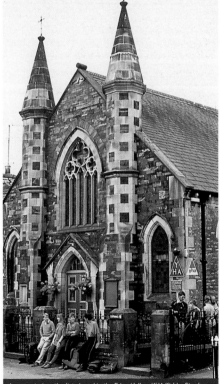
A converted methodist chapel in the Eden Valley: YHA Kirkby Stephen.

● FAMILY   ● CITY   ● GROUP   ● TRADITIONAL   ● CAMPING BARN   ● COASTAL   ● RURAL

Family rooms: Yes. **Rent-a-Hostel:** Yes.
Classroom: No. **Education packages:** No.
Facilities: Lounge, self-catering kitchen, dining room, showers, drying room, luggage store and laundry facilities.
Daytime access: All areas. 🚫
Meals: Breakfast, picnic lunch, evening meal.
Reception open: Staff available before 10.00hrs and after 17.00hrs.
Getting there: From M6 J38, take second exit on left from roundabout, signed Kirkby Stephen. From A66 Penrith direction, follow signs for Brough then turn right for A685 (Kendal direction). From Coast-to-Coast path, pass Spar shop and traffic lights. The hostel is on the west side of the main street.
Parking: Roadside or free car park 100 metres away.
Nearest other hostels: Keld 11 miles, Hawes 15, Dufton 16.
Public transport: BUS: Various connections from Kirkby Stephen station, also Primrose Coaches 352 Newcastle-upon-Tyne–Blackpool. RAIL: Kirkby Stephen 1.5 miles.

● LEYBURN

campingbarns@yha.org.uk
Booking: 0870 770 6113
Arrival time: Mr & Mrs Iveson, 01969 622204

This camping barn at Craken House Farm has featured in the TV series All Creatures Great and Small, and the BBC's Countryfile. Only a mile from the market town of Leyburn, it boasts magnificent views over Wensleydale and the Yorkshire Dales and there are plenty of interesting river and fell walks all around.
Great for... visiting Richmond, Hawes and the Yorkshire Dales.
You need to know... bring a pillow case, sleeping bag and £1 coins for the meter.
Accommodation: Sleeps 12 in partitioned bunk beds.
Facilities: Electric light, heaters, fridge and shower (all metered), wash basins, toilets, gas cooker, cutlery, crockery, pans, multi-fuel stove, TV outlet and extra plugs for own equipment. Dogs welcome.
Nearest pub: 1 mile. **Nearest shop:** 1 mile.
Location: OS 99, GR 121895.

●● LINTON ☆

Nr Grassington, Linton-in-Craven, Skipton, North Yorkshire BD23 5HH;
Tel: 0870 770 5920 Fax: 0870 770 5921

A 17th century rectory built of mellow stone, this hostel is in a quiet Wharfedale village, a mile from the busier settlement of Grassington. Linton's old world cottages, ancient clapper bridge and packhorse bridge by the ford are a delight. You'll also want to visit Linton Falls (0.5 miles away), Bolton Abbey (eight miles) and Kilnsey Crag (four miles). A popular base for families.
Location: OS 98, GR 998627.
Great for... a quiet break in the country.
You need to know... this hostel may close during 2003. Please enquire before planning your stay.
Accommodation: 36 beds: 2x4-, 3x6- and 1x10-bed rooms.
Family rooms: No. **Rent-a-Hostel:** Yes.

Classroom: No. **Education packages:** No.
Facilities: Self-catering kitchen, dining room, drying room, cycle store and garden. **Daytime access:** Restricted. 🚫
Meals: Breakfast, picnic lunch, evening meal.
Reception open: 17.00hrs.
Getting there: The hostel is adjacent to the village green on the east side of the packhorse bridge, over the river.
Parking: Yes.
Nearest other hostels: Malham 7 miles (by path), Kettlewell 8, Earby 15.
Public transport: BUS: Pride of the Dales 72, Keighley & District 67A from Skipton station, 74 from Ilkley, Dalesbus from West Yorkshire. RAIL: Skipton 8 miles.

●● LOCKTON ☆

Old School, Lockton, Pickering, North Yorkshire YO18 7PY
Tel: 0870 770 5938 Fax: 0870 770 5939

An old village school in a rural hamlet, Lockton offers basic facilities for those who want to get away from it all. A few miles away is Levisham Station on the North York Moors Steam Railway, allowing

www.britainonview.com

Take a trip on the North York Moors Steam Railway near YHA Lockton.

● FAMILY ● CITY ● GROUP ● TRADITIONAL ● CAMPING BARN ● COASTAL ● RURAL

linear walks over uncrowded moorland terrain. Alternatively, there is excellent walking in Cropton Forest and Levisham Beck or you can enjoy a peaceful cycle ride along Dalby Forest Drive. If you recognise the countryside then you'll remember that this is where the TV series Heartbeat is filmed.

Location: OS 94, GR 844900.

Great for... a secluded break for keen walkers and cyclists.

You need to know... there is no drying room.

Accommodation: 22 beds: 1x4-, 1x8- and 1x10-bed rooms.

Family rooms: No. **Rent-a-Hostel:** Yes.

Classroom: No. **Education packages:** No.

Facilities: Self-catering kitchen, lounge, showers, cycle store and car park. **Daytime access:** All areas. ☺

Meals: Self-catering only.

Reception open: Staff available before 10.00hrs and after 17.00hrs.

Getting there: From the A169, turn west at the sign for Lockton and Levisham.

Parking: Yes, at hostel.

Nearest other hostels: Boggle Hole 15 miles, Whitby 15, Scarborough 19 (12 by path).

Public transport: BUS: Yorkshire Coastliner 840 Whitby–Malton (passes close to Whitby and Malton station). RAIL: Malton 14 miles, Levisham (North Yorks Moors Railway, connecting with Esk Valley line at Grosmont) 2.

● LOVESOME HILL

campingbarns@yha.org.uk

Booking: 0870 770 6113

Arrival time: Mr & Mrs Pearson, 01609 772311 (fax: 01609 774715)

www.britainonview.com

Feeding the farm animals: Lovesome Hill Farm.

THE REGION'S BEST HISTORICAL SITES

Rievaulx Abbey, N Yorks YHA Osmotherley: "Huge and very impressive. Shows just how important monasteries were in medieval England."

Museum of Army Transport YHA Beverley Friary: "An excellent rainy-day museum. Mostly under cover with plenty of tanks and trucks to climb over. Don't miss the last remaining Beverley Blackburn plane."

Hull's museums YHA Beverley Friary: "Heard of 'The Deep'? This is where you can journey into the ocean depths! Hull also has seven museums with free admission, covering everything from transport to our maritime past."

Scarborough Castle YHA Scarborough: "Dates from the 12th century, but its site, on the edge of a cliff, has over 3,000 years of history. An eerie insight into the past."

This former corn store, now a camping barn, is in the farmyard at Lovesome Hill Farm. Centrally placed for exploring the Yorkshire Dales and the North York Moors National Parks, the barn is just 200 metres from the Coast-to-Coast walk. The bustling market town of Northallerton is four miles away. From there, it is 4 miles north along the A167 on the right-hand side.

Great for... experiencing life on a working farm and exploring the Dales and Moors.

You need to know... small groups can book breakfast by arrangement; you can hire sheets and duvets.

Accommodation: Sleeps 10 in bunks in two rooms on the first floor.

Facilities: Electric light, two heaters, cooker, shower, toilets and metered electricity. Food available at barn (order in advance).

Nearest pub: 2.5 miles. **Nearest shop:** 2.5 miles.

Location: OS 99, GR 361998.

● LOW ROW

campingbarns@yha.org.uk

Booking: 0870 770 6113

Arrival time: Mrs Clarkson, 01748 884601

This camping barn is on Low White Farm, an outstanding location in Swaledale at the heart of the Yorkshire Dales National Park. It is a mile from the Coast-to-Coast walk and there are many routes close by, including the Corpse Road running between Keld and Reeth.

Great for... exploring the Yorkshire Dales.

You need to know... there is a car park next to the barn.

Accommodation: Sleeps 15 in bunk beds on the first floor, mattresses are provided.

Facilities: Dining area, fully equipped kitchen with gas cooker,

● FAMILY   ● CITY   ● GROUP   ● TRADITIONAL   ● CAMPING BARN   ● COASTAL   ● RURAL

cutlery, crockery and pans, electric light, oil central heating on a meter, showers, toilets and washbasin. Dogs welcome.
Nearest pub: 1.25 miles. **Nearest shop:** 2 miles.
Location: OS 92, GR 003983.

●● MALHAM ☆☆☆
Malham, Skipton, North Yorkshire BD23 4DE;
malham@yha.org.uk
Tel: 0870 770 5946 Fax: 0870 770 5947

Designed by John Dower, one of the most influential figures in the initiative to establish National Parks in Britain, this is a purpose-built Youth Hostel. Walking and cycling are the main attractions and the Pennine Way and Yorkshire Dales Cycleway both pass through this village at the heart of the Yorkshire Dales National Park. The hostel has great facilities for educational groups as well as youngsters, with a safe, secure garden, a range of toddler's equipment for hire and a child-friendly menu. The famous Limestone pavements and Malham Tarn are within walking distance.
Location: OS 98, GR 901629.
Great for... walkers and cyclists.
Accommodation: 82 beds: 1x2-, 4x4-, 1x5- and 9x6–8-bed rooms.
Family rooms: Yes. **Rent-a-Hostel:** Yes.
Classroom: Yes. **Education packages:** No.
Facilities: Lounge, self-catering kitchen, showers, lockers, laundry, shop and grounds. **Daytime access:** All areas.
Meals: Breakfast, picnic lunch, evening meal.
Reception open: Staff available before 10.00hrs and after 17.00hrs.
Getting there: The hostel is situated in the centre of the village, next to the Listers Arms pub.
Parking: Yes. Take first left after YHA Malham sign to the car park.
Nearest other hostels: Stainforth 8 miles, Kettlewell 10 (by path).
Public transport: BUS: Pennine 210 from Skipton (passes close to Skipton station), Postbus from Skipton, Dales Bus from West Yorkshire. RAIL: Settle 7 miles, Skipton 13.

●● MANKINHOLES ☆☆☆☆
Mankinholes, Todmorden, Lancashire OL14 6HR;
mankinholes@yha.org.uk
Tel: 0870 770 5952 Fax: 0870 770 5952

Once the local manor house dating back to the 17th century, this refurbished hostel on the edge of moorland is a charming place to stay. The Pennine Way and Calderdale Way are close by and you'll find an abundance of other footpaths, bridleways and packhorse trails to explore. Despite the quiet, rural location, it's within easy reach of other attractions should the weather prove inclement. Eurekal, the interactive childrens' museum in Halifax, Haworth, The Keighley & Worth Valley Steam Railway and Hollingworth Lake & Activity Centre are all nearby.
Location: OS 103, GR 960235.
Great for... walkers keen on clocking up the miles.
You need to know... it's self-catering accommodation only.
Accommodation: 32 beds: 2x2-, 4x4- and 2x6-bed rooms.
Family rooms: Yes. **Rent-a-Hostel:** Yes.

A 17th century refurbished manor house: YHA Mankinholes.

Classroom: No. **Education packages:** No.
Facilities: Self-catering kitchen, dining room, lounge, showers, cycle store, laundry facilities and grounds. **Daytime access:** All areas. ⊗
Meals: Self-catering only.
Reception open: Staff available before 10.00hrs and after 17.00hrs.
Getting there: Follow road to Lumbutts. The hostel is 0.25 miles east of the Top Brink public house.
Parking: Yes.
Nearest other hostels: Haworth 12 miles (18 by Pennine Way), Crowden 24 (by Pennine Way), Earby 25 (by Pennine Way).
Public transport: BUS: First Calderline T6/T8 from Todmorden (passes close to Todmorden station). RAIL: Todmorden 2 miles. FERRY: Liverpool to Belfast 55 miles, Hull to Europe 85 (both accessible via M62 motorway).

●● OSMOTHERLEY ☆☆
Cote Ghyll, Osmotherley, Northallerton, North Yorkshire DL6 3AH; osmotherley@yha.org.uk
Tel: 0870 770 5982 Fax: 0870 770 5983

You'll find this hostel, formerly a mill, in a secluded valley on the edge of the North York Moors National Park. It's popular with walkers but also those wishing to tour the coast and the Yorkshire Moors and Dales, which are all within an hour's drive. There are plenty of attractions to suit all tastes nearby, such as Mount Grace Priory, Rievaulx Abbey, World of James Herriot and Lightwater Valley Theme Park.
Location: OS 100, GR 461981.
Great for... families and groups wanting to walk and tour the area.
Accommodation: 72 beds: 1x2-, 2x3-, 1x4- and 5x6-bed rooms, some en-suite.
Family rooms: Yes. **Rent-a-Hostel:** No.

For more information visit www.yha.org.uk

FAMILY   ● CITY   ● GROUP   ● TRADITIONAL   ● CAMPING BARN   ○ COASTAL   ● RURAL

Classroom: Yes. **Education packages:** Yes.
Facilities: Lounge/reception, TV room, self-catering kitchen, showers, drying room, dining/games room, cycle store, laundry, grounds and residential licence. **Daytime access:** All areas. ☻
Meals: Breakfast, picnic lunch, evening meal.
Reception open: 13.00hrs.
Getting there: Go north out of the village and after quarter of a mile turn right down a private drive past a caravan/camping site.
Parking: Yes.
Nearest other hostels: Helmsley 15 miles, Ellingstring 23, Grinton 31.
Public transport: BUS: Arriva 80/89 Northallerton station–Stokesley, alight Osmotherley 0.75 miles.
RAIL: Northallerton 8 miles. FERRY: Newcastle 50 miles, Hull 70.

● RICHMOND
campingbarns@yha.org.uk
Booking: 0870 770 6113
Arrival time: Mr & Mrs Atkinson, 01748 822940

These three former byres at East Applegarth Farm have been converted into a camping barn with magnificent views across Swaledale. It is a great base for exploring the Yorkshire Dales National Park with many scenic local trails and the Coast-to-Coast walk passing close by.
Accommodation: Sleeps 12 in two rooms, mattresses provided.
Facilities: Electric light, heat and cooking facilities on meter, cutlery, crockery, pans. Dogs welcome. Food available at barn.
Nearest pub: 3 miles. **Nearest shop:** 3 miles.
Location: OS 92, GR 135017.

www.britainonview.com

Scarborough makes an ideal destination for family fun.

YHA Scarborough: peace and quiet by the riverside.

●● SCARBOROUGH ☆☆☆
Burniston Road, Scarborough, North Yorkshire YO13 0DA; scarborough@yha.org.uk
Tel: 0870 770 6022 Fax: 0870 770 6023

This former water mill – built around 1600 – provides the perfect antidote to a day spent exploring Scarborough's many attractions such as the Sea Life Centre, Kinderland and Atlantis Water Park. Only two miles from the hectic town centre, its wooded riverside location attracts herons, foxes, kingfishers, deer and, occasionally, otters. This hostel has good facilities for children and is just 15 minutes' walk from the sea, making it perfect for a traditional seaside holiday.
Location: OS 101, GR 026907.
Great for... summer fun for seaside-loving families.
Accommodation: 48 beds: 3x4- and 6x6-bed rooms.
Family rooms: Yes. **Rent-a-Hostel:** Yes.
Classroom: No. **Education packages:** No.
Facilities: Lounge, self-catering kitchen, showers, drying room, laundry and cycle store. **Daytime access:** Restricted. ☻
Meals: Breakfast, picnic lunch, evening meal.
Reception open: 17.00hrs.
Getting there: From Scarborough, follow signs to North Bay attractions, then the A165 to Whitby. The hostel is 2 miles north of the town centre. There is a very sharp turn immediately after the

Yorkshire & South Pennines

● FAMILY　　● CITY　　● GROUP　　● TRADITIONAL　　● CAMPING BARN　　● COASTAL　　● RURAL

bridge – you are advised to drive past and turn around in the lay-by (see map on page 175).

Parking: Yes.

Nearest other hostels: Boggle Hole 13 miles, Lockton 19 (12 by path), Whitby 20.

Public transport: BUS: Frequent from surrounding areas. RAIL: Scarborough 2 miles. FERRY: Hull 45 miles. **NATIONALEXPRESS** Westwood coach park 2 miles.

● SINNINGTON

campingbarns@yha.org.uk

Booking: 0870 770 6113

Arrival time: Mrs Scaling, 01751 473792

This former granary is now a camping barn on the family-run Cliff Farm. Enjoy local walks, visit the steam railway or take a day trip to Flamingoland, the North York Moors or the coast.

Great for... access to the North York Moors and Ryedale.

You need to know... the shower, washing and toilet facilities are in an adjacent building and shared with a small campsite.

Accommodation: Sleeps 12, mattresses provided.

Facilities: Electric light, heat, shower and cooking facilities on meter, toilets, washing facilities, cutlery, crockery, pans and fridge. Dogs welcome by prior arrangement.

Nearest pub: 1 mile. **Nearest shop:** 2.5 miles.

Location: OS 94, GR 752849.

●● SLAIDBURN ☆☆☆

King's House, Slaidburn, Clitheroe, Lancashire BB7 3ER; slaidburn@yha.org.uk

Tel: 0870 770 6034

Those of you who love the outdoors life will adore Slaidburn's location. In the middle of the Forest of Bowland, there's an excellent network of quiet roads and cycle paths while walking routes will take you across moorland and alongside the river and reservoir. For peace

In the middle of the Forest of Bowland: YHA Slaidburn.

and solitude, head to the relatively undiscovered fells and valleys of the nearby Area of Outstanding Natural Beauty. The hostel is a comfortable retreat to return to – a 17th century village inn, the listed building has recently been refurbished to a high standard.

Location: OS 103, GR 711523.

Great for... adults happy to spend a week walking or cycling.

You need to know... Slaidburn offers self-catering accommodation.

Accommodation: 30 beds: 1x3-, 4x4-, 1x5- and 1x6-bed rooms.

Family rooms: Yes. **Rent-a-Hostel:** Yes.

Classroom: No. **Education packages:** No.

Facilities: Lounge, dining room, self-catering kitchen, showers and cycle store. Limited shop. Credit cards accepted for advance bookings only. **Daytime access:** Restricted. ⊗

Meals: Self-catering only.

Reception open: 17.00hrs.

Getting there: From Clitheroe, take B6478 Settle road. The hostel is in the centre of the village opposite the pub.

Parking: Yes.

Nearest other hostels: Ingleton 15 miles, Stainforth 15, Earby 19, Arnside 32.

Public transport: BUS: Tyrer 110/1 from Clitheroe (passing Clitheroe station). RAIL: Clitheroe 8 miles.

YHA Stainforth is a refurbished Georgian country house.

●● STAINFORTH ☆☆☆

Stainforth, Settle, North Yorkshire BD24 9PA; stainforth@yha.org.uk

Tel: 0870 770 6046 Fax: 0870 770 6047

This refurbished Georgian country house nestles in wooded grounds on the edge of the Yorkshire Dales National Park, just minutes from the village. It makes an ideal base for families and groups with easy walks to waterfalls, caves and limestone scenery and within reach of the River Ribble and Three Peaks walk. The Falconry and Conservation Centre and the market town of Settle are close by, while Skipton and its castle are 20 minutes away.

Location: OS 98, GR 821668.

Great for... families used to the outdoors life.

For all the latest YHA news visit www.yha.org.uk

● FAMILY ● CITY ● GROUP ● TRADITIONAL ● CAMPING BARN ● COASTAL ● RURAL

Accommodation: 47 beds: 1x2-, 2x4-, 2x6-, 1x7-, 1x8- and 1x10-bed rooms, some en-suite.
Family rooms: Yes. **Rent-a-Hostel:** No.
Classroom: Yes. **Education packages:** No.
Facilities: Lounge, dining room, self-catering kitchen, showers, drying room and cycle store. **Daytime access:** All areas. ⊗
Meals: Breakfast, picnic lunch, evening meal.
Reception open: 15.00hrs.
Getting there: The hostel is 2 miles north of Settle in the Yorkshire Dales National Park, 0.25 mile south of village on main B6479 Settle–Horton-in-Ribblesdale. It is 3.5 miles south of the Pennine Way at Dale Head and 4 miles south of the Pennine Way at Horton.
Parking: Yes.
Nearest other hostels: Malham 8 miles, Ingleton 10, Kettlewell 15.
Public transport: BUS: Bibby's/Kirkby Lonsdale Coaches Settle–Horton (passes Settle station). RAIL: Settle 2.5 miles, Giggleswick 3.

Get close to birds of prey at the Falconry near YHA Stainforth.

● TRAWDEN

campingbarns@yha.org.uk
Booking: 0870 770 6113
Arrival time: Mr & Mrs Mann, 01282 865257

This recently restored camping barn is in an idyllic setting surrounded by meadows, one mile from Trawden village. There are plenty of opportunities for walking in the Forest of Trawden and on the expansive South Pennine moors. Skipton and its castle are 20 minutes away.
Great for... walking on Pendle Hill and Boulsworth.
You need to know... you must make sure you come to Middle Beardshaw Farm; there is also a Lower Beardshaw Farm and a Higher!
Accommodation: Sleeps 15 to 20 in a sleeping gallery, camp-beds are provided.
Facilities: Sitting area with wood-burning stove (fuel can be purchased), bathrooms with hot showers, fully equipped kitchen with gas rings and microwave, toilets, electric light, heater, fridge, metered electricity. Pool room with darts and table tennis. Meals can be enjoyed in attached conservatory in summer.
Nearest pub: 1 mile. **Nearest shop:** 1 mile.
Location: OS 103, GR 903381.

● WESTERDALE

campingbarns@yha.org.uk
Booking: 0870 770 6113
Arrival time: Mr & Mrs Alderson, 01287 660259

This former byre, now a camping barn, has lovely views of Westerdale Moor and Castleton Rigg. In the farmyard at Broadgate Farm in the North York Moors National Park, it is within three miles of the Coast-to-Coast and Lyke Wake walks. There are also numerous local trails including the Rosedale Circuit.
Great for... enthusiastic walkers.
Accommodation: Sleeps 12 in bunkbeds in two rooms on the ground floor.
Facilities: Electric lights, heaters, hot water, shower and gas cooker. Dogs welcome.
Nearest pub: 2 miles. **Nearest shop:** 2 miles.
Location: OS 94, GR 671049.

●● WHITBY ☆

East Cliff, Whitby, North Yorkshire YO22 4JT;
whitby@yha.org.uk
Tel: 0870 770 6088 Fax: 0870 770 6089

Perched dramatically on the headland, YHA Whitby has panoramic views of the harbour, coastline and imposing abbey ruins. Watch the brightly coloured fishing boats bringing in their catch or spend a day on the sandy beaches within walking distance of the hostel. Explore the nearby moors and dales and cycle along the disused railway line to Robin Hood's Bay. All in all, it's the perfect seaside holiday for outdoor-minded families.
Location: OS 94, GR 902111.
Great for... active families seeking a seaside break.

Yorkshire & South Pennines

● FAMILY   ● CITY   ● GROUP   ● TRADITIONAL   ● CAMPING BARN   ● COASTAL   ● RURAL

You need to know... the car park is half a mile away.
Accommodation: 58 beds: 1x2-, 3x4-, 2x6-, 1x10- and 1x22-bed rooms.
Family rooms: Yes. **Rent-a-Hostel:** No.
Classroom: No. **Education packages:** Yes.
Facilities: Lounge, self-catering kitchen, dining room, showers, drying room, lockers and garden. **Daytime access:** Restricted. ⊗
Meals: Breakfast, picnic lunch, evening meal.
Reception open: 17.00hrs.
Getting there: By road, follow signs to Abbey up Green Lane, turn left and continue beyond the Abbey to the car park. The hostel is nearby. On foot, climb the 199 steps from town.
Parking: Drop-off point near to hostel – park in Abbey car park (0.5 miles away and free 19.00hrs–09.00hrs).
Nearest other hostels: Boggle Hole 7 miles, Scarborough 20.

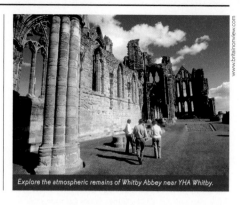

Explore the atmospheric remains of Whitby Abbey near YHA Whitby.

HOSTEL MANAGERS CHOOSE...

THE TOP 10 ATTRACTIONS IN...
YORK

1. YORK MINSTER
"It took 200 years to build and was finished before Columbus sailed for America. York Minster still towers over the surrounding medieval streets."

2. GHOST TRAILS
"Join a ghost walk and be guided around one of Europe's most haunted cities!"

3. JORVIK VIKING CENTRE
"Experience the sights (and smells!) of Viking York in this reconstruction of the 10th century city."

4. YORK DUNGEON
"Steel yourself for a highly entertaining, if rather gruesome, journey through the centuries. The darkest chapters of York's grim and bloody past are recreated."

5. YORK FESTIVALS
"There is no shortage of pageantry in York. Don't miss the Jorvik Viking Festival in February and the Cycle Rally each June."

6. NATIONAL RAILWAY MUSEUM
"The largest of its kind in the world, this museum houses icons including Queen Victoria's carriage and the Japanese Bullet Train."

7. CASTLE MUSEUM
"In York's old prison, this museum shows life in York since 1580. Wander through Victorian Streets and peep into Dick Turpin's cell."

8. MURTON PARK
"It's four attractions in one (Danelaw Dark Age Village, Brigantium Roman Fort, Yorkshire Museum of Farming and Derwent Valley Light Railway). Quite simply, this is a great family day out."

9. CITY WALLS
"An afternoon's stroll round three miles of city walls and bars (gatehouses) will give you a fascinating insight into the city's past."

10. THE SHAMBLES
"One of the best preserved medieval streets in Europe, the Shambles takes its name from 'shammels', shelves used by butchers to display their meat."

For more information visit www.yha.org.uk

● FAMILY ● CITY ● GROUP ● TRADITIONAL ● CAMPING BARN ● COASTAL ● RURAL

Public transport: BUS: Frequent.
RAIL: Whitby (not Sun, except June to Sept) 0.5 miles.
NATIONALEXPRESS>> Langborne Road 0.5 miles.

●● YORK ☆☆☆

Water End, Clifton, York, North Yorkshire
YO30 6LP; york@yha.org.uk
Tel: 0870 770 6102 Fax: 0870 770 6103

The ancient and beautiful walled city of York has attracted visitors for centuries, some more welcome than others. The Romans, Anglo-Saxons, Vikings and Normans have all left their mark on the city, giving tourists of the 21st century plenty to see and do. This hostel, an attractive Victorian building, allows easy access to the city centre via a soothing stroll along the River Ouse. For extra comfort, premium rooms are available.

Location: OS 105, GR 589528.
Great for... a friendly and efficient base to explore York.
You need to know... with 150 beds, this hostel can get very busy.
Accommodation: 150 beds: mostly 4-bed rooms, plus 4x6- and 3x8-bed options. Premium 1-, 2-, 3- and 4-bed rooms.
Family rooms: Yes. **Rent-a-Hostel:** No.
Classroom: Yes. **Education packages:** No.
Facilities: Restaurant with full menu and table licence, lounge, TV, games room, self-catering kitchen, showers, cycle and luggage stores, laundry facilities, internet access, garden and patio. Conference facilities and night security. **Daytime access:** All areas (except bedrooms between 10.00hrs and 13.00hrs).
Meals: Breakfast, picnic lunch, evening meal.
Reception open: 7.00hrs to 22.30hrs (access 24hrs).
Getting there: From the minster, take A19 to Clifton Green, turning left at Old Grey Mare pub into Water End. Hostel is 300 metres on the right. From A1237 ring road, take A19 towards the city, turning right into Water End at the second set of traffic lights. From the station, turn left and approach the river, turn left and walk up the river bank for 0.5 miles until you reach Water End bridge (see map on page 175).

Parking: Yes, cars and coaches.
Nearest other hostels: Helmsley 24 miles, Beverley Friary 30, Haworth 45, Scarborough 45.
Public transport: BUS: Frequent from surrounding areas.
RAIL: York 1 mile. **FERRY:** Hull 41 miles.
NATIONALEXPRESS>> McMillans Bar, York station 1 mile.

www.britainonview.com

Spend an entertaining evening at the Theatre Royal near YHA York.

YHA York is just a riverside stroll from the city centre.

FIND PEACE AND QUIET

Many of the hostels in Yorkshire & South Pennines offer a secluded stay in stunning countryside. For details, turn to page 20.

The Youth Hostels of...

North West cities & Peak District

Stunning hills: Mam Tor near YHA Castleton is just one of the great locations that attract thousands to the Peaks every year.

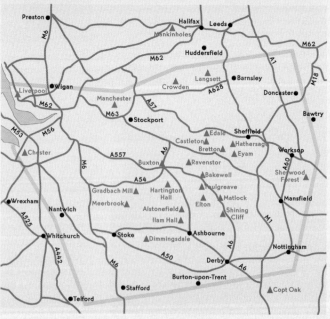

For further information visit www.yha.org.uk

● FAMILY   ● CITY   ● GROUP   ● TRADITIONAL   ● CAMPING BARN   ● COASTAL   ● RURAL

● ABNEY

campingbarns@yha.org.uk
Booking: 0870 770 6113
Arrival time: Mr & Mrs Chadwick, 01433 650481

You'll find this camping barn in the small village of Abney, 1,000 feet up on the gritstone hills at the head of Abney Clough. The moors hereabouts are noted for their fine viewpoints.
Accommodation: Sleeps 8 in 2 separate areas.
Facilities: Electric light, heaters, cooking area with two rings, fridge and microwave, BBQ, outdoor seating and adjacent toilet. Electricity on a meter.
Nearest pub: 2.5 miles. **Nearest shop:** 3 miles.
Location: OS 110, GR 198798.

●● ALSTONEFIELD ☆☆☆

Gypsy Lane, Alstonefield, nr Ashbourne, Derbyshire DE6 2FZ; reservations@yha.org.uk
Tel: 0870 770 5670 Fax: 0870 770 5670
Bookings more than 7 days ahead: 0870 770 6113

Overlooking Dovedale, this is a comfortable base from which to explore the Manifold Valley and Beresford and Wolfscote Dales on foot or by bike, with Chatsworth House and Alton Towers both nearby. The hostel consists of two barns, each with its own lounge, dining area and self-catering kitchen. All five bedrooms are en-suite and there is a large patio and garden area.
Location: OS 119, GR 133556.
Great for... a modern base with a range of activities nearby.
You need to know... it's self-catering accommodation only.
Accommodation: 20 beds: 5x4-bed rooms, all en-suite.
Family rooms: Yes. **Rent-a-Hostel:** Yes.
Classroom: No. **Education packages:** No.
Facilities: Lounge, dining room, self-catering kitchen, drying room, showers, bedrooms and grounds. **Daytime access:** All areas. ⊗
Meals: Self-catering only.
Reception open: Staff available before 10.00hrs and after 17.00hrs.
Getting there: From A515 to Alstonefield, go past Overdale B&B into Gypsy Lane. Hostel is on the left.
Parking: Yes.
Nearest other hostels: Ilam Hall 3.5 miles, Hartington Hall 4.5, Meerbrook 12.
Public transport: BUS: Postbus from Leek (with connections from Stoke-on-Trent), Warrington 441 from Ashbourne (Thurs, Sat only), connections from Derby and Manchester.
RAIL: Cromford 13 miles, Buxton 14.

● ALSTONEFIELD

campingbarns@yha.org.uk
Booking: 0870 770 6113
Arrival time: Mr & Mrs Flower, 01335 310349

This camping barn is near the attractive village of Alstonefield, in the heart of the Peak District between Dovedale and the Manifold Valley.

It enjoys fine views of the surrounding limestone hills and is an ideal base for walkers and cyclists. It's also convenient for Alton Towers and visiting historic houses.
Great for... discovering the delights of both Derbyshire and Staffordshire.
You need to know... parking is limited.
Accommodation: Sleeps 12 in a separate upstairs area.
Facilities: Communal cooking area with picnic bench seating, toilet and basin.
Nearest pub: 1 mile. **Nearest shop:** 1 mile.
Location: OS 119, GR 125569.

●● BAKEWELL ☆

Fly Hill, Bakewell, Derbyshire DE45 1DN;
bakewell@yha.org.uk
Tel: 0870 770 5682 Fax: 0870 770 5682

With fine views over the historic market town of Bakewell and the Wye Valley, this relaxed hostel is the ideal base from which to explore the many delights of the Peak District. Chatsworth House and Haddon Hall, Lathkill Dale and Monsal Dale are all within easy walking distance and there are great public transport links. Bakewell itself is a hive of activity. Famous for its puddings and tarts with a market tradition stretching back over 700 years old, this wonderful town is full of hidden surprises.
Location: OS 119, GR 215685.

Cooling down at Chatsworth House near YHA Bakewell.

www.britainonview.com

● FAMILY   ● CITY   ● GROUP   ● TRADITIONAL   ● CAMPING BARN   ● COASTAL   ● RURAL

Great for... exploring the Peak District National Park.

You need to know... parking is limited.

Accommodation: 28 beds: 2x2- and 4x6-bed rooms.

Family rooms: No. **Rent-a-Hostel:** No.

Classroom: No. **Education packages:** Yes.

Facilities: Lounge, drying room, self-catering kitchen, showers and small shop. **Daytime access:** All areas. ♿

Meals: Breakfast, picnic lunch, evening meal.

Reception open: Staff available before 10.00hrs and after 17.00hrs.

Getting there: From the A6 Buxton–Matlock road at Bakewell follow YHA sign up North Church Street near the roundabout and the Rutland Hotel. Follow road up the hill, past the church on the left and take the second right on to Fly Hill (hostel is signposted).

Parking: Small car park, further parking in town centre.

Nearest other hostels: Youlgreave 3.5 miles, Matlock 8, Buxton 12.

Public transport: BUS: Frequent from surrounding areas. RAIL: Matlock 8 miles.

NATIONAL EXPRESS If travelling towards Nottingham, stop is 100 metres from Rutland Arms on A6 towards Matlock. If travelling to Manchester, stop is adjacent to Rutland Arms on A6 to Buxton.

Groups of all ages will discover stimulating activities in the Peaks.

● BIRCHOVER

campingbarns@yha.org.uk

Booking: 0870 770 6113

Arrival time: Mr Heathcote, 01629 650245

This camping barn is on a beef farm and campsite at the edge of Birchover, between Bakewell and Matlock. Nearby is Stanton Moor with its Nine Ladies stone circle.

You need to know... it's a minimum booking of five.

Accommodation: Sleeps 10.

Facilities: Communal area with tables, adjacent cooking shelter with stone bench, toilets and showers in farmyard, hot water and shower.

Nearest pub: 0.5 miles. **Nearest shop:** 0.5 miles.

Location: OS 119, GR 241622.

●● BRETTON ☆

Bretton, nr Eyam, Hope Valley, Sheffield, Yorkshire S32 5QD; reservations@yha.org.uk

Tel: 0870 770 5720 **Fax:** 0870 770 5720

Bookings more than 7 days ahead: 0870 770 6113

The smallest and highest hostel in the Peaks, Bretton is situated above the historic plague village of Eyam with stunning views of the surrounding countryside. An open fire and Rayburn stove provide a homely welcome and add to the traditional character and friendly atmosphere. Walkers will be in their element here, with clear paths and trails over the White Peak within easy reach.

Location: OS 119, GR 200780.

Great for... active people looking for a small, cosy base.

You need to know... it's self-catering accommodation only; credit cards are only accepted for advance bookings.

Accommodation: 18 beds: 1x4-, 1x6-, and 1x8-bed rooms.

Family rooms: No. **Rent-a-Hostel:** Yes.

Classroom: No. **Education packages:** No.

Facilities: Lounge/dining room, self-catering kitchen, shower,

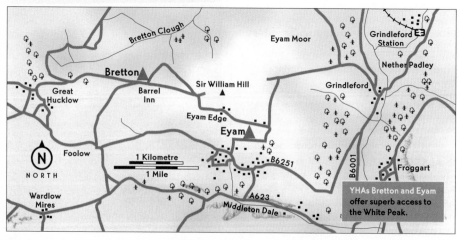

YHAs Bretton and Eyam offer superb access to the White Peak.

For offers and discounts visit www.yha.org.uk

drying room, cycle store and grounds. No hostel shop.

Daytime access: Restricted. ⊗

Meals: Self-catering only.

Reception open: 17.00hrs.

Getting there: Off the A623 Chapel-le-Frith to Baslow Road, follow sign to Foolow. Take first left after the Bulls Head pub (signposted Bretton) and follow road up steep hill. The track to the hostel is on the left, 20 metres before the Barrel Inn.

Parking: Yes.

Nearest other hostels: Eyam 1.5 miles, Hathersage 5, Ravenstor 6.

Public transport: BUS: Various services from Sheffield, Buxton and Chesterfield (passing close to Sheffield, Buxton and Chesterfield stations), alight Foolow 1 mile.

RAIL: Grindleford 4 miles, Hathersage 4.

● BUTTERTON A

campingbarns@yha.org.uk

Booking: 0870 770 6113

Arrival time: Jason Renshaw, 01538 304226

Perched high above the Manifold Valley, Waterslacks Barn is a secluded base from which to enjoy the limestone valleys and attractive villages of the southern Peak District.

Great for... walking in the White Peak, rock climbing, caving and cycling on the Manifold track.

You need to know... campfire wood can be pre-booked from Mr Renshaw on the telephone number above.

Accommodation: Sleeps 15.

Facilities: Communal area with table and benches, cooking area,

---

HOSTEL MANAGERS CHOOSE...

THE REGION'S BEST CYCLE TRAILS

Tissington Trail YHA Ilam Hall: "Especially suitable for families with young kids as it doesn't go onto roads at all. Hire bikes at Ashbourne and Parsley Hay."

High Peak Trail YHA Matlock: "17 miles of traffic-free riding. On an old railway track, it runs past abandoned engine houses, sidings and signals, as well as hundreds of wildflowers in the summer."

The Silent Valley YHA Castleton: "Pedal around these lakes that harbour a ghostly secret. Two villages were flooded to form the reservoirs — if you listen to the wind you may hear the lost villagers. Fascinating by day, stunning by moonlight."

Manifold Trail YHA Hartington Hall: "I defy anyone not to enjoy this! Safe, secure and mostly off-road, the Manifold Trail follows a disused railway track through a dramatic landscape. Cycle hire is available at Waterhouses."

Monsal Trail YHA Bakewell: "Put your brakes on at Monsal Head. This great railway viaduct has fantastic views over Monsal Dale."

---

toilet, shower, heating, electric light and metered electricity. Campfire allowed.

Nearest pub: 1 mile. **Nearest shop:** 1 mile.

Location: OS 118/119, GR 087561.

● BUTTERTON B

campingbarns@yha.org.uk

Booking: 0870 770 6113

Arrival time: Jason Renshaw, 01538 304226

Wills Barn is a short walk out of Butterton village and lies beside the minor road to Wetton Mill. It's convenient for exploring the Manifold and Dove Valleys.

Great for... walking in the White Peak, rock climbing, caving and cycling on the Manifold track.

You need to know... campfire wood can be pre-booked from Mr Renshaw.

Accommodation: Sleeps 6.

Facilities: Living area with tables and benches, cooking area, toilet and washbasin, shower, lighting and metered electricity. Campfire allowed.

Nearest pub: 0.75 miles. **Nearest shop:** 1 mile.

Location: OS 118/119, GR 083564.

● BUXTON ☆

Sherbrook Lodge, Harpur Hill Road, Buxton, Derbyshire SK17 9NB; buxton@yha.org.uk

Tel: 0870 770 5738 Fax: 0870 770 5738

A Victorian house in wooded grounds, YHA Buxton is within easy walking distance of the centre of this spa town in the Peak District.

The mountain of Mam Tor, near YHA Castleton and Losehill.

For more information visit www.yha.org.uk

● FAMILY   ● CITY   ● GROUP   ● TRADITIONAL   ● CAMPING BARN   ● COASTAL   ● RURAL

It's perfectly positioned for starting the Limestone Loop walk while attractions in the area include Alton Towers, Lyme Park and Chatsworth House. With spacious car parking and the railway station close by, the hostel is easily accessible.

Location: OS 119, GR 062722.

Great for... exploring the Peak District National Park.

You need to know... this hostel may close during 2003. Please enquire before planning your stay.

Accommodation: 56 beds: mostly 4–8-bed rooms plus 1x10-bed and 1x12-bed.

Family rooms: No. **Rent-a-Hostel:** No.

Classroom: No. **Education packages:** Yes.

Facilities: Lounge, self-catering kitchen, dining room, showers, drying room, cycle and luggage store and grounds.

Daytime access: Restricted.

Meals: Breakfast, picnic lunch, evening meal.

Reception open: 17.00hrs.

Getting there: 1 mile south of Market Place, head for London Road and A515. Then turn right after the hospital signposted YHA 80 yards. The hostel is on the left.

Parking: Yes.

Nearest other hostels: Gradbach 7 miles, Ravenstor 7, Castleton 12, Manchester 22.

Public transport: BUS: Frequent from surrounding areas (tel: 01298 23098). RAIL: Buxton 1.5 miles.

NATIONAL EXPRESS Market Place 1 mile.

●● CHESTER ☆☆

40 Hough Green, Chester, Cheshire CH4 8JD;
chester@yha.org.uk
Tel: 0870 770 5762 Fax: 0870 770 5763

This is an ideal location for a historical break in Britain's only completely walled city. The hostel, a large, comfortable Victorian house built in 1856, offers easy access to the city centre and its cathedral just a mile away. Explore the Roman remains and wander through the historic medieval shopping galleries that line the streets. Go boating on the River Dee or visit the world famous zoo. Further afield, visit the Boat Museum and Blue Planet Aquarium at Ellesmere Port, the many historic houses of Cheshire, Jodrell Bank Science Centre, and the castles, coast and mountains of north Wales.

Location: OS 117, GR 397651.

Great for... a civilised city break with historical interest.

Accommodation: 117 beds: all 2–10-bed rooms.

Family rooms: Yes. **Rent-a-Hostel:** No.

Classroom: Yes. **Education packages:** No.

Facilities: Lounge, TV lounge, self-catering kitchen, showers, drying room, cycle store, lockers, laundry facilities and shop.

Daytime access: All areas.

Meals: Breakfast, picnic lunch, evening meal (17.30-19.00hrs).

Reception open: All day.

Getting there: The hostel is southwest of city centre on A5104 (signposted to Saltney), 350 metres from traffic lights on right (see map on page 174).

●● CASTLETON ☆

Castleton, Hope Valley, Derbyshire S33 8WG;
castleton@yha.org.uk
Tel: 0870 770 5758 Fax: 0870 770 5759

Originally Castleton Hall, this building dates back to the 13th century and, together with the former vicarage, stands at the heart of the village square. Walkers staying at this hostel on two separate sites will be spoilt for choice. There are many fine routes around the valley which is overlooked by the spectacular Winnats Pass and Mam Tor, known as the shivering mountain. Peveril Castle and a choice of underground caves are all within walking distance.

Location: OS 110, GR 150828.

Great for... walkers of all levels and active families.

You need to know... the vicarage is available for exclusive use, as is the self-contained stable and hayloft.

Accommodation: 150 beds: all 2-, 4-, 6- and 8-bed rooms, half of which are en-suite.

Family rooms: Yes. **Rent-a-Hostel:** Yes.

Classroom: Yes. **Education packages:** Yes.

Facilities: Lounges, TV room, games rooms, self-catering kitchen, showers, drying room, cycle store and luggage store.

Daytime access: All areas. ⊗

Meals: Breakfast, picnic lunch, evening meal.

Reception open: All day.

Getting there: Follow A625 from Sheffield. Once in village, turn left into Market Place. Or follow A625 from Manchester and turn into Winnats Pass.

Parking: Nearby.

Nearest other hostels: Edale 4 miles, Hathersage 6, Eyam 7.

Public transport: BUS: Mainline/Stagecoach East Midland 272/4 from Sheffield (passes Hope station). RAIL: Hope 3 miles.

Ideal for Rent-a-Hostel: YHA Castleton (The Vicarage).

⬤ FAMILY   ⬤ CITY   ⬤ GROUP   ⬤ TRADITIONAL   ⬤ CAMPING BARN   ⬤ COASTAL   ⬤ RURAL

YHA Crowden is a popular overnight stop on the Pennine Way.

Great for... mixing days out in the city with varied walking.
Accommodation: 38 beds: 2x2-, 4x4- and 3x6-bed rooms.
Family rooms: Yes. **Rent-a-Hostel:** Yes.
Classroom: No. **Education packages:** No.
Facilities: Lounge, self-catering kitchen, showers, drying room, shop and cycle store. **Daytime access:** Restricted. ⊗
Meals: Breakfast, picnic lunch, evening meal.
Reception open: 17.00hrs.
Getting there: Situated on A628, Manchester to Barnsley Road. From end of M67, follow Barnsley (A628) signs, Crowden is 3.5 miles after Tintwistle. Take signposted left turn up to hostel. From Barnsley (M1) direction, follow Manchester (A628). Hostel well signed on right. From Glossop, follow B6105 (signposted Barnsley). At junction with A628, carefully turn left, hostel signposted on right.
Parking: Yes.
Nearest other hostels: Langsett 10 miles, Edale 15 (via Pennine Way), Manchester 20, Mankinholes 24 (via Pennine Way).
Public transport: RAIL: Hadfield 5 miles.
NATIONALEXPRESS National Express 350 Sheffield–Manchester (passes close to Sheffield station). Stops at Coach Stop, A628, Longdendale (200 metres from hostel).

YHA Chester is close to the historic city centre.

Parking: Yes.
Nearest other hostels: Maeshafn 14 miles, Liverpool 20, Llangollen 22, Manchester 39, Conwy 43.
Public transport: BUS: Frequent from surrounding areas. RAIL: Chester 1.5 miles.
NATIONALEXPRESS Delamere Street bus station 1 mile.

⬤⬤ CROWDEN ☆☆

Crowden-in-Longdendale, Glossop, Derbyshire SK13 1HZ
Tel: 0870 770 5784 Fax: 0870 770 5784

Situated in the Peak District, Crowden is a popular overnight stop on the Pennine Way. Groups, families and individuals are all welcome at this comfortably refurbished row of former quarrymen's cottages. There's plenty to do here besides exploring the rugged countryside on foot. With Manchester, Liverpool and Sheffield all less than an hour's drive away, it's within reach of the north's most vibrant cities.
Location: OS 110, GR 073993.

⬤⬤ DIMMINGSDALE (awaiting classification)

Oakamoor, Stoke-on-Trent, Staffordshire ST10 3AS; dimmingsdale@yha.org.uk
Tel: 0870 770 5794 Fax: 0870 770 5794

You take your pick of activities when you stay at Dimmingsdale. With Alton Towers just two miles away, the lure of a fun-filled day is ever-present. The Pottery Museums at Stoke-on-Trent, the Cauldon Canal and several nature reserves offer more sedate entertainment, while an extensive network of rights of way will keep walkers and cyclists busy. Whatever you choose to do, this traditional, purpose-built hostel in secluded woodland offers a quiet base.
Location: OS 119, GR 052436.
Great for... a varied break for small groups.
You need to know... only self-catering accommodation is available; the hostel, which is heated by a wood-burning stove, is in an isolated location some 2 miles from Oakamoor village and the shop is limited.
Accommodation: 20 beds: 2x6- and 1x8-bed rooms.
Family rooms: Yes. **Rent-a-Hostel:** Yes.
Classroom: No. **Education packages:** No.

● FAMILY ● CITY ● GROUP ● TRADITIONAL ● CAMPING BARN ● COASTAL ● RURAL

●● EDALE ☆

**Rowland Cote, Nether Booth, Edale, Hope Valley, Derbyshire S33 7ZH; edale@yha.org.uk
Tel: 0870 770 5808 Fax: 0870 770 5809**

Take a deep breath before you book a bed here because Edale is a dedicated Activity Centre. On the slopes of Kinder Scout in the Peak District National Park, the Edale Valley is one the best known walking and adventure locations in the country. It's the perfect place to try some of the activities on offer at this hostel, such as caving, climbing, kayaking, canoeing, abseiling, orienteering and archery. Whether travelling alone or as part of a group, this is the hostel for you if you want to have fun and improve your outdoor skills.

Location: OS 110, GR 139865.
Great for... active people fuelled by adrenalin.
You need to know... it's advisable to book in advance.
Accommodation: 143 beds: mostly 2–8- plus 2x12-bed rooms.
Family rooms: No. **Rent-a-Hostel:** No.
Classroom: Yes. **Education packages:** Yes.
Facilities: Lounge, games room with TV, self-catering kitchen, showers, drying room, cycle store, laundry and grounds. Outdoor activities (book in advance). **Daytime access:** All areas.
Meals: Breakfast, picnic lunch, evening meal.

Reception open: All day.
Getting there: 1 mile east of Edale village marked 'Rowland Cote' on Ordnance Survey map.
Parking: Yes.
Nearest other hostels: Castleton 4 miles, Hathersage 8, Crowden 15 (by Pennine Way).
Public transport: BUS: No service to hostel, but good connections to Sheffield and Manchester. Use train for last part of the journey. Centre minibus meets all trains between 1600hrs and 2000hrs on Fridays. RAIL: Edale 2 miles.

Choose from a wide range of outdoor activities at YHA Edale.

Wild excitement at Alton Towers near YHA Dimmingsdale.

www.britainonview.com

Facilities: Common room, self-catering kitchen, showers, drying room, cycle store, BBQ and limited shop.
Daytime access: All areas. ⊗
Meals: Self-catering only.
Reception open: Staff available before 10.00hrs and after 17.00hrs.
Getting there: From Oakamoor off B5417, take road at south end of bridge past Admiral's House B&B. Take road to top of hill, turn left up farm track to hostel.
Parking: Yes.
Nearest other hostels: Ilam 12 miles, Alstonefield 15, Meerbrook 16, Gradbach 17.
Public transport: BUS: First PMT 238 from Uttoxeter (passes close Uttoxeter station), alight Oakamoor 2 miles. RAIL: Blythe Bridge 6.5 miles.

● EDALE

**campingbarns@yha.org.uk
Booking: 0870 770 6113
Arrival time: Mr & Mrs Gee, 01433 670273**

This camping barn at Cotefield Farm overlooks the famous Mam Tor, at the heart of a popular walking area and at the start of the Pennine Way. The high moorland of Kinder and the wooded Derwent Valley are readily accessible.
You need to know... you have to leave your car at the farm and walk along the footpath across two fields to the barn.
Accommodation: Sleeps 8.
Facilities: Small communal living area with table and benches,

● FAMILY ● CITY ● GROUP ● TRADITIONAL ● CAMPING BARN ● COASTAL ● RURAL

cooking area with external access and separate toilet.
Nearest pub: 1 mile. **Nearest shop:** 1 mile.
Location: OS 110, GR 132869.

Edale: stretch your legs in stunning countryside.

●● ELTON ☆
Old Hall, Main Street, Elton, Matlock, Derbyshire DE4 2BW; elton@yha.org.uk
Tel: 0870 770 5818 Fax: 0870 770 5818

Set in great walking country surrounded by a maze of footpaths, this hostel is a ramblers' paradise. It's close to the market towns of Matlock and Bakewell, and within easy reach of Chatsworth and Haddon Hall. The hostel dates back to the 17th century and provides simple, traditional accommodation.
Location: OS 119, GR 224608.
Great for... exploring the Derbyshire dales.
You need to know... this hostel may close during 2003; please enquire before planning your stay. Bring provisions with you as the hostel shop is limited.
Accommodation: 22 beds: 1x2-, 2x4- and 2x6-bed rooms.
Family rooms: No. **Rent-a-Hostel:** No.
Classroom: No. **Education packages:** No.
Facilities: Lounge, self-catering kitchen, shower, drying room, shop and cycle store. **Daytime access:** Restricted. ⊗

●● HARTINGTON HALL ☆☆☆☆
Hartington, Buxton, Derbyshire SK17 0AT; hartington@yha.org.uk
Tel: 0870 770 5848 Fax: 0870 770 5849

This magnificent 17th century manor house features log fires, oak panelling and a room where Bonnie Prince Charlie stayed. Refurbished with the help of a members' appeal and a grant from the National Heritage Lottery Fund, the hostel offers accommodation and facilities of a high standard and is an ideal base for walkers and cyclists. There is a stream of stately homes to visit, as well as 11th century Pilsbury Castle and tranquil Dovedale. Children are very welcome with a pets' area and adventure playground on site.
Location: OS 119, GR 131603.
Great for... families who appreciate history.
You need to know... a self-catering cottage in the hostel's grounds sleeps 8.
Accommodation: 122 beds: 3x1-, 4x2-, 3x3-, 9x4-, 3x5-, 2x6-, 1x7-, 4x8- and 1x9-bed rooms, 18 en-suite.
Family rooms: Yes. **Rent-a-Hostel:** No.
Classroom: Yes. **Education packages:** Yes.
Facilities: Dining rooms, lounges, self-catering facilities, drying room, laundry, TV room, shop, toilets and showers, games room, cycle store, luggage store and internet access. Adventure playground and wildlife garden. Facilities for people with disabilities. **Daytime access:** All areas.

Meals: Breakfast, picnic lunch, evening meal.
Reception open: Staff available before 10.00 and after 17.00hrs.
Getting there: From village centre, turn up the lane by the school. The hostel is 200 metres up hill on left.
Parking: Small car park and roadside parking.
Nearest other hostels: Alstonefield 5 miles, Youlgreave 6, Ilam 9.
Public transport: BUS: Bowers 442 from Buxton station. RAIL: Buxton 12 miles, Matlock 13.

YHA Hartington Hall: Bonnie Prince Charlie stayed here!

North West cities & Peak District

● FAMILY ● CITY ● GROUP ● TRADITIONAL ● CAMPING BARN ● COASTAL ● RURAL

Meals: Self-catering only.
Reception open: 17.00hrs.
Getting there: Hostel is at east end of Elton village on Main Street.
Parking: Main Street. Please observe hostel's parking guidelines.
Nearest other hostels: Youlgreave 5 miles (2.5 by path), Matlock 6, Bakewell 7.
Public transport: BUS: Hulleys 172 Matlock–Bakewell (passes close to Matlock station). RAIL: Matlock 5 miles.

●● EYAM ☆

Hawkhill Road, Eyam, Hope Valley, Derbyshire
S32 5QP; eyam@yha.org.uk
Tel: 0870 770 5830 Fax: 0870 770 5831

This Victorian folly resembles a tiny, turreted castle and perches on the hillside overlooking the historic village of Eyam, famous for its tragic past. Two thirds of the village population was wiped out during the Great Plague of the 17th century, and you can trace the tale with a wander through the village to see the Plague Cottages and parish church. As the hostel sits on the boundary of the contrasting landscapes of the White Peak and Dark Peak, there's also a varied array of excellent walking.
Location: OS 119, GR 219769.
Great for... walkers interested in history.
You need to know... there are limited self-catering facilities.
Accommodation: 60 beds, 4x2-, 6x4-, 2x6- and 2x8-bed rooms.
Family rooms: Yes. **Rent-a-Hostel:** No.
Classroom: Yes. **Education packages:** Yes.
Facilities: Lounge, games room, self-catering kitchen, drying room and cycle store. **Daytime access:** All areas. ⊗
Meals: Breakfast, picnic lunch, evening meal.

Explore the Peak District from a Victorian folly: YHA Eyam.

Reception open: Staff available before 10.00hrs and after 17.00hrs.
Getting there: Follow hostel signs from village. Go past the museum and car park, continue up the hill and hostel is around 600 metres on left.
Parking: Yes.
Nearest other hostels: Bretton 1.5 miles, Hathersage 6, Bakewell 7, Ravenstor 7.
Public transport: BUS: Various services from Sheffield, Buxton and Chesterfield (passing close to Sheffield, Buxton and Chesterfield stations), alight Eyam. RAIL: Grindleford 3.5 miles, Hathersage 5.5.

●● GRADBACH MILL ☆

Gradbach, Quarnford, Buxton, Derbyshire
SK17 0SU; gradbachmill@yha.org.uk
Tel: 0870 770 5834 Fax: 0870 770 5835

A former mill in its own secluded grounds on the banks of the River Dane, this hostel is close to the Staffordshire moorlands and gritstone Roaches. If you're a National Trust member then there's

The dramatic landscape of the Roaches near YHA Gradbach Mill.

plenty to do as National Trust properties Quarry Bank Mill at Styal, Little Morton Hall, Tatton Park, Dunham Massey and Biddulph Grange are all nearby. Or, for a dose of fun, Alton Towers is 15 miles away.
Location: OS 118, GR 993661.
Great for... outdoor enthusiasts looking for a varied break.
You need to know... the hostel is in two separate buildings, with one available separately through the Rent-a-Hostel scheme.
Accommodation: 91 beds: 5x2-, 1x3-, 9x4- and 7x6-bed rooms.
Family rooms: Yes. **Rent-a-Hostel:** Yes.
Classroom: No. **Education packages:** No.
Facilities: Lounge, self-catering kitchen, showers, drying room, cycle store, luggage store, laundry facilities and grounds.
Daytime access: All areas. ⊗
Meals: Breakfast, picnic lunch, evening meal.

● FAMILY ● CITY ● GROUP ● TRADITIONAL ● CAMPING BARN ● COASTAL ● RURAL

Reception open: 13.00hrs.
Getting there: Hostel is clearly signposted from Flash village, just off the A53 Buxton–Leek road.
Parking: Yes.
Nearest other hostels: Buxton 7 miles, Hartington 12, Ravenstor 12.
Public transport: BUS: First PMT X18 Sheffield–Leek (passes close to Sheffield, Stoke-on-Trent and Buxton stations), alight Flash Bar Stores, 3 miles. RAIL: Buxton 7 miles, Macclesfield 9.

●● HATHERSAGE ☆☆

Castleton Road, Hathersage, Hope Valley, Derbyshire S32 1EH; hathersage@yha.org.uk
Tel: 0870 770 5852 Fax: 0870 770 5852

This Victorian house is on the edge of a village which is associated with both Little John and Charlotte Brontë's Jane Eyre. It's on the White Peak Way circular walk and is overlooked by Stanage Edge which attracts climbers of all abilities. As well as countryside pursuits, shoppers will be happy as Sheffield is just 10 miles away.
Location: OS 110, GR 226814.
Great for... those using public transport, rock-climbers.
You need to know... there are plenty of shops in the village.
Accommodation: 40 beds: 1x2-, 2x4- and 5x6-bed rooms.
Family rooms: No. **Rent-a-Hostel:** Yes.
Classroom: No. **Education packages:** Yes.
Facilities: Lounge, self-catering kitchen, showers, dining room, cycle store and grounds. **Daytime access:** All areas. ♿
Meals: Breakfast, picnic lunch, evening meal.
Reception open: Staff available before 10.00hrs and after 17.00hrs.
Getting there: Hostel is 100 metres on right past the George Hotel on the road from Sheffield to Castleton.
Parking: Limited to six cars.
Nearest other hostels: Bretton 5 miles, Castleton 6, Eyam 6, Edale 12.
Public transport: BUS: First Mainline 214 from Hathersage–Matlock, 272 Sheffield–Castleton, 175 Derwent–Bakewell, 257 Sheffield–Derwent (weekends only). RAIL: Hathersage 0.5 miles.

●● ILAM HALL ☆☆☆☆

Ilam Hall, Ilam, Ashbourne, Derbyshire DE6 2AZ; ilam@yha.org.uk
Tel: 0870 770 5876 Fax: 0870 770 5877

This is a Youth Hostel to remember! A Victorian gothic manor house owned by the National Trust, it makes for a civilised break. Its grounds stretch to 84 acres of country park on the banks of the River Manifold, making outdoor games, woodland wanders and riverside walks an appealing possibility. Walk in the gently undulating White Peak area of the Peak District National Park, visit Dovedale or cycle along the Tissington and Manifold Trails.
Location: OS 119, GR 131506.
Great for... a country house break with gentle pursuits.
You need to know... there's a charge for parking (unless you are an NT member); there is separate accommodation for wheelchair users.

YHA Ilam Hall is a gothic manor in 84 acres of country park.

Accommodation: 135 beds: 1x2-, 1x3-, mostly 4-8-, 1x11- and 1x14-bed rooms, some en-suite.
Family rooms: Yes. **Rent-a-Hostel:** No.
Classroom: Yes. **Education packages:** Yes.
Facilities: Lounge, TV room, games room, self-catering kitchen, showers, drying room, cycle store, laundry facilities, residential licence and grounds. **Daytime access:** All areas.
Meals: Breakfast, picnic lunch, evening meal.
Reception open: All day.
Getting there: From Ilam village centre enter National Trust Country Park and follow drive.

Stepping stones in Dovedale: near YHAs Ilam Hall and Hartington Hall.

www.britainonview.com

● FAMILY   ● CITY   ● GROUP   ● TRADITIONAL   ● CAMPING BARN   ● COASTAL   ● RURAL

Parking: NT car park (NT charge – tickets from reception).
Nearest other hostels: Alstonefield 3 miles, Hartington 9, Dimmingsdale 12, Matlock 20.
Public transport: BUS: Infrequent from Ashbourne, alight Ilam crossroads 2.5 miles.
RAIL: Matlock 14 miles, Uttoxeter 15, Derby 18.
NATIONALEXPRESS Ashbourne bus station, 5 miles.

●● LANGSETT ☆

Langsett, Stocksbridge, Sheffield S36 4GY;
reservations@yha.org.uk
Tel: 0870 770 5912 Fax: 0870 770 5912
Bookings more than 7 days ahead: 0870 770 6113

Langsett offers open fires and comfortable facilities in a rural location with extensive views, yet is close to good transport links. The hostel is surrounded by superb heather moorland with Margery Hill, the Derwent Valley and Holmfirth, the setting for Last of the Summer Wine, all within easy reach.
Location: OS 110, GR 211005.
Great for... a rural retreat for walkers.
You need to know... there are basic facilities only; credit cards are accepted for advance bookings only; there's no hostel shop.
Accommodation: 27 beds: 4x4-, 1x5- and 1x6-bed rooms.
Family rooms: No. **Rent-a-Hostel:** Yes.
Classroom: No. **Education packages:** No.
Facilities: Lounge/dining room, self-catering kitchen, showers, drying room, cycle store and garden. **Daytime access:** Restricted. ⌖
Meals: Self-catering only.
Reception open: 17.00hrs (19.00hrs on Fridays).
Getting there: Hostel is 1 mile southeast of Flouch roundabout,

on north side of A616, 100 metres up track between café and Gilbert Hill, on opposite side of road to Waggon & Horses pub. Slow down on approaching Langsett as road is fast. Also 1 mile from Trans-Pennine trail.
Parking: Yes.
Nearest other hostels: Crowden 10 miles, Hathersage 18, Edale 20.
Public transport: BUS: Yorkshire Traction 23, 23A, 24, 24A from Barnsley (Penistone station). RAIL: Penistone 3 miles.
NATIONALEXPRESS Stocksbridge 3.5 miles.

YHA Liverpool is conveniently located close to the Albert Dock.

●● LIVERPOOL ☆☆☆☆

25 Tabley Street, off Wapping, Liverpool,
Merseyside L1 8EE; liverpool@yha.org.uk
Tel: 0870 770 5924 Fax 0870 770 5925

This is a modern, purpose-built hostel with excellent facilities. Adjacent to the Albert Dock and just a 10-minute walk from the heart of the city, it's a great location for visiting Liverpool's main attractions. On the dock, you'll find the Beatles Story, Tate Gallery and Merseyside Maritime Museum. Take a tour of the famous football ground or visit the Museum of Life. Premium rooms are available.
Location: OS 108, GR 344895.
Great for... a comfortable base to tour Liverpool's attractions.
You need to know... breakfast is included in the overnight fee.
Accommodation: 100 beds: all 3-, 4- and 6-bed en-suite rooms.
Family rooms: Yes. **Rent-a-Hostel:** No.
Classroom: Yes. **Education packages:** Yes.
Facilities: Lounge with TV, games rooms, self-catering kitchen, showers, cycle store, luggage store, lockers, laundry facilities and grounds. **Daytime access:** All areas.
Meals: Breakfast, picnic lunch, evening meal.
Reception open: 24hrs.
Getting there: From Lime Street station follow signs for Albert

YHA Langsett offers a comfortable rural retreat.

To make a booking visit www.yha.org.uk

● FAMILY ● CITY ● GROUP ● TRADITIONAL ● CAMPING BARN ● COASTAL ● RURAL

A modern, purpose-built hostel with excellent facilities: YHA Liverpool.

Accommodation: 144 beds: 30x4- and 4x6-bed en-suite rooms.
Family rooms: Yes. **Rent-a-Hostel:** No.
Classroom: Yes. **Education packages:** Yes.
Facilities: Lounge, TV room, games room, self-catering kitchen, showers, toilets, cycle store, luggage store, lockers, laundry facilities and conference rooms. **Daytime access:** All areas.
Meals: Breakfast, picnic lunch, evening meal.
Reception open: 24hrs.
Getting there: From bus station and Piccadilly train station, follow signs for Castlefield/Museum of Science and Industry (MSI), or take the Metrolink to the G-Mex station. By road, follow signs for Castlefield/MSI. Hostel is opposite MSI and behind Castlefield Hotel (see map on page 174).

Dock. Turn left onto main dock road (called Wapping). Hostel is on left after Baltic Fleet pub. From James Street station turn right then left onto Wapping, past the Albert Dock on your right – hostel is on the left after Baltic Fleet pub (see map on page 174).
Parking: Yes.
Nearest other hostels: Chester 20 miles, Manchester 32.
Public transport: BUS: Frequent from surrounding areas.
RAIL: James Street 0.75 miles, Liverpool Lime Street 1.25.
FERRY: Ireland/Isle of Man Terminal 1 mile.
NATIONALEXPRESS» Liverpool coach station, Norton St 1 mile.

● LOSEHILL
campingbarns@yha.org.uk
Booking: 0870 770 6113
Arrival time: 01433 620373 during office hours

Owned by the Peak District National Park, this camping barn is in the Hope Valley below the steep slopes of Back Tor and Lose Hill, near the village of Castleton.
Accommodation: Sleeps 8.
Facilities: Communal area with table and bench, cooking area and separate toilet in adjoining lean-to.
Nearest pub: 1 mile. **Nearest shop:** 1 mile.
Location: OS 110, GR 153838.

●● MANCHESTER ☆☆☆
Potato Wharf, Castlefield, Manchester, M3 4NB;
manchester@yha.org.uk
Tel: 0870 770 5950 Fax: 0870 770 5951

Purpose-built in 1995, this hostel enjoys a canal-side location close to the heart of the rejuvenated city centre. Ideally situated for a city break, it's within easy reach of some of the best shopping, restaurants, cinemas, concert halls, museums and theatres in northern England. It's hard to narrow down just what to do but don't miss the Manchester United museum and stadium tour and the Trafford Centre. Breakfast is included in the overnight charge and premium rooms are available.
Location: OS 109, GR 831976.
Great for... a stylish city break.

Taking a break from seeing the city sights around YHA Manchester.

For all the latest YHA news visit www.yha.org.uk

North West cities & Peak District

● FAMILY ● CITY ● GROUP ● TRADITIONAL ● CAMPING BARN ● COASTAL ● RURAL

Purpose-built in a canalside location: YHA Manchester.

Parking: Yes.
Nearest other hostels: Crowden 20 miles, Liverpool 32, Chester 39.
Public transport: BUS: GM Metrolink: G-Mex, 0.25 miles (connections from Manchester Piccadilly station).
RAIL: Deansgate, few minutes' walk, Manchester Victoria 1 mile.
NATIONALEXPRESS Manchester coach station 0.75 miles.

●● MATLOCK ☆

40 Bank Road, Matlock, Derbyshire DE4 3NF;
matlock@yha.org.uk
Tel: 0870 770 5960 Fax: 0870 770 5961

This hostel started life as Smedley's Memorial Hydropathic Hospital, serving as a place of rest and rehabilitation for the needy. It still offers a welcome retreat though nowadays it's mainly from the many activities on offer close by. The Heights of Abraham, the Lead Mining

YHA Matlock was once Smedley's Memorial Hydropathic Hospital.

Museum, Alton Towers and the American Adventure Theme Park are all nearby, as is excellent walking in the Peak District National Park. Children will be made very welcome, with toddler-friendly facilities and a menu for under-10s.
Location: OS 119, GR 300603.
Great for... a busy family holiday.
Accommodation: 53 beds: 4x1-, 4x2-, 2x3-, 5x4-, 1x6- and 1x9-bed rooms.
Family rooms: Yes. **Rent-a-Hostel:** No.
Classroom: Yes. **Education packages:** No.
Facilities: Lounge, TV room, games room, self-catering kitchen, showers, drying room, cycle store, laundry facilities, grounds, training and conference rooms. **Daytime access:** All areas. ◯
Meals: Breakfast, picnic lunch, evening meal.
Reception open: 13.00hrs.
Getting there: YHA Matlock is 200 metres up Bank Road on right, clearly signposted from Crown Square roundabout in town centre.
Parking: Yes.
Nearest other hostels: Bakewell 8 miles, Youlgreave 10, Hartington 13.
Public transport: BUS: Frequent from surrounding areas.
RAIL: Matlock 400 metres.
NATIONALEXPRESS Matlock bus station 300 metres.

HOSTEL MANAGERS CHOOSE...

THE BEST MUSEUMS & COUNTRY HOUSES

Jodrell Bank Science Centre YHA Chester: "Unravel the mysteries of space! In the shadow of the world famous telescope, there are hands-on exhibits and a planetarium."
Sudbury Hall (National Trust) YHA Ilam Hall: "Houses a Museum of Childhood, including a chimney climb for adventurous youngsters."
Haddon Hall YHA Hartington Hall: "The most complete medieval manor house in the country. Wander through tapestry-lined rooms or explore the rose-filled garden."
Eyam Hall YHA Hartington Hall: "Its exhibits tell the incredible story of this famous plague village."
Chatsworth House YHA Castleton: "Magnificent country house with extensive gardens. All kids will enjoy playing in the adventure playground."
National Tramway Museum, Crich YHA Matlock: "Voted in the top three museums for people with disabilities."
Museum of Science & Industry, Manchester YHA Buxton: "An excellent family day out with free admission."
Manchester United FC YHA Manchester: "A must for all fans! Contact the hostel for further details."
Bass Museum of Brewing YHA Hartington Hall: "It's got shire horses, a children's play area and plenty of tastings."

For offers and discounts visit www.yha.org.uk

92

● FAMILY ● CITY ● GROUP ● TRADITIONAL ● CAMPING BARN ● COASTAL ● RURAL

The Peak District offers tracks and trails for all ages and abilities.

● MEERBROOK ☆

Old School, Meerbrook, Leek, Staffordshire ST13 8SJ; dimmingsdale@yha.org.uk
Tel: 0870 770 5966 Fax: 0870 770 5966
Bookings more than 7 days ahead: 0870 770 5794

At the centre of Meerbrook in a quiet corner of the Staffordshire moorlands, this hostel offers basic facilities in an old village school complete with original beamed ceiling. The nearby Roaches are a popular location for climbing and the moorland provides excellent walking. Staffordshire's museums, factory shops and potteries are within easy reach should the weather turn inclement.
Location: OS 118, GR 989608.
Great for... outdoor folk who like small, cosy hostels.
You need to know... it's self-catering accommodation only.
Accommodation: 22 beds: 2x2-, 1x8- and 1x10-bed rooms.
Family rooms: No. **Rent-a-Hostel:** Yes.
Classroom: No. **Education packages:** No.
Facilities: Lounge, self-catering kitchen, shower, drying room, cycle store, BBQ, grounds and basic hostel shop. Credit cards accepted.
Daytime access: Restricted. 🚫
Meals: Self-catering only.
Reception open: 17.00hrs.
Getting there: From A53 Buxton–Leek road, take turning by Three Horseshoes pub, signposted Meerbrook. Hostel is in village centre on right-hand side, past pub.
Parking: Yes.
Nearest other hostels: Gradbach 5 miles, Buxton 11, Hartington 12, Dimmingsdale 16.
Public transport: BUS: First PMT X18 Sheffield–Keele (passes close to Stoke-on-Trent and Buxton stations), alight Blackshaw Moor 1.5 miles. RAIL: Buxton 10 miles, Stoke-on-Trent 15.
NATIONAL EXPRESS>> Leek Bus Station 4.25 miles.

● MIDDLETON-BY-YOULGREAVE

campingbarns@yha.org.uk
Booking: 0870 770 6113
Arrival time: Mr Butterworth, 01629 636746

This camping barn is part of a working farm on the edge of the small village of Middleton-by-Youlgreave. It is a good base for walking in

Bradford Dale and Lathkill Dale, an area full of wildlife interest.
Great for... discovering the Peak District National Park.
You need to know... well-behaved dogs on leads are accepted (this is a working farm).
Accommodation: Sleeps 12 on the first floor, access by external stone steps.
Facilities: Communal living area, separate cooking area, toilet in adjacent building, electric light, metered electricity.
Nearest pub: 1 mile. **Nearest shop:** 1 mile.
Location: OS 119, GR 196634.

● NAB END

campingbarns@yha.org.uk
Booking: 0870 770 6113
Arrival time: Mr & Mrs Cox, 01298 83225

In one of the quieter parts of the National Park, Nab End camping barn lies between Hollinsclough and Longnor. The upper valley of the River Dove, marking the boundary between limestone and gritstone, is nearby and the river's source, high up on Axe Edge, lies to the northwest.
Accommodation: Sleeps 16 on the first floor.
Facilities: Living area on first floor, kitchen, toilets and washroom on ground floor, metered electricity, electric light, fridge and shower.
Nearest pub: 1.5 miles. **Nearest shop:** 1.5 miles.
Location: OS 119, GR 077662.

●● RAVENSTOR ☆☆☆

Millers Dale, Buxton, Derbyshire SK17 8SS; ravenstor@yha.org.uk
Tel: 0870 770 6008 Fax: 0870 770 6009

This National Trust property stands high above the dales of the River Wye in 60 acres of grounds. Surrounded by the fascinating

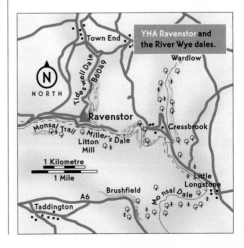

YHA Ravenstor and the River Wye dales.

● FAMILY ● CITY ● GROUP ● TRADITIONAL ● CAMPING BARN ● COASTAL ● RURAL

A wonderful National Trust property: YHA Ravenstor.

limestone scenery of the White Peak, the hostel is on the White Peak Way and there is excellent walking for all abilities nearby. It is also within easy visiting distance of Litton Mill.

Location: OS 119, GR 152732.

Great for... walkers looking for a tranquil base from which to explore the Peaks.

Accommodation: 83 beds: 1x2-, 1x3-, 1x5-, 1x7-, 1x8-, 1x10-, 1x12-, 1x16- and 1x20-bed rooms.

Family rooms: Yes. **Rent-a-Hostel:** No.

Classroom: Yes. **Education packages:** Yes.

Facilities: Lounge, dining room, TV room/study, self-catering kitchen, showers, shop and cycle store. **Daytime access:** All areas.

Meals: Breakfast, picnic lunch, evening meal.

Reception open: 13.00hrs.

Getting there: From A6 between Bakewell and Buxton take the B6049 to Tideswell. The hostel is 1 mile past Millers Dale.

Parking: Yes.

Nearest other hostels: Bretton 6 miles, Bakewell 7, Buxton 7, Eyam 7, Castleton 8.

Public transport: BUS: From Sheffield, Buxton (passes close to Sheffield and Buxton stations). RAIL: Buxton 8 miles.

●● SHERWOOD FOREST ☆☆☆☆

Forest Corner, Edwinstowe, Nottinghamshire NG21 9RN; sherwood@yha.org.uk

Tel: 0870 770 6026 Fax: 0870 770 6027

This modern, purpose-built Youth Hostel is set on the edge of Sherwood Forest and offers a high standard of en-suite family accommodation. Follow in Robin Hood's footsteps through ancient woodland to the Major Oak, visit the excellent visitor centre just 10 minutes' walk from the hostel and enjoy cycling on the network

of trails. Nottinghamshire also has many other attractions from magnificent stately homes, country parks and castles to the historic towns of Newark and Southwell.

Location: OS 120, GR 625673.

Great for... a fun-filled family holiday.

Accommodation: 39 beds: all 2-5-bed rooms, mostly en-suite.

Family rooms: Yes. **Rent-a-Hostel option:** No.

Classroom: No. **Education packages:** No.

Facilities: Lounge, dining room, toilets, showers, drying room, self-catering kitchen and cycle store. Facilities for people with disabilities. **Daytime access:** All areas. ⊗

Meals: Breakfast, picnic lunch, evening meal.

Reception open: All day.

Getting there: From M1 northbound, exit motorway at J28 and follow A38 to Mansfield town centre. Follow signs for A60 to Worksop until junction with A6075 to Edwinstowe. Once in Edwinstowe turn left at traffic lights at Royal Oak pub crossroads. Turn left onto Forest Corner 400 metres up this road. From M1 southbound, exit motorway at J31 and follow A57 to Worksop. Stay on this road until signs for Sherwood Forest, Clumber Park and Edwinstowe B6034. On reaching a double roundabout follow signs for A616 Ollerton and Newark. After approx 2 miles turn right onto B6034, signed Edwinstowe and YHA. On entering Edwinstowe, turn right into Forest Corner, signed YHA and Craft Centre.

Parking: Yes.

Nearest other hostels: Lincoln 30 miles, Matlock 30, Copt Oak 40.

Public transport: BUS: From Mansfield bus station, Stagecoach

HOSTEL MANAGERS CHOOSE...

THE BEST CAVES & ROCKS IN THE PEAKS

Devil's Arse YHA Castleton: "Yes, that is its name! It's a show cave just five minutes from the hostel. Travel into the bowels of the earth on the underground rope walks."

Mam Tor YHA Castleton: "I'd recommend all our guests try this. Stand in the mystic ruins of the old hill fort and watch the sun rise over its slopes before returning to the hostel for breakfast."

Castleton Underground YHA Castleton: "No, it's not an urban public transport system, but a maze of passages and caverns in and around the village. Take a stroll in the show cave or a caving trip with an instructor."

Poole's Cavern YHA Buxton: "Spectacular! Boasts the longest stalactite in Derbyshire."

National Stone Centre YHA Hartington Hall: "It charts the history of stone and is home to the Millennium Wall, a dry-stone wall built in regional styles. You can also pan for gold."

Speedwell Cavern YHA Hartington Hall: "Very eerie indeed. Travel through an old lead mine by boat."

For current prices visit www.yha.org.uk

YHA Sherwood Forest: purpose-built on the edge of Robin Hood's lair.

13/15 Mon–Sat. Bus 110/113 Sun and Bank Holiday Mon. From Nottingham, Victoria bus station Stagecoach 33 (Nottingham train station is not near 33 bus route or Victoria bus station – a walk across Nottingham city centre is required). RAIL: Mansfield 8 miles.

●● SHINING CLIFF ☆

Jackass Lane, nr Ambergate, Derbyshire
DE56 2RE; reservations@yha.org.uk
Tel: 0870 770 6028 Fax: 0870 770 6029
Bookings more than 7 days ahead: 0870 770 6113

Get away from it all in this unique hostel that lies in the heart of an ancient wood. Facilities are basic – self-catering is your only option and you must bring provisions with you as none are available at the hostel. It's also recommended that you bring a torch. But for many walkers and cyclists, that's the very charm of this small hostel.
Location: OS 119, GR 335522.
Great for... a quiet break.
You need to know... it's a 10-minute walk from the car park (no access by car).
Accommodation: 20 beds: 2x4- and 2x6-bed rooms.
Family rooms: No. **Rent-a-Hostel option:** Yes.
Classroom: No. **Education packages:** No.
Facilities: Common room, self-catering kitchen, cycle store and grounds. No hostel shop. Credit cards not accepted. Bring a torch.
Daytime access: Restricted. ⊗
Meals: Self-catering only.
Reception open: 17.00hrs.

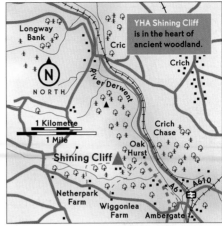

YHA Shining Cliff is in the heart of ancient woodland.

Getting there: From Ambergate, cross river by church. Cars/cycles up hill, turn right into woods by third farm (Netherpark). Walkers turn right by river. At fork take lower path, through works yard then left up path through woods, following signs.
Parking: Yes, then 10-minute walk to hostel.
Nearest other hostels: Matlock 8 miles, Elton 10, Youlgreave 12.5.
Public transport: BUS: Stagecoach 142-143, Doyles 144 and TP from Derby, alighting at Ambergate 1 mile (path), 2 miles (road). RAIL: Ambergate 2 miles.

● TADDINGTON

campingbarns@yha.org.uk
Booking: 0870 770 6113
Arrival time: Mr & Mrs Gillott, 01298 85730

This camping barn is in the centre of Taddington village, midway between Buxton and Bakewell at 1,000 feet. Surrounded by hills and dales, there are fine walks and views in all directions.
Accommodation: Sleeps 10.
Facilities: Communal area with tables and benches, cooking area, toilets, shower, heater, electric light and metered electricity. No dogs.
Nearest pub: 50 metres. **Nearest shop:** 5 miles.
Location: OS 119, GR 145710.

● UNDERBANK

campingbarns@yha.org.uk
Booking: 0870 770 6113
Arrival time: Mr & Mrs Waller, 01260 227229

This camping barn is part of Blaze Farm, a dairy farm near the western edge of the National Park. It overlooks the Wildboarclough Valley and is close to the well-known viewpoint of Shuttlingsloe. A tea room selling homemade dairy ice-cream is open daily.

North West cities & Peak District

● FAMILY ● CITY ● GROUP ● TRADITIONAL ● CAMPING BARN ● COASTAL ● RURAL

Great for... walking, climbing at the Roaches, fishing.
Accommodation: Sleeps 10 on the first floor.
Facilities: Living area, kitchen, toilet, shower, electric light, metered electricity. Dogs welcome.
Nearest pub: 0.5 miles. **Nearest shop:** 1 mile.
Location: OS 118, GR 973677.

Wildboarclough, on the edge of the National Park near Underbank.

● UPPER BOOTH

campingbarns@yha.org.uk
Booking: 0870 770 6113
Arrival time: Mr & Mrs Helliwell, 01433 670250

Part of a farm owned by the National Trust, this camping barn stands at 1,000 feet, near the head of Edale. Lying close to the Pennine Way, it is well placed for exploring Kinder Scout and for ridge walking high above Edale.
Great for... a relaxing break, outdoor activities.
You need to know... there is a campsite adjacent to the barn.
Accommodation: Sleeps 12.
Facilities: Communal living space with tables and benches, two small cooking areas, washbasins, shower, hot water and toilets in separate outbuildings.
Nearest pub: 2 miles. **Nearest shop:** 2 miles.
Location: OS 110, GR 103854.

Once the village Co-op, now a comfortable hostel: YHA Youlgreave.

●● YOULGREAVE ☆☆☆

Fountain Square, Youlgreave, near Bakewell, Derbyshire DE45 1UR; youlgreave@yha.org.uk
Tel: 0870 770 6104 **Fax:** 0870 770 6104

Above the River Bradford and Lathkill Dale, Youlgreave was once the old Co-op village store and it still retains some of the original characteristics – look for the stone beehive (symbol of the Co-op) and the windows inscribed with the shop's services. Rooms are named after the store departments and there are interesting displays to give you a flavour of the period. Many adventures await outside in the White Peak, where walkers, cyclists and mountain bikers will be in their element.
Location: OS 119, GR 210641.
Great for... active people who want to step into yesteryear.
You need to know... you must park in the village.
Accommodation: 42 beds: 1x2-, 5x4-, 2x6- and 1x8-bed rooms.
Family rooms: Yes. **Rent-a-Hostel:** No.
Classroom: No. **Education packages:** No.
Facilities: Lounge/dining room, self-catering kitchen, drying room, cycle store and showers. **Daytime access:** All areas. ⊗
Meals: Breakfast, picnic lunch, evening meal.
Reception open: Staff available before 10.00hrs and after 17.00hrs.
Getting there: The hostel is in village centre on main street opposite Fountain Well.
Parking: No.
Nearest other hostels: Elton 2.5 miles, Bakewell 3.5, Matlock 10.
Public transport: BUS: Hulleys 170/1 from Bakewell (connections from Chesterfield and Matlock stations). RAIL: Matlock 11 miles.
NATIONALEXPRESS» Bakewell, Rutland Arms 3.5 miles.

Traditional Bakewell tarts on sale near YHA Youlgreave.

TRY A YHA ACTIVITY BREAK

Many of the hostels in the Peak District offer fun-filled activity breaks and special interest holidays. For details, turn to page 28.

For all the latest YHA news visit www.yha.org.uk

The Youth Hostels of...

Wales

Over the hills and far away: Wales is the perfect destination to escape modern life.

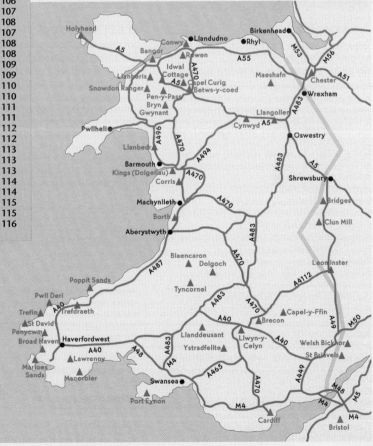

● FAMILY ● CITY ● GROUP ● TRADITIONAL ● CAMPING BARN ● COASTAL ● RURAL

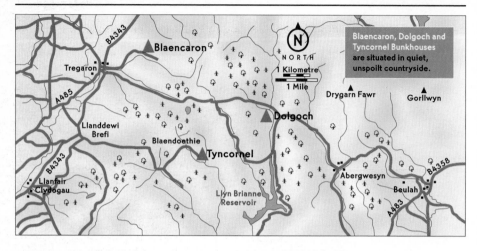

Blaencaron, Dolgoch and Tyncornel Bunkhouses are situated in quiet, unspoilt countryside.

●● BANGOR ☆☆

Tan-y-Bryn, Bangor, Gwynedd LL57 1PZ;
bangor@yha.org.uk
Tel: 0870 770 5686 Fax: 0870 770 5687

For a holiday jam-packed with a diverse range of activities, YHA Bangor, a large, Victorian house just minutes from the town centre, makes a great base. The mountains of Snowdonia are just a 15-minute drive away, offering a range of gentle wanders in the foothills and energetic all-day hikes. There's an awesome array of beaches close by on the Isle of Anglesey and the historic castles at Penrhyn and Caernarfon are within easy visiting distance. To help you explore to the full, mountain bikes, tandems and trailer bikes can be hired by arrangement.

Location: OS 115, GR 590722.
Great for... families with plenty of energy.
You need to know... you should book early as this hostel is popular during term time with school parties.
Accommodation: 70 beds: 1x2-, 3x4-, 6x6- and 2x10-bed rooms.
Family rooms: Yes. **Rent-a-Hostel:** No.
Classroom: Yes. **Education packages:** Yes.
Facilities: Reception, lounge, games room, self-catering kitchen, table licence, showers, drying room, cycle store, laundry facilities, shop, dining room and grounds. **Daytime access:** All areas.
Meals: Breakfast, picnic lunch, evening meal (18.00-19.00hrs).
Reception open: All day.
Getting there: From A55, take the A5 into Bangor. The hostel is on the left by the speed limit sign. From the station, go straight over the traffic lights. Bear left at the first roundabout and straight over the second. Keep on the same road and the hostel is at the top of the hill after Nelson's pub.
Parking: Yes.
Nearest other hostels: Idwal Cottage 9 miles, Llanberis 11, Conwy 15.
Public transport: BUS: Frequent from surrounding areas.
RAIL: Bangor 1.25 miles. FERRY: Holyhead/Dublin 17 miles.
NATIONAL EXPRESS » Garth Road bus station 0.75 miles.

● BETWS-Y-COED

Swallow Falls, Betws-y-Coed, Gwynedd,
LL24 0DW; betwsycoed@yha.org.uk
Tel: 01690 710796 Fax: 01690 710191

Don't be misled by this hostel's location near the village that shares its name, it's actually part of a very lively and busy hotel and bar complex. The pub has live music and the hostel itself is best suited to travellers rather than school parties or young families.
Location: OS 17, GR 764576.
Great for... Outdoor types who love walking, cycling and canoeing.
You need to know... the hostel is expected to open in Spring 2003.
Accommodation: 53 beds, all 4-8-bed rooms.
Family rooms: Yes. **Rent-a-Hostel:** No.
Classroom: No. **Education packages:** Yes.
Facilities: Small lounge area, self-catering kitchen, showers, toilets, drying room, cycle storage, hotel's bars and large cafeteria.
Daytime access: All areas.
Meals: Self-catering at hostel or comprehensive choice of value-for-money meal options at hotel complex.
Reception open: All day.
Getting there: Take the A5 to Betws-y-Coed; the hostel is 2 miles outside the village adjacent to the Swallow Falls Hotel.
Parking: Large car park and coach park.
Nearest other hostels: Capel Curig 3 miles, Idwal 5.
Public transport: BUS: 96 runs past the hostel.
RAIL: Betws-y-Coed 2 miles.

●● BLAENCARON BUNKHOUSE ☆

Blaencaron, Tregaron, Ceredigion SY25 6HL;
reservations@yha.org.uk
Tel: 0870 770 5700
Bookings more than 7 days ahead: 0870 770 6113

Walkers who yearn to lose themselves in unspoilt countryside will

FAMILY CITY GROUP TRADITIONAL CAMPING BARN COASTAL ● RURAL

be happy here. This former village school is in the quiet Arfon Groes Valley with plenty of activities that will appeal to outdoor folk. Birdwatching is particularly good and there are plenty of mountain bike trails and walking tracks. Cors Caron National Nature Reserve, Strata Florida Abbey and the Devil's Bridge Railway and Waterfall are all within easy reach.

Location: OS 146, GR 713608.

Great for... a quiet break in the country and birdwatching.

You need to know... this hostel only has basic amenities.

Accommodation: 16 beds: 2x4- and 1x8-bed rooms.

Family rooms: No. **Rent-a-Hostel:** No.

Classroom: No. **Education packages:** No.

Facilities: Self-catering kitchen/dining/common room, drying room, shower and toilet. Credit cards not accepted. No hostel shop.

Daytime access: Restricted. ⊗

Meals: Self-catering only.

Reception open: 17.00hrs.

Getting there: From Red Lion Inn, Tregaron, take B4343 north. Take first right for 2 miles to phone box and turn right again for 1 mile to reach the hostel.

Parking: Opposite, limited.

Nearest other hostels: Dolgoch 12 miles (9 by mountain path), Tyncornel 14 (8 by mountain path).

Public transport: BUS: Arriva Cymru 516, James 589 Aberystwyth Station–Tregaron, alight 2 miles north of Tregaron, then 2 miles. RAIL: Aberystwyth 20 miles, Devil's Bridge (Vale of Rheidol Railway, seasonal) 17 miles.

●● BORTH ☆☆

**Morlais, Borth, Ceredigion SY24 5JS;
borth@yha.org.uk
Tel: 0870 770 5708 Fax: 0870 770 5709**

The name of this Edwardian house is Morlais, which translates as 'the voice of the sea'. You'll understand why once you see its position overlooking Cardigan Bay just 20 metres from the beach. Enjoy striking sunsets from the headland or play on the dunes and four miles of sandy beach. The Ynyslas and Ynys Hir nature reserves, Nant Yr Arian Forestry Centre and the world renowned Centre for Alternative Technology are all within reach by bicycle, public transport or car.

Location: OS 135, GR 608907.

Great for... those who love the sea.

Accommodation: 60 beds: 4-, 6- and 8-bed rooms.

Family rooms: Yes. **Rent-a-Hostel:** Yes.

Classroom: Yes. **Education packages:** Yes.

Facilities: Lounge, TV room, showers, cycle store, shop and dining room, conference room, internet access. Lockers available, groups welcome, discounts available, green hostel.

Daytime access: All areas.

Meals: Breakfast, picnic lunch, evening meal.

Reception open: Staff available before 10.00hrs and after 17.00hrs.

Getting there: The hostel is on B4353 between Borth village and the Ynyslas golf links.

Parking: Yes.

●● BRYN GWYNANT ☆☆

**Nantgwynant, Caernarfon, Gwynedd LL55 4NP; bryngwynant@yha.org.uk
Tel: 0870 770 5732 Fax: 0870 770 5733**

Experience Snowdonia at its most serene in this early Victorian mansion in the heart of the National Park. Set in 40 acres of wooded grounds with stunning views over Llyn Gwynant and Snowdon, this is the perfect escape from the rat race. Walkers will be at home here, with plenty of low and high level routes all around. Don't miss the classic Watkin path up Snowdon, which begins less than a mile from the hostel and leads you into incredible mountain scenery – just don't forget your camera.

Location: OS 115, GR 641513.

Great for... walkers and families who want a quiet escape.

You need to know... thermos flasks can be hired from the hostel.

Accommodation: 74 beds: mainly 2-, 3-, 4-, 5- and 6-bed rooms, with 1x8-, 1x9- and 1x10-bed option.

Family rooms: Yes. **Rent-a-Hostel:** Yes.

Classroom: Yes. **Education packages:** Yes.

Facilities: Lounge, self-catering kitchen, pool table, drying room, shop, showers, cycle store and camping.

Daytime access: All areas. ⊗

Meals: Breakfast, picnic lunch, evening meal.

Reception open: Staff are available before 10.00hrs and after 17.00hrs.

Getting there: The hostel is on the A498, 8 miles west of Capel Curig and 4 miles east of Beddgelert.

Parking: Yes.

Nearest other hostels: Pen-y-Pass 4 miles, Capel Curig 8, Snowdon Ranger 9.

Public transport: BUS: Snowdon Sherpa 97A Porthmadog station–Betws-y-Coed station. RAIL: Betws-y-Coed 13 miles, Bangor 25. FERRY: Holyhead/Dublin 35 miles.

Magnificent views: YHA Bryn Gwynant.

Wales

FAMILY ● CITY ● GROUP ● TRADITIONAL ● CAMPING BARN ● COASTAL ● RURAL

Nearest other hostels: Corris 19 miles, Kings (Dolgellau) 34.
Public transport: BUS: Arriva Cymru 512 runs hourly between Borth and Aberystwyth and will drop you off outside the hostel on request. RAIL: Borth 0.5 miles. FERRY: Fishguard to Rosslare 55 miles. **NATIONALEXPRESS** Birmingham to Aberystwyth.

●● BRECON (TY'N-Y-CAEAU) ☆☆☆
Groesffordd, Brecon, Powys LD3 7SW;
brecon@yha.org.uk
Tel: 0870 770 5718 Fax: 0870 770 5719

This Victorian country house is a couple of miles from the historic market town of Brecon, which boasts a wealth of listed properties, narrow streets and a cathedral. A warm and friendly welcome awaits you here, with the hostel making a comfortable, convenient base to explore the area. The Brecon Beacons National Park offers great walking from gentle strolls to spectacular ascents, or save your legs and see the countryside from the saddle on a pony trek. Boating, sailing and canoeing are possible on Llangorse Lake four miles away.
Location: OS 160, GR 074288.
Great for... active families wanting a mix of town and country.
You need to know... special family packages are available, which include free admission to many local attractions.
Accommodation: 54 beds: all 2–10-bed rooms, some en-suite.
Family rooms: Yes. **Rent-a-Hostel:** No.
Classroom: No. **Education packages:** Yes.
Facilities: Self-catering kitchen, dining room, drinks licence, TV, showers, drying room, laundry facilities, cycle store, shop, grounds, picnic area and BBQ. **Daytime access:** All areas. ♿
Meals: Breakfast, picnic lunch, evening meal.
Reception open: Staff available before 10.00hrs and after 17.00hrs.
Getting there: From the A40 (Abergavenny–Brecon road) take the Llanfrynach exit. Then follow signs to Groesffordd. Continue through the village following the hostel signs. The hostel is on the right.
Parking: Yes.

The Brecon Beacons National Park near YHA Brecon.

Nearest other hostels: Llwyn-y-Celyn 9 miles, Capel-y-Ffin 23.
Public transport: BUS: Abergavenny–Brecon 21, bus station 0.5 miles from Abergavenny train station; Stagecoach 39 and Yeomans Canyon 40 from Hereford (passes close to Hereford station). Bus 42 from Merthyr Tydfil station. RAIL: Abergavenny 19 miles, Merthyr Tydfil 20.

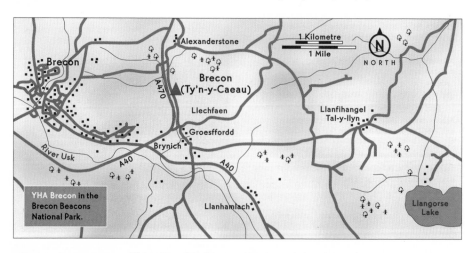
YHA Brecon in the Brecon Beacons National Park.

To make a booking visit www.yha.org.uk

● FAMILY ● CITY ● GROUP ● TRADITIONAL ● CAMPING BARN ● COASTAL ● RURAL

●● BROAD HAVEN ☆☆☆

Broad Haven, Haverfordwest, Pembrokeshire SA62 3JH; broadhaven@yha.org.uk
Tel: 0870 770 5728 Fax: 0870 770 5729

You'd better be good at making decisions if you stay here. Should you spend the day learning to ride a horse, or climbing and abseiling on spectacular cliffs? Or would sea kayaking, surfing, canoeing, windsurfing or scuba diving be more fun? All these activities can be arranged at this modern, purpose-built single-storey hostel. There are safe beaches just 100 metres away, the Pembrokeshire Coastal Footpath running past the hostel and boat trips to nearby islands. But whatever you decide to do, toast the day with a glass of wine at the hostel while you watch the sun set over St Brides Bay.

HOSTEL MANAGERS CHOOSE...

THE BEST SPOTS FOR BIRDWATCHING

Ynys-hir RSPB reserve YHA Borth: "A tranquil spot. Keep your eyes peeled for red kites."
Lavan Sands YHA Bryn Gwynant: "This is a huge mudflat at the eastern end of the water separating Anglesey from the mainland. It's a haven for waterfowl and waders."
Conwy RSPB reserve YHA Conwy: "Visit in spring and autumn to see migrants, including ospreys."
Marloes Sands Beach YHA Marloes Sands "Spectacular views well away from the crowds, plus seals and birds galore."
Mawddach Estuary YHA Kings: "Attracts raptors such as ospreys and goshawks. Nearby, Coed Garth Gell RSPB reserve is also an excellent site for Welsh woodland species."

Location: OS 157, GR 863141.
Great for... action men (and women!) keen to try a new skill.
You need to know... the hostel has disabled facilities.
Accommodation: 75 beds: mostly 4- and 7-bed rooms, plus 1x2-bed room, most en-suite.
Family rooms: Yes. **Rent-a-Hostel:** Yes.
Classroom: Yes. **Education packages:** Yes.
Facilities: Self-catering kitchen, dining room, lounge, games area, drying room, showers, suitable for people with disabilities.
Daytime access: All areas. ⊗
Meals: Breakfast, picnic lunch, evening meal.
Reception open: 15.00hrs.
Getting there: From the M40 west, take A40 to Haverfordwest. Then follow signs for Broad Haven (7 miles). On approaching village turn immediately right into Main Beach car park and hostel is on right.
Parking: Yes.
Nearest other hostels: Penycwm 8 miles, Marloes 10 (13 by path), St David's 17 (25 by path), Manorbier 28.
Public transport: BUS: First Cymru/Silcox 311 from Haverfordwest (passes close to Haverfordwest station). RAIL: Haverfordwest 7 miles. FERRY: Pembroke Dock 10 miles, Fishguard 22 miles.

●● CAPEL CURIG ☆☆

Plas Curig, Capel Curig, Betws-y-Coed, Conwy LL24 0EL; capelcurig@yha.org.uk
Tel: 0870 770 5746 Fax: 0870 770 5747

The views of Moel Siabod and the Snowdon Horseshoe from this hostel will have you itching to put on your walking boots and explore Snowdonia. Scale the mountains or enjoy easy wanders through the forest or alongside the River Llugwy. For the more adventurous, Plas-y-Brenin Outdoor Activity Centre is close by, which offers a smorgasbord of adrenalin-filled skills to master.
Location: OS 115, GR 726579.
Great for... active people who want an overdose of fresh air.

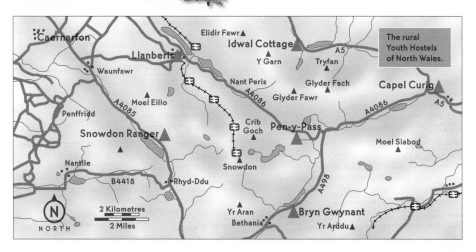

For all the latest YHA news visit www.yha.org.uk

101

YHA Capel Curig is superbly situated for exploring Snowdonia.

You need to know... parking is limited.
Accommodation: 52 beds: mostly 2-, 4- and 5-bed rooms, plus 1x6- and 1x8-bed option.
Family rooms: Yes. **Rent-a-Hostel:** No.
Classroom: No. **Education packages:** No.
Facilities: Self-catering kitchen, dining room, two lounges, showers, toilets, drying room, cycle store and shop.
Daytime access: Restricted.
Meals: Breakfast, picnic lunch, evening meal.
Reception open: 17.00hrs.
Getting there: Access is difficult from Betws-y-Coed direction. Continue to junction with A4086, turn around and return to hostel up steep driveway. By bus, ask driver to stop at hostel.
Parking: Limited.
Nearest other hostels: Pen-y-Pass 5 miles, Idwal Cottage 6, Conwy 18.
Public transport: BUS: Silver Star 96B from Bethesda (with connections from Bangor), Snowdon Sherpa 96, 97A from Llandudno (pass Betws-y-Coed station). RAIL: Betws-y-Coed 5 miles.

●● CAPEL-Y-FFIN ☆☆
Capel-y-Ffin, Llanthony, nr Abergavenny,
Monmouthshire NP7 7NP
Tel: 0870 770 5748

Nestled in the Llanthony Valley in the Black Mountains of the Brecon Beacons, this small hostel was once a hill farm. It's now an excellent base for walkers and cyclists with routes leading through unspoilt countryside in all directions, including the Cambrian Way, Offa's Dyke trails and Sustrans Route 42. Those with literary interests will want to visit Hay-on-Wye eight miles away, while there are more than enough monastery ruins nearby to satisfy history buffs. Horseriders will also be happy here, with riding arranged directly from the hostel. The hostel has a conservation site and bird hide.
Location: OS 161, GR 250328.
Great for... couples and small groups, especially riders, cyclists and walkers.
You need to know... parking is limited.
Accommodation: 38 beds: 1x3-, 1x4-, 1x6-, 1x8- and 1x18/20-bed rooms.
Family rooms: Yes. **Rent-a-Hostel:** Yes.
Classroom: No. **Education packages:** No.
Facilities: Lounge/dining room, self-catering kitchen, showers, drying room, cycle store, shop and camping. Licenced premises and accredited member of Taste of Wales quality food scheme.
Daytime access: Restricted. ⊗
Meals: Breakfast, picnic lunch, evening meal.
Reception open: 17.00hrs.
Getting there: From A449, A4042 take A465 towards Hereford from Abergavenny. Turn off at Llanfihangel Crucorney, follow signs to Llanthony then to Capel-y-Ffin. Hostel is 1 mile on other side of Capel-y-Ffin village on left. From Hay-on-Wye, turn left opposite Swan Hotel (road signed Capel-y-Ffin). Follow road and signs. Go over mountain road and two cattle grids. Hostel is down road on right-hand side.
Parking: In lay-by.
Nearest other hostels: Brecon 23 miles (16 by mountain path), Welsh Bicknor 33.
Public transport: BUS: Stagecoach 39, Yeomans Canyon 40 Hereford–Brecon (passes close to Hereford station), alight Hay-on-Wye 8 miles. RAIL: Abergavenny 16 miles.
NATIONAL EXPRESS » Abergavenny 14 miles.

● CARDIFF ☆☆☆
2 Wedal Road, Roath Park, Cardiff CF14 3QX;
cardiff@yha.org.uk
Tel: 0870 770 5750 Fax: 0870 770 5751

As the capital city of Wales, Cardiff is a stylish, cosmopolitan city with a rich heritage and a reputation for hosting national and international sporting events. Expect history-filled days (Cardiff Castle and the Museum of Welsh Life at St Fagans are both close by) and excellent nightlife. Located in the student area, the hostel makes a convenient base to explore all the city has to offer.
Location: OS 171, GR 185308.
Great for... experiencing Cardiff's vibrant atmosphere.
You need to know... the overnight price includes a light breakfast.

● FAMILY　● CITY　● GROUP　● TRADITIONAL　● CAMPING BARN　● COASTAL　● RURAL

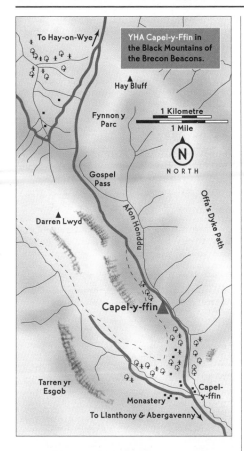

To Hay-on-Wye

YHA Capel-y-Ffin in the Black Mountains of the Brecon Beacons.

Hay Bluff

Fynnon y Parc

1 Kilometre
1 Mile

N
NORTH

Gospel Pass

Darren Lwyd

Afon Honddu

Offa's Dyke Path

Capel-y-ffin

Tarren yr Esgob

Monastery

Capel-y-ffin

To Llanthony & Abergavenny

Accommodation: 64 beds: 2x4-, 2x6-, 2x14- and 1x16-bed rooms.
Family rooms: No. **Rent-a-Hostel:** No.
Classroom: No. **Education packages:** No.
Facilities: Two lounges, TV, dining room, self-catering kitchen, showers, shop, laundry, cycle store and luggage store.
Daytime access: All areas.
Meals: Light breakfast only. Evening meals for pre-booked groups.
Reception open: All day.
Getting there: From M4, take J29 and follow A48M to the exit for A470. Take first left off roundabout. Follow Whitchurch Road to traffic lights and turn left into Fairoak Road. Follow road to the roundabout then turn left into Wedal Road and the hostel is on the right.
Parking: Yes.
Nearest other hostels: Llwyn-y-Celyn 42 miles, Port Eynon 56.
Public transport: BUS: Cardiff Bus 28, 29, 29B. RAIL: Cardiff Central 2 miles. FERRY: Swansea to Cork 50 miles, Fishguard 100 miles.
NATIONALEXPRESS Cardiff bus station 2 miles.

●● CONWY ☆☆☆☆

Larkhill, Sychnant Pass Road, Conwy LL32 8AJ;
conwy@yha.org.uk
Tel: 0870 770 5774 Fax: 0870 770 5775

This is a modern hostel. Expect high quality accommodation in spacious communal areas with panoramic views. All rooms have en-suite showers and children are well catered for with baby changing facilities, cots and a special menu. It's an ideal base for visiting the North Wales coast and Snowdonia National Park, with the medieval castle and town centre of Conwy a 10-minute walk away.
Location: OS 115, GR 775773.
Great for... families and youth organisations.
You need to know... advance booking is essential.
Accommodation: 80 beds: 2- and 4-bed rooms, en-suite showers.
Family rooms: Yes. **Rent-a-Hostel:** No.
Classroom: Yes (35 to 60 people). **Education packages:** Yes.
Facilities: Lounges, TV room, games room, self-catering kitchen, drying room, shop, cycle store, lockers, laundry facilities, residential licence, internet access, large grounds with summer house, roof terrace, picnic and BBQ area. Disabled facilities.
Daytime access: All areas.
Meals: Cafeteria/restaurant, alcohol licence.
Reception open: 14.00hrs.
Getting there: From A55, take J17 second exit for Conwy, A547. Head to Conwy centre and at town walls turn right into Mount Pleasant then right again at T-junction. The hostel is on the left after 150 metres.
Parking: Yes.
Nearest other hostels: Bangor 15 miles, Capel Curig 18, Chester 44.
Public transport: BUS: Frequent from surrounding areas. RAIL: Conwy 0.25 miles, Llandudno Junction 1.5.
FERRY: Holyhead to Dun Laoghaire 32 miles.
NATIONALEXPRESS Llandudno Junction 0.5 miles.

Just ask!: YHA staff are always willing to help.

For more information visit www.yha.org.uk

● FAMILY   ● CITY   ● GROUP   ● TRADITIONAL   ● CAMPING BARN   ● COASTAL   ● RURAL

●● CORRIS ☆☆☆

Canolfan Corris, Old School, Corris, Machynlleth, Powys SY20 9QT; corrishostel@canolfancorris.com
Tel: 0870 770 5778 Fax: 0870 770 5778

Do you know your essential oils and understand the greenhouse effect? If so, you'll find a welcoming smile at this award-winning hostel that's run on environmental and Celtic themes and focuses on conservation and inner harmony. This hostel, once a school, has won a Green Tourism award. You'll find it in the Dyfi Eco Valley, close to the Centre for Alternative Technology, Dyfi Biosphere and King Arthur's Labyrinth. Cader Idris mountain, ancient sites and Sustrans National Cycle Route 8 are all within easy reach.

Location: OS 124, GR 753080.
Great for... folk looking for a caring, holistic atmosphere.
You need to know... credit cards are not accepted (make cheques payable to Canolfan Corris).
Accommodation: 48 beds: 1x2-, 1x10-, 1x22- and few 4–6-bed rooms.
Family rooms: Yes. **Rent-a-Hostel:** No.
Classroom: No. **Education packages:** No.
Facilities: Lounge/dining room, self-catering kitchen, showers, drying room, lockers, laundry room, cycle store and grounds.
Daytime access: All areas. ⊗
Meals: Breakfast, picnic lunch, evening meal.
Reception open: Staff available before 10.00hrs and after 17.00hrs.
Getting there: From A487 at Briach Goch Hotel turn off downhill (signposted) into village. After 400 metres at Slaters Arms pub and crossroads (signposted), turn left uphill. A small car park is 150 metres on right and the hostel is a further 30 metres uphill on right.
Parking: Yes.
Nearest other hostels: Kings (Dolgellau) 15 miles, Borth 19, Llanbedr 28.
Public transport: BUS: Arriva Cymru 30, 32, 34 Aberystwyth–Dolgellau (passes Machynlleth station), Trawscambria 701.
RAIL: Machynlleth 6 miles.

●● CYNWYD ☆☆

The Old Mill, Cynwyd, Corwen, Denbighshire LL21 0LW
Tel: 0870 770 5786 Fax: 0870 770 5786

This small hostel, which offers basic amenities, provides access to unlimited walking and cycling. Follow a mountain path to Pistyll Rhaeadr, the highest waterfall in Wales, or head further afield to Bala Lake, where a plethora of watersports is on offer. Llangollen, Chirk Castle and Lake Vyrnwy RSPB Reserve are also close by. After an action-packed day, this former woollen mill offers a riverside retreat to rest your weary bones.

Location: OS 125, GR 057409.
Great for... walkers and cyclists wanting a rural retreat.
You need to know... it's self-catering accommodation only.

Chirk Castle, near YHA Cynwyd.

Accommodation: 30 beds: 1x2-, 1x4-, 1x6-, 1x8- and 1x10-bed room, plus self-catering cottage with 4 beds (book separately).
Family rooms: No. **Rent-a-Hostel:** No.
Classroom: No. **Education packages:** No.
Facilities: Lounge/dining room, self-catering kitchen, showers, toilets, drying room, cycle store, shop, grounds and camping.
Daytime access: Restricted. ⊗
Meals: Self-catering only.
Reception open: 17.00hrs.
Getting there: The hostel is on B4401 from Corwen. In Cynwyd, bear left before bridge and follow road for 100 metres. From Bala, turn right immediately before bridge on B4401, then first left. Go

---

HOSTEL MANAGERS CHOOSE...
THE BEST WELSH CASTLES TO VISIT

Skenfrith Castle YHA Broad Haven: "For me, of all the castles in this area, Skenfrith is the most impressive. Its site is stunningly beautiful."

Caernarfon Castle YHA Snowdon Ranger: "Just eight miles from the hostel, Caernarfon Castle and the walled town is a World Heritage site. It's one of the six 13th century castles built by Edward I and makes an impressive contrast to the smaller castles of the Welsh princes."

Beaumaris Castle YHA Bryn Gwynant: "Although never completed, this is Britain's most technically advanced moated castle. Enjoy a picnic in the grounds and see the ducks and swans on the castle moat."

Conwy Castle YHA Conwy: "The views from the battlements are amazing — looking over to the coast you'll see Llandudno and the Ormes, with the mountains of Snowdonia in the opposite direction."

Dolwyddelan Castle YHA Bryn Gwynant: "Buried deep in Snowdonia, this is a true Welsh creation, built by Llywelyn the Great and offering fantastic views from its battlements."

● FAMILY ● CITY ● GROUP ● TRADITIONAL ● CAMPING BARN ● COASTAL ● RURAL

over second bridge and turn immediately right.
Parking: Yes.
Nearest other hostels: Llangollen 14 miles, Maeshafn 18, Lledr Valley 26.
Public transport: BUS: Arriva Cymru 94 Wrexham–Barmouth (passes close to Ruabon and Barmouth stations). RAIL: Ruabon 18 miles. FERRY: Liverpool or Holyhead 40 miles.

●● DOLGOCH BUNKHOUSE ☆

Dolgoch, Tregaron, Ceredigion SY25 6NR;
reservations@yha.org.uk
Tel: 0870 770 5796 Fax: 0870 770 5797
Bookings more than 7 days ahead: 0870 770 6113

Head into the wilds to this remote, gas-lit farmhouse in the lonely Tywi Valley for an experience to remember. There is no electricity and the only heating is an open fire. You'll have to make your own entertainment, but with excellent birdwatching and walking country all around, you won't have trouble keeping yourself busy. Pony trekking is available and the Welsh National Cycle Route runs nearby.

YHA Dolgoch is in the wild and remote Tywi Valley.

Location: OS 147, GR 806561.
Great for... an escape into the wilds of Wales.
You need to know... the track to the hostel is very rough.
Accommodation: 19 beds: 1x4-, 1x5- and 1x10-bed rooms.
Family rooms: No. **Rent-a-Hostel:** No.
Classroom: No. **Education packages:** No.
Facilities: Self-catering kitchen/dining room, shower and shop.
Daytime access: Restricted. ⊗
Meals: Self-catering only.
Reception open: 17.00hrs.
Getting there: From Tregaron take Abergwesyn mountain road for 9 miles. From Beulah on A483, take road to Abergwesyn and then Tregaron mountain road for 6 miles. Hostel is 0.75 miles south of Bridge in Tywi Valley along an uneven forestry track.
Parking: In hostel grounds only, limited.
Nearest other hostels: Blaencaron 12 miles (9 by mountains), Tyncornel 19 (5 by mountains).
Public transport: BUS: Arriva Cymru 516, James 589 Aberystwyth Station–Tregaron, alight Tregaron 9 miles. RAIL: Llanwrtyd Wells 10 miles. FERRY: Fishguard to Rosslare 66 miles.

● HOLYHEAD

Break Water Country Park, Holyhead, Anglesey;
reservations@yha.org.uk
Tel: 0870 770 6122 Fax: 0870 770 6123

Enjoy your stay at our latest addition to the YHA North Wales network. Situated at the heart of the Break Water Country Park, five minutes from Holyhead, this hostel is an ideal base to explore the island of Anglesey's beautiful countryside. Enjoy the stunning scenery and walk the coastal footpath or just relax at the nearby Llyn Llwynog lake where you can fish and watch the model boats in the company of moorhens and mallards. There are a variety of walks for all levels including access to Holyhead Mountain and South Stacks.
Location: OS 124, GR 683161.
Great for... a varied break with plenty of attractions.
You need to know... this hostel will open in summer 2003.
Accommodation: 24 beds.
Family rooms: No. **Rent-a-Hostel:** Yes.
Classroom: No. **Education packages:** No.
Facilities: Lounge, self-catering kitchen, toilets and showers, disabled access, drying room, cycle storage.
Daytime access: All areas. ⊗
Meals: Self-catering only.
Reception open: Before 10.00hrs and after 17.00hrs.
Getting there: Take the A55 to Holyhead then follow directions for Break Water Country Park.
Parking: Car and minibus parking.
Nearest other hostels: Bangor 17 miles.
Public transport: BUS: 4 Bangor to Holyhead.
RAIL: Holyhead 0.5 miles. FERRY: Holyhead 0.5 miles.
NATIONALEXPRESS》 Bangor 17 miles.

●● KINGS (DOLGELLAU) ☆☆

Kings, Penmaenpool, Dolgellau, Gwynedd
LL40 1TB; kings@yha.org.uk
Tel: 0870 770 5900 Fax: 0870 770 5901

Combine a beach holiday with countryside pursuits at YHA Kings, at the southern end of the Snowdonia National Park. Large sandy

Horse riding in Dolgellau.

beaches are close by in Barmouth, or try mountain biking, pony trekking, watersports and fishing in Dolgellau. Walkers will be busy at this country house and can choose between a high-level hike up Cader Idris or gentle trails leading to the Mawddach Estuary, whose low tide sands and woodlands are a haven for wildlife and migrant waders.

Location: OS 124, GR 683161.

Great for... individuals and groups combining quiet days on the beach with energetic walking.

You need to know... it's open to organised groups all year.

Accommodation: 42 beds: all 6-bed rooms.

Family rooms: Yes. **Rent-a-Hostel:** Yes.

Classroom: No. **Education packages:** No.

Facilities: Lounge, dining room, showers, drying room, shop, cycle store and grounds. **Daytime access:** Restricted. ♿

Meals: Self-catering. Full catering for pre-booked groups from April to July.

Reception open: 17.00hrs.

Getting there: The hostel is off the A493 Dolgellau–Tywyn road. 1 mile west of Penmaenpool, turn uphill opposite Abergwynant Trekking Centre. Then drive for 1 mile along lane. From Barmouth, take the wooden toll bridge.

Parking: Yes.

Nearest other hostels: Corris 15 miles, Llanbedr 17.

Public transport: BUS: Arriva Cymru 28 Dolgellau–Tywyn (passes close to Fairbourne station), alight 1.5 miles west of Penmaenpool, then 1 mile. RAIL: Morfa Mawddach 5 miles.

●● LAWRENNY ☆☆☆

Lawrenny, Pembrokeshire SA68 0PN

Tel: 0870 770 5914 Fax: 0870 770 5915

Pembrokeshire National Park is a rich habitat for waders, wildfowl... and summer tourists. Escape the crowds at this former village school in a quiet corner of the park close to several waterways and footpaths. There are dozens of on- and off-road cycle routes, while Oakwood Pleasure Park, Folly Farm and Carew Castle are all nearby.

Location: OS 158, GR 018070.

Great for... exploring the quieter parts of Pembrokeshire.

You need to know... it's self-catering accommodation and there's no hostel shop; no credit cards accepted.

Accommodation: 23 beds: 1x3-, 3x4- and 1x8-bed rooms.

Family rooms: No. **Rent-a-Hostel:** Yes.

Classroom: No. **Education packages:** No.

Facilities: Lounge, self-catering kitchen, showers and drying room.

Daytime access: Restricted. ♿

Meals: Self-catering only.

Reception open: 17.00hrs.

Getting there: Follow A40 west from Carmarthen to Canaston Bridge. Take A4075 Tenby Road past Oakwood Leisure Park to CC2000/ Canaston Bowl. Turn right, follow signs to Lawrenny (6 miles).

Parking: Yes.

Nearest other hostels: Manorbier 9 miles, Marloes Sands 23.

Public transport: BUS: Postbus from Narberth. RAIL: Kilgetty 8 miles, Narberth 10. FERRY: Pembroke Dock 12 miles.

●● IDWAL COTTAGE ☆☆☆☆☆

Nant Ffrancon, Bethesda, Bangor, Gwynedd LL57 3LZ; idwal@yha.org.uk

Tel: 0870 770 5874 Fax: 0870 770 5875

Stay below the impressive Glyder mountains with views of the Nant Ffrancon Valley at this former quarry manager's cottage. Recently refurbished, you can be sure of a warm welcome at this environmentally-conscious hostel. All levels of walks can be found in the immediate area, and you won't need to travel far for world-class mountain bike trails. It's perfectly placed for strolls to see Rhaeadr Ogwen Waterfalls or Cwm Idwal nature reserve (with its dramatic lake) and Devil's Kitchen.

Location: OS 115, GR 648603.

Great for... a relaxing stay in the mountains of Snowdonia.

You need to know... it's self-catering accommodation only.

Accommodation: 38 beds: mostly small-, medium-sized bedrooms.

Family rooms: Yes. **Rent-a-Hostel:** No.

Classroom: No. **Education packages:** No.

Facilities: Excellent self-catering kitchen, gathering room, showers, drying room, cycle store, grounds and camping. Shop with extensive store including frozen meals.

Daytime access: All areas. ♿

Meals: Self-catering only.

Reception open: Staff available before 10.00 and after 17.00hrs.

Getting there: The hostel is off the A5 at the west end of Llyn Ogwen, 5 miles south of Bethesda.

Parking: Yes, private car park opposite hostel.

Nearest other hostels: Capel Curig 6 miles, Pen-y-Pass 10 (5 by mountain path), Bangor 10, Llanberis 12 (7 by mountain path).

Public transport: BUS: Arriva 66 Bangor–Bethesda then Snowdon Sherpa 96B Bethesda–Pen-y-Pass, via Idwal Cottage. RAIL: Bangor 12 miles, Betws-y-Coed 11.

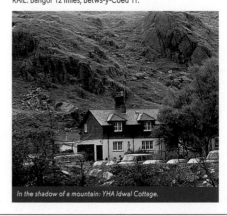

In the shadow of a mountain: YHA Idwal Cottage.

● FAMILY ● CITY ● GROUP ● TRADITIONAL ● CAMPING BARN ● COASTAL ● RURAL

●● LLANBERIS ☆☆
**Llwyn Celyn, Llanberis, Caernarfon, Gwynedd
LL55 4SR; llanberis@yha.org.uk
Tel: 0870 770 5928 Fax: 0870 770 5929**

Mountain bikers, climbers and walkers will find plenty to do at this mountainside hostel. The quickest route up Snowdon, whose summit is visible from the hostel, starts close by, or choose less strenuous valley walks to waterfalls. Llyn Padarn, where you can be instructed in the arts of fishing, canoeing, windsurfing and sailing, is less than a mile from the hostel, or take to the saddle with a day's pony trekking. Castles and craft workshops also abound for the less energetic.

Location: OS 115, GR 574596.
Great for... active, adventurous people.
Accommodation: 56 beds: 3x2-, 1x3-, 4x4-, 1x5-, 2x6- and 1x8-bed rooms, 3 fully en-suite with double beds.
Family rooms: Yes. **Rent-a-Hostel:** No.
Classroom: Yes. **Education packages:** No.
Facilities: Lounge, TV room, self-catering kitchen, dining room, showers, drying room, cycle store and shop.
Daytime access: Restricted. ☺
Meals: Breakfast, picnic lunch, evening meal.
Reception open: 17.00hrs.
Getting there: From High Street, take Capel Coch Road (Spar is on the corner) and keep left at the fork in the road halfway up the hill. The hostel is on the left through a farm gate. Please contact hostel for coach access.

Parking: Cars and minibuses only.
Nearest other hostels: Pen-y-Pass 6 miles, Snowdon Ranger 11 (4 by mountain), Bangor 11, Bryn Gwynant 11.
Public transport: BUS: KMP 85, 86 from Bangor, Arriva Cymru 77 from Bangor (pass close to Bangor station), or both alight at Spar on High Street. RAIL: Bangor 11 miles.

www.britainonview.com

Rewarding views of Snowdonia National Park near YHA Llanberis.

●● LLANBEDR (HARLECH) ☆☆
**Plas Newydd, Llanbedr, Barmouth LL45 2LE;
llanbedr@yha.org.uk
Tel: 0870 770 5926 Fax: 0870 770 5927**

Bring the kids to this Youth Hostel and feel like the best parents in the world. If you can drag them away from the swing park and football pitch next to the hostel, there are beaches and mountains aplenty to explore. Cycle the Mawddach Trail, walk the Rhinog mountains and mountain bike on world-class tracks in Coed-y-Brenin Forest. Shell Island, Harlech Castle and Llanfair Slate Caverns are all within three miles of the hostel.

Location: OS 124, GR 585267.
Great for... active families with children of walking age.
Accommodation: 42 beds: all 3-, 4- and 6-bed rooms.
Family rooms: Yes. **Rent-a-Hostel:** Yes.
Classroom: No. **Education packages:** No.
Facilities: Lounge, self-catering kitchen, dining room, shop, games room, showers, drying room, cycle store and garden with BBQ.
Daytime access: Restricted. ☺
Meals: Breakfast, picnic lunch, evening meal.
Reception open: 17.00hrs.
Getting there: The hostel is on A496 in centre of village beside stone bridge over river. Tight turn into hostel drive.
Parking: Yes.

www.britainonview.com

The freedom of the hills by foot, bike or horse: Wales's National Parks.

For offers and discounts visit www.yha.org.uk

Wales

● FAMILY   ● CITY   ● GROUP   ● TRADITIONAL   ● CAMPING BARN   ● COASTAL   ● RURAL

Close to beaches and mountains: YHA Llanbedr.

Nearest other hostels: Kings 17 miles, Bryn Gwynant 31, Snowdon Ranger 33, Borth 48.

Public transport: BUS: Arriva Cymru 38 Barmouth–Blaenau Ffestiniog. RAIL: Llanbedr 0.5 miles.

●● LLANDDEUSANT ☆☆☆

The Old Red Lion, Llanddeusant, Carmarthenshire SA19 9UL
Tel: 0870 770 5930 Fax: 0870 770 5930

A break in this rural retreat will restore your spirits. Set in the least developed area of the Brecon Beacons, the hostel overlooks the magical Sawdde Valley. Trails lead up to the legendary Llyn y Ffan glacial lake and the heights of the Carmarthen Fans. Circular walks will take you to an Iron Age fort, Roman camps and standing stones. The hostel, a former inn built in 1789, retains many of its original features and offers a warm welcome with an open fire in the lounge.

www.britainonview.com

Walk to the glacial lake of Llyn y Ffan near YHA Llanddeusant.

The Black Mountain Red Kite feeding station is a mile away.
Location: OS 160, GR 776245.
Great for... getting away from it all.
You need to know... the hostel has no shop.
Accommodation: 26 beds: 3x4-, 1x6- and 1x8-bed rooms.
Family rooms: Yes. **Rent-a-Hostel:** Yes.
Classroom: No. **Education packages:** No.
Facilities: Self-catering kitchen, common room, showers, cycle store, drying room and camping. **Daytime access:** Restricted. ⊗
Meals: Self-catering only.
Reception open: 17.00hrs.
Getting there: From M4 either J29 (A449 to A40) or J32 (A470 to A40). From A40 Brecon–Llandovery road, turn left in Trecastle at Castle Coaching Inn. After 9 miles on Llanddeusant Road turn left opposite Cross Inn, then 1 mile to hostel on right. From Carmarthen, take A40 via Llandeilo then right for A4069 (Llangadog to Brynamman Road). Turn left opposite Three Horseshoes pub. Follow road round to right in Twynllannan, turn right and immediately left. Look for hostel signs on the left by the church.
Parking: Cars/minibuses only.
Nearest other hostels: Ystradfellte 23 miles, Llwyn-y-Celyn 25, Brecon 29.
Public transport: RAIL: Llangadog 7 miles.

●● LLANGOLLEN ☆☆☆

Tyndwr Road, Llangollen, Denbighshire
LL20 8AR; llangollen@yha.org.uk
Tel: 0870 770 5932 Fax: 0870 770 5933

Tyndwr Hall is a large Victorian manor and coach house which was built in the early 1800s. Situated in over seven acres of grounds, it still retains many original features such as stained glass windows, decorative fireplaces and a bell tower. The market town of Llangollen has more than enough to occupy your days with good walking, canal trips, a steam train and Dr Who Exhibition. Whitewater rafting, canoeing, mountain biking and golf are all available nearby.
Location: OS 117, GR 232413.
Great for... busy days and relaxing evenings.
You need to know... this hostel is in two separate buildings.
Accommodation: 134 beds: 2-, 4- and 6-bed rooms, with several 10–20-bed options.
Family rooms: Yes. **Rent-a-Hostel:** Yes.
Classroom: Yes. **Education packages:** Yes.
Facilities: Self-catering kitchen, lounge, dining room, drying room, cycle store, showers, games room, table licence and dance floor.
Daytime access: All areas.
Meals: Breakfast, picnic lunch, evening meal.
Reception open: 15.00hrs.
Getting there: From A5 east of Llangollen, turn left after golf club and follow hostel signs. From town, follow A5 towards Shrewsbury and, after fire station, bear right up Birch Hill. Turn right at Y-junction, then 0.5 miles to hostel.
Parking: Yes.
Nearest other hostels: Cynwyd 14 miles, Maeshafn 16, Chester 23, Capel Curig 38.

For more information visit www.yha.org.uk

● FAMILY ● CITY ● GROUP ● TRADITIONAL ● CAMPING BARN ● COASTAL ● RURAL

Public transport: BUS: Arriva Cymru 94, Bryn Melyn X5, GHA 5 Wrexham–Llangollen (pass Ruabon Station), alight Llangollen then 1.5 miles. RAIL: Chirk 5 miles, Ruabon 5.
NATIONALEXPRESS Market St, Memorial Hall 2 miles.

●● MAESHAFN ☆☆
Maeshafn, Mold, Denbighshire CH7 5LR;
reservations@yha.org.uk
Tel: 0870 770 6113 Fax: 0870 770 6127

Maeshafn is a priceless gem of YHA history. This Swiss chalet-style building was constructed in 1931 as the first purpose-built hostel, designed by Portmeirion's architect Clough Williams Ellis. It nestles into the foot of Moel Findeg and its country park, close to Loggerheads Country Park, Offa's Dyke and the Clwydian Hills. There are plenty of activities to try in the area, including walking, cycling, abseiling and ice skating, as well as exploring historic cities, castles and the countryside.

●● LLWYN-Y-CELYN ☆☆
Libanus, Brecon, Powys LD3 8NH;
llwynycelyn@yha.org.uk
Tel: 0870 770 5936 Fax: 0870 770 5937

This hostel offers access to some of the best walking in Wales. Choose gentle strolls alongside the Brecon and Monmouth Canal or ascend across the spectacular ridges and peaks of Pen-y-Fan (2,907 feet) and Corn Du (2,863 feet). Guided walks are organised by the National Park between April and October. Cosy accommodation greets your return to the hostel, an 18th century Welsh farmhouse set in 15 acres of ancient woodland.
Location: OS 160, GR 973225.
Great for... walkers of all abilities.
Accommodation: 41 beds: 5x2-, 3x4-, 1x5-, 1x6- and 1x8-bed rooms.
Family rooms: Yes. **Rent-a-Hostel:** No.

Location: OS 117, GR 208606.
Great for... walking and cycling.
You need to know... it's self-catering accommodation only.
Accommodation: 22 beds: 1x2-bed room plus a partitioned area divided into 5x4-bunkbed sectioned alcoves.
Family rooms: No. **Rent-a-Hostel:** Yes.
Classroom: No. **Education packages:** No.
Facilities: Lounge/dining room, self-catering kitchen, showers, drying room and cycle store. **Daytime access:** Restricted. ⊗
Meals: Self-catering only.
Reception open: 17.00hrs.
Getting there: Turn off A494 Mold to Ruthin road at the Maeshafn and YHA sign. Continue on this minor road for 1.5 miles. Turn left at village and hostel is 0.5 miles on left.
Parking: Yes.
Nearest other hostels: Chester 14 miles, Llangollen 16, Cynwyd 20, Conwy 41.

Classroom: Yes. **Education packages:** No.
Facilities: Self-catering kitchen, full meals service, dining room, lounge with open fire, showers, drying room, shop, cycle store, small seminar rooms, grounds with nature trail and camping.
Daytime access: All areas. ⊗
Meals: Breakfast, picnic lunch, evening meal.
Reception open: Staff available before 10.00 and after 17.00hrs.
Getting there: From M4 take J32 north to A470. Hostel is 13 miles north of Merthyr Tydfil, signed on road. From Brecon take A470 towards Merthyr Tydfil. Hostel is on left, 2 miles beyond Libanus village. Access on foot from Taff Trail 1 mile north of Storey Arms.
Parking: Yes.
Nearest other hostels: Brecon 9 miles, Ystradfellte 12, Llanddeusant 25, Capel-y-Ffin 33, Cardiff 35.
Public transport: BUS: 60/60 Coaches service 43 Brecon–Merthyr Tydfil stops at hostel drive.
RAIL: Merthyr Tydfil 15 miles, Abergavenny 28.

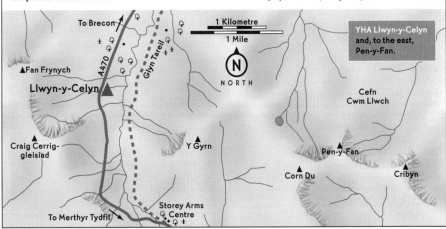

● FAMILY ● CITY ● GROUP ● TRADITIONAL ● CAMPING BARN ● COASTAL ● RURAL

Public transport: BUS: Arriva Cymru B5 from Mold, with connections from Wrexham, Flint and Chester stations, alight Maeshafn Road end, then 1.5 miles. **RAIL:** Buckley 8 miles, Wrexham 13, Chester 16.

●● MARLOES SANDS ☆☆

Runwayskiln, Marloes, Haverfordwest,
Pembrokeshire SA62 3BH;
reservations@yha.org.uk
Tel: 0870 770 5958 Fax: 0870 770 5959
Bookings more than 7 days ahead: 0870 770 6113

Wake up to the sounds of the sea. A cluster of National Trust farm buildings with exceptional sea views, YHA Marloes Sands is on the Pembrokeshire Coastal Path. Famous bird sanctuary and marine reserve, Skomer Island, can be reached by ferry from nearby Martin's Haven or try your hand at watersports at Dale.
Location: OS 157, GR 778080.
Great for... walkers and outdoor folk looking for a seaside haven.
You need to know... parking is limited to six cars.
Accommodation: 30 beds: 1x2-, 3x4-, 1x6- and 1x10-bed rooms.
Family rooms: No. **Rent-a-Hostel:** Yes.
Classroom: No. **Education packages:** No.
Facilities: Combined lounge/dining room/self-catering kitchen, showers, drying room, cycle store and small shop.
Daytime access: Restricted. ⊗

YHA Marloes Sands: a cottage by the sea.

Meals: Self-catering only.
Reception open: 17.00hrs.
Getting there: Follow B4327 from Haverfordwest for 11 miles and turn right to Marloes. At village church, turn left to car park. The hostel is down a private track on left approx 200 metres (coaches not allowed, speed limit 5mph).
Parking: Limited to six cars. Minibuses in National Trust car park.
Nearest other hostels: Broad Haven 13 miles (path), St David's 22.
Public transport: BUS: From Haverfordwest or Milford Haven to Marloes (infrequent), then 1 mile. **RAIL:** Milford Haven 11 miles, Haverfordwest 14. **FERRY:** Pembroke to Ireland 7 miles.

●● MANORBIER ☆☆☆

Manorbier, nr Tenby, Pembrokeshire
SA70 7TT; manorbier@yha.org.uk
Tel: 0870 770 5954 Fax: 0870 770 5955

An action-packed break awaits at YHA Manorbier in the Pembrokeshire Coast National Park. From the clifftops overlooking Caldey Island, the coastal path and Church Doors beach will no doubt beckon. But it's the children who will be in their element here. Visit Oakwood, Wales's largest theme park. Or, for open spaces and a dose of Welsh history, try Heatherton Country Park, Wedlock Dinosaur Park, or Pembroke and Carew Castles. Even staying in this hostel, a futuristic former Ministry of Defence building is an adventure!
Location: OS 158, GR 081975.
Great for... families with energetic kids.
You need to know... self-catering apartments are also available.
Accommodation: 59 beds: 1x3-, 1x4-, 6x6- and 2x8-bed rooms, plus 2 separate apartments sleeping 4–6.
Family rooms: Yes. **Rent-a-Hostel:** Yes.
Classroom: Yes. **Education packages:** Yes.
Facilities: Lounge/TV room, games room, self-catering kitchen, dining room, shop, showers, cycle store, laundry facilities, grounds and camping. **Daytime access:** Restricted.
Meals: Breakfast, picnic lunch, evening meal.
Reception open: 17.00hrs.

Getting there: From Tenby follow A4139 towards Pembroke. Turn left at junction of B4585 to Manorbier. This is also signposted to the Royal Artillery Range (RAR Station). Turn left at signpost to hostel and Shrinkle Haven. Go straight over roundabout by children's playground and up hill. At the top, turn left in front of RAR gates. Hostel is on left 0.5 miles along this road on clifftops.
Parking: Yes.
Nearest other hostels: Lawrenny 9 miles, Broad Haven 28.
Public transport: BUS: First Cymru 349 Tenby–Haverfordwest, alight Shrinkle 1 mile. **RAIL:** Manorbier 2.5 miles.
FERRY: Pembroke to Rosslare 10 miles.
NATIONALEXPRESS» Tenby, Upper Park Road 4.25 miles.

Futuristic: YHA Manorbier was once a Ministry of Defence base.

⬤ FAMILY ⬤ CITY ⬤ GROUP ⬤ TRADITIONAL ⬤ CAMPING BARN ⬤ COASTAL ⬤ RURAL

HOSTEL MANAGERS CHOOSE...

THE BEST WELSH BEACHES

Poppit Sands YHA Poppit Sands: "This is a fantastic Blue Flag sandy beach with interesting rock pools and dunes to explore."

Newgale Beach YHA Broad Haven: "It compares with beaches in Cornwall for surfing."

Newborough YHA Snowdon Ranger: "The best beach in North Wales, with great coves to explore."

Tenby South & North YHA Manorbier: "Just five miles from the hostel at Manorbier, there's plenty of sand plus the harbour and boat trips."

Abersoch, Beaumaris & Pwllheli YHA Bryn Gwynant: "Abersoch is a great family bucket-and-spade beach and is good for watersports, Beaumaris has a nice pier and is good for crabbing while Pwllheli offers safe swimming close to the shore."

Caernarfon YHA Bryn Gwynant: "Good views of the castle and Anglesey. A nice place to have lunch away from the crowds."

Whitesands Beach YHA Broad Haven: "It's got safe, sandy beach for families."

Rhossili Beach YHA Cardiff: "There's a very active surfing scene here."

Manorbier Beach and Freshwater West YHA Manorbier: "Two great beaches for surfers, 10 and 15 minutes away from the hostel by car."

Black Rock Sands and Red Wharf Bay YHA Bryn Gwynant: "The former is an excellent surfing and jet ski beach in winter. Drive right onto the sands and stroll for miles. The second is a super place for a spot of lunch where you can watch the boats go by."

●● PENYCWM ☆☆☆☆☆
Whitehouse, Penycwm, Haverfordwest, Pembrokeshire SA62 6LA; penycwm@yha.org.uk
Tel: 0870 770 5988 Fax: 0870 770 5989

This is the very first hostel in Britain to be awarded a five-star grade so expect a warm welcome, wholesome food, en-suite rooms (some with double beds) with TV and an exceptional level of comfort. It makes a great base to explore Pembrokeshire. The award-winning hostel is close to a number of Blue Flag beaches including the extensive beach at Newgale and the attractive harbour village of Solva. There are walks to suit all and watersports, boat rides and horseriding are easy to arrange.
Location: OS 157, GR 857250.
Great for... a comfortable family holiday.
You need to know... you must book evening meals 24 hours ahead.
Accommodation: 26 beds: 2x2-, 4x4- and 1x6-bed rooms, all en-suite.
Family rooms: Yes. **Rent-a-Hostel:** No.
Classroom: Yes. **Education packages:** Yes.

Facilities: Lounge, TV room, self-catering kitchens, showers, cycle store, luggage store, indoor recreation area and lawned grounds. No hostel shop. **Daytime access:** All areas. ⊗
Meals: Breakfast, picnic lunch, evening meal.
Reception open: Staff available before 10.00hrs and after 17.00hrs.
Getting there: Access via A487 Newgale to Solva road. At Penycwm take minor road north towards Letterston/Mathry and follow signs to the hostel.
Parking: Yes.
Nearest other hostels: Broad Haven 8 miles, Trefin 8, St David's 9 (17 by path).
Public transport: BUS: Richards 411, alight Penycwm, then 1.5 miles. RAIL: Haverfordwest 12 miles. FERRY: Fishguard to Rosslare 12 miles.

●● PEN-Y-PASS ☆☆
Pen-y-Pass, Nantgwynant, Caernarfon, Gwynedd LL55 4NY; penypass@yha.org.uk
Tel: 0870 770 5990 Fax: 0870 770 5991

This hostel was once the haunt of Victorian climbers – George Mallory of Everest fame once stayed here on his early climbing trips to Wales. With such a prestigious history, it now makes the ideal base to ascend Snowdon and explore the surrounding mountains.
Location: OS 115, GR 647556.
Great for... walkers wanting easy access to Snowdon.

George Mallory of Everest fame stayed here: YHA Pen-y-Pass.

For all the latest YHA news visit www.yha.org.uk

111

● FAMILY   ● CITY   ● GROUP   ● TRADITIONAL   ● CAMPING BARN   ● COASTAL   ● RURAL

You need to know... parking is limited.

Accommodation: 79 beds: a few 2-, mostly 4–6-bed rooms, plus 1x12-bed option.

Family rooms: Yes. **Rent-a-Hostel:** No.

Classroom: Yes. **Education packages:** No.

Facilities: Two lounges, residents' bar and lounge, games room, self-catering kitchen, dining room, shop, showers, drying room, cycle store and lockers. **Daytime access:** All areas.

Meals: Breakfast, picnic lunch, evening meal.

Reception open: All day.

Getting there: From A55 coast road follow signs for Llanberis then A4086 to hostel. From A5 turn onto A4086 at Capel Curig. Turn right at Pen-y-Gwryd Hotel. The hostel is on the right.

Parking: Public car park opposite – limited permits available.

Nearest other hostels: Bryn Gwynant 4 miles, Capel Curig 5, Idwal Cottage 5 (by path), Llanberis 6.

Public transport: BUS: Snowdon Sherpa 96A from Llanberis, 96, 97A from Llandudno Pass, 97A from Porthmadog station. RAIL: Bangor 18 miles.

●● POPPIT SANDS ☆☆☆

Sea View, Poppit, Cardigan, Pembrokeshire SA43 3LP; poppit@yha.org.uk

Tel: 0870 770 5996 Fax: 0870 770 5996

YHA Poppit Sands is set in five acres of grounds that reach to the sea. It overlooks a fantastic Blue Flag sandy beach and bay where, if you keep your eyes peeled, you may spot dolphins and seals. Activity courses are run from the hostel, which has been extensively refurbished and is now run using sustainable technologies. Horseriding, cycling, birdwatching, fishing and boat trips are all available in the area.

Location: OS 145, GR 144487.

Great for... families who love the outdoors.

You need to know... it's self-catering accommodation only.

Accommodation: 40 beds: 2-, 3-, 4-, 5-, 6- and 8-bed rooms.

Family rooms: Yes. **Rent-a-Hostel:** Yes.

Classroom: Yes. **Education packages:** Yes.

Facilities: Lounge, self-catering kitchen/dining room, showers, drying room, shop and camping. **Daytime access:** All areas. ⊗

Meals: Self-catering only.

Reception open: Staff available before 10.00hrs and after 17.00hrs.

Getting there: From Carmarthen take the A484 to Cardigan. Follow the signs to St Dogmaels (B4545) and then to Poppit Sands. From Aberystwyth take the A487 to Cardigan then the B4545 to St Dogmaels and Poppit Sands. The hostel is signposted from the lifeboat station (you will find the hostel down a flight of concrete steps).

Parking: Yes.

Nearest other hostels: Trefdraeth 11 miles, Pwll Deri 25, Llanddeusant 43, Borth 48.

Public transport: BUS: Richards Bros 407/9 from Cardigan to Poppit Sands car park to within 0.5 miles, Poppit Rocket runs between Fishguard and Cardigan. RAIL: Fishguard Harbour 20 miles, Carmarthen 26. FERRY: Fishguard to Rosslare 20 miles.

●● PORT EYNON ☆☆☆

Old Lifeboat House, Port Eynon, Swansea SA3 1NN; porteynon@yha.org.uk

Tel: 0870 770 5998 Fax: 0870 770 5999

Once a lifeboat station, YHA Port Eynon is in a beautiful position on the Gower with an award-winning beach on its doorstep. The beach has enough sand and rock pools to keep the children entertained for hours. The bay is also extremely popular for all watersports and there is storage for surfboards, canoes and other bulky equipment at the hostel. With the Gower Coastal Path and cycle trails crossing this Area of Outstanding Natural Beauty and its 34 miles of heritage coast, YHA Port Eynon is an outdoor enthusiast's dream.

Location: OS 159, GR 468848.

Great for... outdoor activities in a quiet setting.

Family fun: YHA Port Eynon has this award-winning beach close by.

You need to know... parking is 400 metres away so you'll have to carry that surfboard.

Accommodation: 28 beds: 3x2-, 2x4-, 1x6- and 1x8-bed rooms.

Family rooms: Yes. **Rent-a-Hostel:** Yes.

Classroom: No. **Education packages:** No.

Facilities: Lounge/dining room, self-catering kitchen, showers, drying room, shop and cycle store. **Daytime access:** Restricted. ⊗

Meals: Self-catering only.

Reception open: 17.00hrs.

Getting there: If approaching from Severn Bridge, exit from M4 at J42 in Swansea. Follow the brown and white tourist signs for Gower then the A4118 for Port Eynon. If you are approaching from Carmarthen, exit the M4 at J47 following signs for Gower then South Gower. In Port Eynon follow the road down to the car park at the beach. From the car park walk down the track signed 'parking for

● FAMILY   ● CITY   ● GROUP   ● TRADITIONAL   ● CAMPING BARN   ● COASTAL   ● RURAL

permit holders only' to hostel.
Parking: Use seafront car park, 400 metres away.
Nearest other hostels: Llanddeusant 44 miles, Cardiff 56.
Public transport: BUS: First Cymru 18/A from Swansea (passes close to Swansea station). Sundays and bank holidays, use bus 49.
RAIL: Swansea 16 miles. FERRY: Swansea to Cork 20 miles.
NATIONALEXPRESS>> Swansea 16 miles.

Breathtaking view: the Conwy Valley near YHA Rowen.

●● PWLL DERI ☆☆

**Castell Mawr, Trefasser, Goodwick,
Pembrokeshire SA64 0LR
Tel: 0870 770 6004 Fax: 0870 770 6004**

Perched in an idyllic clifftop setting, this hostel boasts spectacular views and glorious sunsets. Watch the seals and birds as you follow the coastal path that passes alongside the hostel or visit Llangloffan Farmhouse Cheese Centre and Melin Tregwynt Woollen Mill.
Location: OS 157, GR 891387.
Great for... a relaxed break by the sea.
You need to know... it's self-catering accommodation only.
Accommodation: 31 beds: 2x2-, 1x4-, 1x7- and 2x8-bed rooms.
Family rooms: No. **Rent-a-Hostel:** No.
Classroom: No. **Education packages:** No.
Facilities: Lounge/dining room, self-catering kitchen, shower, drying room, shop and cycle store. **Daytime access:** Restricted. ⊗

Stunning: sea views and striking sunsets typify the Welsh experience.

Meals: Self-catering only.
Reception open: 17.00hrs.
Getting there: Take Pwll Deri road out of Goodwick, keep following signs for Pwll Deri. From St David's–Fishguard road, approach via St Nicholas.
Parking: Nearby.
Nearest other hostels: Trefin 9 miles (by path), Trefdraeth 13 (22 by path), St David's 21, Poppit Sands 37 (by path).
Public transport: BUS: Richards 410 Fishguard–Goodwick (connections from Haverfordwest station), alight Goodwick, then 4 miles. Puffin Shuttle Bus operates between Fishguard and St David's (alight at Trefasser 0.5 miles from hostel) July–Sept.
RAIL: Fishguard Harbour 4.5 miles. FERRY: Fishguard 4.5 miles.

●● ROWEN ☆☆☆

**Rhiw Farm, Rowen, Conwy LL32 8YW
Tel: 0870 770 6012
Bookings more than 7 days ahead: 0870 770 6111**

This traditional Welsh hill farmhouse retains much of its rustic charm and original character. Situated at the top of a very steep, narrow lane, it offers breathtaking views over the Conwy Valley and across to Snowdonia. A friendly welcome awaits walkers with open fires in the lounge and dining room to warm you after a day on the hills.
Location: OS 115, GR 747721.
Great for... keen walkers wanting a rural haven.
You need to know... access to the hostel is up a very steep hill (1:3 gradient) on a narrow, rough road and shouldn't be attempted in cars in poor weather.
Accommodation: 24 beds: 1x2-, 1x4-, 1x8- and 1x10-bed rooms.
Family rooms: No. **Rent-a-Hostel:** Yes.
Classroom: No. **Education packages:** No.
Facilities: Lounge, dining room, self-catering kitchen, shower, small shop and cycle store. No credit cards accepted.
Daytime access: Restricted. ⊗
Meals: Self-catering only.

Wales

● FAMILY   ● CITY   ● GROUP   ● TRADITIONAL   ● CAMPING BARN   ● COASTAL   ● RURAL

Reception open: 17.00hrs.
Getting there: From B5106 follow signs for Rowen to post office. Continue along main street for 500 metres and turn right at hostel sign. Continue straight uphill. Hostel is 0.75 miles further on left. Access is unsuitable for some vehicles.
Parking: Yes.
Nearest other hostels: Conwy 5 miles, Bangor 12 (by mountain path), Capel Curig 12, Idwal Cottage 17 (by mountain path).
Public transport: BUS: Arriva Cymru 19 Llandudno–Llanrwst (passes close to Llandudno Junction and Betws-y-Coed stations), alight Rowen post office, then 1 mile up hill. RAIL: Tal-y-Cafn 3 miles. NATIONALEXPRESS Llandudno Junction 5.5 miles.

Start your ascent of Snowdon from the door: YHA Snowdon Ranger.

●● SNOWDON RANGER ☆☆☆
Rhyd Ddu, Caernarfon, Gwynedd LL54 7YS;
snowdon@yha.org.uk
Tel: 0870 770 6038 Fax: 0870 770 6039

This former inn nestles at the foot of Snowdon and offers lake swimming from its own beach. In an area steeped in Welsh culture, you won't be short of places to visit. The village of Beddgelert, Sygun Copper Mine, Caernarfon Castle and the Maritime Museum are all nearby. The Snowdon Ranger Path up Snowdon also begins here.
Location: OS 115, GR 565550.
Great for... exploring the mountains, lakes and valleys of Snowdonia National Park.
You need to know... the hostel is in a roadside location.
Accommodation: 65 beds: mostly 2- and 4-bed rooms.
Family rooms: No. **Rent-a-Hostel:** No.
Classroom: No. **Education packages:** No.
Facilities: Lounge, games room, dining room, self-catering kitchen, showers, drying room, cycle store, shop and grounds.
Daytime access: Restricted. ⊛
Meals: Breakfast, picnic lunch, evening meal.
Reception open: 17.00hrs.
Getting there: The hostel is on the A4085, 8 miles south of Caernarfon, 5 miles north of Beddgelert and 12 miles from A55 coastal expressway.

Parking: Yes.
Nearest other hostels: Bryn Gwynant 9 miles (7 by path), Llanberis 11 (4 by path), Pen-y-Pass 14 (10 by path), Bangor 17.
Public transport: BUS: Snowdon Sherpa 95 Caernarfon–Beddgelert (connections from Bangor station). RAIL: Porthmadog 13 miles, Bangor 16, narrow gauge Welsh Highland Railway station by hostel. FERRY: Holyhead to Dun Laoghaire 30 miles.

●● ST DAVID'S ☆
Llaethdy, Whitesands, St David's,
Pembrokeshire SA62 6PR
Tel: 0870 770 6042 Fax: 0870 770 6043

There's plenty of entertainment to be had around St David's, Britain's smallest city. It offers a cathedral, Bishop's Palace, Oceanarium and watersports centre plus Ramsey Island RSPB reserve across the bay. Whitesands Bay, one of the best beaches and seaside resorts in Wales, is also close by. After a hectic day, escape the hurly-burly of life in this Youth Hostel, which has simple accommodation in an old farmhouse and outbuildings set below Carn Llidi.
Location: OS 157, GR 739276.
Great for... busy days and quiet evenings.

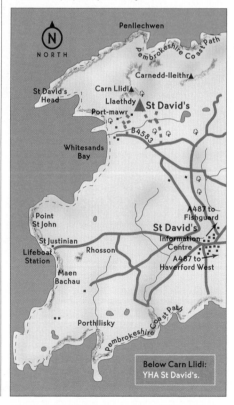

For current prices visit www.yha.org.uk

● FAMILY ● CITY ● GROUP ● TRADITIONAL ● CAMPING BARN ● COASTAL ● RURAL

You need to know... parking is along a rough track.
Accommodation: 40 beds: 1x8-, 1x12- and 1x16-bed rooms, plus 1x4-bed self-contained flat in separate building.
Family rooms: Yes. **Rent-a-Hostel:** No.
Classroom: No. **Education packages:** No.
Facilities: Lounge, self-catering kitchen/dining room, showers, drying room and shop. **Daytime access:** Restricted.
Meals: Self-catering only.
Reception open: 17.00hrs.
Getting there: Leave A487 Fishguard road just outside St David's on B4583 and follow signs to Whitesands Bay. The hostel is signed from golf club.
Parking: Yes.
Nearest other hostels: Penycwm 9 miles, Trefin 11 (by path), Pwll Deri 21 (by path).
Public transport: BUS: Richards 411 Haverfordwest–Fishguard (passes close to Fishguard Harbour station), alight St David's, then 2 miles. RAIL: Fishguard Harbour 15 miles, Haverfordwest 18. FERRY: Fishguard to Rosslare 15 miles, St David's–Whitesands (summer only).

Wild ponies still roam freely on the Welsh hills near YHA Trefdraeth.

www.britainonview.com

●● TREFDRAETH ☆☆☆

Lower St Mary Street, Newport, Pembrokeshire SA42 0TS; reservations@yha.org.uk
Tel: 0870 770 6072 Fax: 0870 770 6072
Bookings more than 7 days ahead: 0870 770 6113

Families will find themselves busy here. A short walk from the shops, pubs, beach, coastal path and bird sanctuary of Newport, the hostel also offers easy access to the Preseli Hills where wild ponies still roam freely. Those interested in the past will enjoy exploring Iron Age forts, hut circles and burial chambers, as well as Castell Henllys. Fishing and pony trekking are also nearby.
Location: OS 145, GR 058393.
Great for... a family holiday packed with activities.
You need to know... parking is limited at this self-catering hostel,

and there's no day access.
Accommodation: 28 beds: 2x2-, 3x4- and 2x6-bed rooms.
Family rooms: Yes. **Rent-a-Hostel:** Yes.
Classroom: No. **Education packages:** No.
Facilities: Lounge, self-catering kitchen/dining room, showers and cycle store. No hostel shop. **Daytime access:** Restricted. ☺
Meals: Self-catering only.
Reception open: 17.00hrs.
Getting there: From Fishguard take A487 to Cardigan road. At Newport turn left down St Mary's Street just before Golden Lion pub. From Aberystwyth take A487 to Cardigan road and continue to Newport. Follow signs to hostel after Golden Lion pub. Hostel is behind the Eco Centre.
Parking: Limited.
Nearest other hostels: Poppit Sands 11 miles (by coastal path), Pwll Deri 13 (22 by coastal path), Trefin 15.
Public transport: BUS: Richards 412 Haverfordwest station–Cardigan. RAIL: Fishguard Harbour 9 miles, Clarbeston Road 14. FERRY: Fishguard to Rosslare 9 miles (by two buses).

● TREFIN ☆☆☆

Ffordd-yr-Afon, Trefin, Haverfordwest, Pembrokeshire SA62 5AU;
reservations@yha.org.uk
Tel: 0870 770 6074 Fax: 0870 770 6074
Bookings more than 7 days ahead: 0870 770 6113

In the centre of a small, friendly village, this hostel used to be a school and still retains a children's playground. Now refurbished, it's a good base for exploring Pembrokeshire Coast National Park. The sea is only 0.5 miles away, as is the coastal path. The fishing village of Abereiddy, famous for its Blue Lagoon and black-sand beaches, is two miles away, or head to St David's for safe swimming and sandcastles galore.
Location: OS 157, GR 840324.
Great for... a family holiday.
You need to know... it's self-catering accommodation only, although the hostel is close to a pub.
Accommodation: 26 beds: 5x4- and 1x6-bed rooms.
Family rooms: No. **Rent-a-Hostel:** Yes.
Classroom: No. **Education packages:** No.
Facilities: Lounge/dining room/self-catering kitchen, showers, cycle store, drying room and toilets. Picnic and BBQ area.
Daytime access: Restricted. ☺
Meals: Self-catering only.
Reception open: 17.00hrs.
Getting there: From A487 take turning to Trefin. Hostel is in the village centre, near the pub.
Parking: Yes.
Nearest other hostels: Penycwm 8 miles, Pwll Deri 9, St David's 11, Trefdraeth 15.
Public transport: BUS: Richards 411 Haverfordwest–Fishguard (passes close to Fishguard Harbour station).
RAIL: Fishguard Harbour 12 miles, Haverfordwest 18.
FERRY: Fishguard to Rosslare 12 miles (tel: 01233 647047).

To make a booking visit www.yha.org.uk

● FAMILY   ● CITY   ● GROUP   ● TRADITIONAL   ● CAMPING BARN   ● COASTAL   ● RURAL

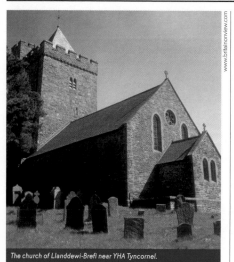

The church of Llanddewi-Brefi near YHA Tyncornel.

●● TYNCORNEL BUNKHOUSE ☆

**Llanddewi-Brefi, Tregaron, Ceredigion
SY25 6PH; reservations@yha.org.uk
Tel: 0870 770 6080 Fax: 0870 770 6081**

This isolated farmhouse is a favourite with folk in search of solitude. Walkers can explore the mountain terrain of the Elenith while the Cors Caron Nature Reserve will thrill wildlife lovers. Wherever you wander, keep your eyes trained upwards to spot red kites. The hostel's facilities complement the next-to-nature setting, with no electricity or phone, and gas-powered shower, lights and cooking.
Location: OS 147, GR 751534.
Great for... a retreat well away from it all.
You need to know... it's self-catering only, no phone or electricity.
Accommodation: 16 beds: 2x8-bed rooms.
Family rooms: No. **Rent-a-Hostel:** No.
Classroom: No. **Education packages:** No.
Facilities: Self-catering kitchen/common room and shower. No credit cards accepted or hostel shop.
Daytime access: Restricted. ⊗
Meals: Self-catering only.
Reception open: 17.00hrs.
Getting there: From Llanddewi–Brefi follow road southeast up Brefi Valley signed to hostel (not southwest to Farmers). Fork left at 4.75 miles. At signpost at 6 miles continue on rough track to hostel (1 mile).
Parking: Yes.
Nearest other hostels: Blaencaron 14 miles (8 by mountains), Dolgoch 19 (5 by mountains).
Public transport: BUS: Arriva Cymru 516, James 589 Aberystwyth station–Tregaron, some calling, some with connections on James 588 to Llanddewi–Brefi, 7 miles or alight Tregaron on others, then 10 miles. RAIL: Aberystwyth 28 miles.

●● YSTRADFELLTE ☆☆

**Tai'r Heol, Ystradfellte, Aberdare, CF44 9JF
Tel: 0870 770 6106 Fax: 0870 770 6106**

These two charming cottages a mile south of the village make a good base for exploring the network of footpaths in the west of the National Park – don't miss the trail that leads to the spectacular waterfalls and natural swimming pool at Porth-yr-Ogof. The National Showcave Centre at Dan-yr-Ogof is also close by.
Location: OS 160, GR 925127.
Great for... keen walkers.
You need to know... it's self-catering accommodation only; there's no hostel shop and credit cards are not accepted.
Accommodation: 28 beds: 1x2-, 3x4-, 1x6- and 1x8-bed rooms.
Family rooms: No. **Rent-a-Hostel:** No.
Classroom: No. **Education packages:** No.
Facilities: Self-catering kitchen/dining room, lounge, showers and drying room. **Daytime access:** Restricted. ⊗
Meals: Self-catering only.
Reception open: 17.00hrs.
Getting there: From M4, exit J43 and take A465 north towards Glynneath. Exit onto A4109 signposted Onllwyn. At traffic lights turn right, take second minor road on left to Pontneddfechan. Continue and hostel is on left.
Parking: Yes.
Nearest other hostels: Llwyn-y-Celyn 12 miles, Brecon 21, Llanddeusant 23.
Public transport: BUS: From Aberdare, alight Penderyn 3.5 miles, First Cymru X5, 160/1 Swansea–Glynneath (pass close to Neath station) then 5 miles. RAIL: Aberdare 10 miles.

Even the youngest family member will enjoy walking in Wales.

For all the latest YHA news visit www.yha.org.uk

The Youth Hostels of…

Heart of England
& The Wye Valley

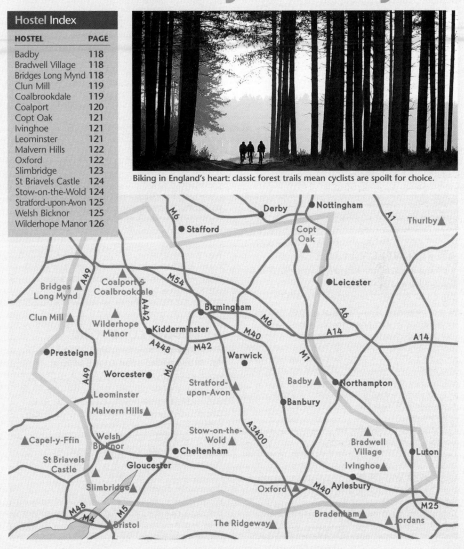

Biking in England's heart: classic forest trails mean cyclists are spoilt for choice.

For further information visit www.yha.org.uk

Heart of England & The Wye Valley

● FAMILY ● CITY ● GROUP ● TRADITIONAL ● CAMPING BARN ● COASTAL ● RURAL

●● BADBY ☆

Church Green, Badby, Daventry,
Northamptonshire NN11 3AS;
badby@yha.org.uk
Tel: 0870 770 5680 Fax: 0870 770 5680

Step into yesteryear and stay in the only thatched Youth Hostel in England and Wales. This cosy 17th century cottage is on the church green in the unspoilt village of Badby and has a large garden and orchard. But don't stand for too long – a sweeping landscape surrounds the hostel where a network of quiet lanes and footpaths will take eager walkers and cyclists to ancient churches and country houses.
Location: OS 152, GR 561588.
Great for... walkers seeking an idyllic break.
You need to know... parking is very limited.
Accommodation: 30 beds: 1x2-, 2x6- and 2x8-bed rooms.
Family rooms: No. **Rent-a-Hostel:** Yes.
Classroom: No. **Education packages:** No.
Facilities: Lounge, self-catering kitchen, dining room, cycle store, shop and garden.
Daytime access: Restricted via numbered keypad. ☺
Meals: Self-catering only.
Reception open: 17.00hrs.
Getting there: Turn off A361, main Daventry–Banbury road, at brown Youth Hostel sign. Follow main street into village. Just past Windmill pub, turn left onto Vicarage Hill until you reach church green. At T-junction turn left down hill and hostel is on left.

Parking: There is no parking available directly outside hostel.
Nearest other hostels: Bradwell 21 miles, Stratford 24.
Public transport: BUS: 41 from Northampton (passes Northampton station), alight Daventry 3 miles, Geoff Amos from Rugby Station, alight Badby 0.25 miles. RAIL: Long Buckby 6 miles, Rugby 12.
NATIONAL EXPRESS》 Daventry bus station 3 miles.

You can't help but relax in these tranquil surroundings: YHA Badby.

●● BRADWELL VILLAGE ☆

Vicarage Road, Milton Keynes, Bucks MK13 9AG;
bradwellvillage@yha.org.uk
Tel: 0870 770 5716 Fax: 0870 770 5717

An attractive 18th century stone farmhouse, this Youth Hostel is within easy reach of Milton Keynes. The city boasts attractions including the UK's biggest indoor 'real' snow slope and a renowned contemporary gallery and theatre. It also has a multitude of parkland and lakes accessible by 200 miles of cycle routes. The home of the Enigma machine and Woburn Abbey and its safari park are nearby.
Location: OS 152, GR 831395.
Great for... year-round winter sports, cyclists of all abilities.
Accommodation: 37 beds: 1x1-, 3x4-, 1x5-, 1x9- and 1x10-bed rooms.
Family rooms: No. **Rent-a-Hostel:** Yes.
Classroom: No. **Education packages:** No.
Facilities: Lounge, dining room, self-catering kitchen, showers, drying room, cycle store and grounds.
Daytime access: Restricted. ☺
Meals: Breakfast only. Full catering for pre-booked parties of 10+.
Reception open: 17.00hrs.
Getting there: From A5 take A422 and turn right into Bradwell. From M1 J14 take A509 to central Milton Keynes. Take V6 (Grafton Street) right, follow signs to Bradwell. Hostel is next to the church.

Parking: At rear of hostel.
Nearest other hostels: Ivinghoe 19 miles, Badby 21, Oxford 38.
Public transport: BUS: Frequent from surrounding areas.
RAIL: Milton Keynes Central 0.75 miles.
NATIONAL EXPRESS》 Milton Keynes coachway 5 miles.

●● BRIDGES LONG MYND ☆

Ratlinghope, Shrewsbury, Shropshire SY5 0SP;
Tel: 01588 650656 Fax: 01588 650531

You'll find this small hostel that was once the old village school hidden away in the Shropshire hills. Walkers will love it here, with the Shropshire Way passing close by and paths leading you to Long Mynd and Stiperstones. Remember to bring your binoculars as there's plenty of birdlife worth watching.
Location: OS 137, GR 395965.
Great for... keen walkers looking for uncrowded paths.
Accommodation: 37 beds: 1x5-, 1x8-, 1x10- and 1x14-bed rooms.
Family rooms: No. **Rent-a-Hostel:** No.
Classroom: No. **Education packages:** No.
Facilities: Lounge, self-catering kitchen, dining room, showers, drying room, cycle store and camping. No credit cards accepted (make cheques payable to Bridges Youth Hostel).
Daytime access: Restricted. ☺

For further information visit www.yha.org.uk

FAMILY ● CITY ● GROUP ● TRADITIONAL ● CAMPING BARNS ● COASTAL ● RURAL

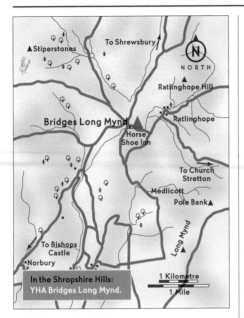

In the Shropshire Hills:
YHA Bridges Long Mynd.

Meals: Self-catering only.
Reception open: Staff available before 10.00hrs and after 17.00hrs.
Getting there: From Clun High Street (B4368) go to the end of Ford Street, turn right and then left. The hostel is 250 metres on the right, past the Memorial Hall.
Parking: Yes.
Nearest other hostels: Bridges 16 miles, Wilderhope 20, Leominster 24.
Public transport: BUS: Whittlebus 743/5 from Ludlow and Craven Arms (pass close to Ludlow and Craven Arms stations), alight Clun 0.25 miles.
RAIL: Broome 7 miles, Hopton 7, Craven Arms 10.

● COALBROOKDALE ☆☆
c/o High Street, Coalport, Telford, Shropshire TF8 7HT; ironbridge@yha.org.uk
Tel: 0870 770 5882 Fax: 0870 770 5883

Ironbridge was once the centre of British industry. This hostel at the 19th century Literary and Scientific Institute provides comfortable accommodation within walking distance of the first iron bridge in the world (constructed in 1777 to advertise iron-based technology) and the museum of iron. History buffs will be happy to indulge their

Meals: Breakfast, picnic lunch, evening meal.
Reception open: 17.00hrs.
Getting there: From Church Stretton, take The Burway and fork right at top of Long Mynd (impassable in winter). From Shrewsbury, take road via Longden and Pulverbatch, then left by Horseshoe Inn.
Parking: Yes.
Nearest other hostels: Wilderhope 13 miles, Clun Mill 16.
Public transport: BUS: Boulton's 551 from Shrewsbury (Tues only). RAIL: Church Stretton 5 miles.

●● CLUN MILL ☆
The Mill, Clun, Craven Arms, Shropshire SY7 8NY
Tel: 0870 770 5766 Fax: 0870 770 5766
Bookings more than 7 days ahead: 0870 770 5916

This restored watermill was once a focal point in the tiny town of Clun and you'll see much of the old machinery still in situ. It now offers accommodation to walkers and cyclists wanting to explore the environmentally sensitive area of the Clun Valley. There's a generous helping of history too, with hill forts and castles nearby.
Location: OS 137, GR 303812.
Great for... a walking break in rolling countryside.
You need to know... it's self-catering accommodation only.
Accommodation: 24 en-suite beds: 1x5-, 1x8- and 1x11-bed rooms.
Family rooms: No. **Rent-a-Hostel:** Yes.
Classroom: No. **Education packages:** No.
Facilities: Lounge/dining room, self-catering kitchen, showers, lockable cycle store, grounds and camping.
Daytime access: All areas.

HOSTEL MANAGERS CHOOSE...
THE BEST DAYS OUT FOR WATER LOVERS

The Upton on Severn cruise YHA Malvern Hills: "You get to see Tewkesbury, the abbey and have a picnic by the river. It's a three-hour round trip for under £10."
The Grand Union Canal YHA Ivinghoe: "There are many canal cruises that take you into the Chiltern hills. All ages will enjoy this"; YHA Bradwell: "The Canal Museum at Stoke Bruerne has a lovely waterside village with historic displays, working models and narrow boat cruises on the canal."
Nene Whitewater Centre YHA Badby: "It's got a man-made canoe slalom and whitewater rafting course."
River Avon YHA Stratford-upon-Avon: "Avon Boating runs half-hour cruises in vintage passenger boats along the River Avon. Hire rowing boats, canoes and punts too."
Cotswold Water Park YHA Stow-on-the-Wold: "Britain's largest water park, with outdoor activities, watersports and a bathing beach."
River Wye YHA St Briavels Castle: "Hire kayaks and canoes to explore the River Wye at Symonds Yat."

For current prices visit www.yha.org.uk

● FAMILY   ● CITY   ● GROUP   ● TRADITIONAL   ● CAMPING BARN   ● COASTAL   ● RURAL

Step back in time: YHA Coalbrookdale and Coalport.

china works in Europe) is set in the heart of the Ironbridge World Heritage site on the thickly wooded banks of the River Severn. History buffs will be happy to indulge their inquisitive brains in no less than 10 industrial heritage museums.
Location: OS 127, GR 671043.
Great for... visiting museums and the Shropshire hills.
You need to know... this is one of two Youth Hostels in Ironbridge.
Accommodation: 85 beds: 1x1-, 4x2-, 2x3-, 8x4-, 1x5-, 1x6-, 2x8- and 1x11-bed rooms, some en-suite.
Family rooms: Yes. **Rent-a-Hostel:** No.
Classroom: Yes. **Education packages:** Yes.
Facilities: Lounge, games rooms, cafeteria (10.00hrs–16.00hrs except in winter) and drying room. **Daytime access:** All areas. ☯
Meals: Breakfast, picnic lunch, evening meal. Buffets available if booked in advance.

inquisitive brains in no less than 10 industrial heritage museums.
Location: OS 127, GR 671043.
Great for... those interested in Britain's past, also for exploring the Shropshire hills.
You need to know... this is one of two Youth Hostels in Ironbridge (Coalport is the other); this hostel is available for pre-booked guests only.
Accommodation: 80 beds: 1x2-, 10x4-, 5x6- and 1x8-bed rooms.
Family rooms: No. **Rent-a-Hostel:** No.
Classroom: Yes. **Education packages:** Yes.
Facilities: Lounge, TV, games room, drying room, toilets, showers.
Daytime access: Restricted. ☯
Meals: Breakfast, picnic lunch, evening meal.
Reception open: 17.00hrs.
Getting there: From Telford centre, follow signs to Ironbridge. With the bridge on the left, turn right at the roundabout into Coalbrookdale. The hostel is 0.5 miles on the right.
Parking: Yes, limited.
Nearest other hostels: Coalport 3 miles, Wilderhope Manor 14.
Public transport: BUS: Telford Link Wellington–Telford (passes close to Wellington Telford West and Telford Central stations). RAIL: Telford Central 5 miles, Wellington Telford West 5.
NATIONALEXPRESS Town Centre, Telford.

● COALPORT ☆☆☆

John Rose Building, High Street, Coalport, Shropshire TF8 7HT; ironbridge@yha.org.uk Tel: 0870 770 5882 Fax 0870 770 5883

Ironbridge was once the centre of British industry. Stay here and you'll be in the thick of its history, as the hostel (once the oldest

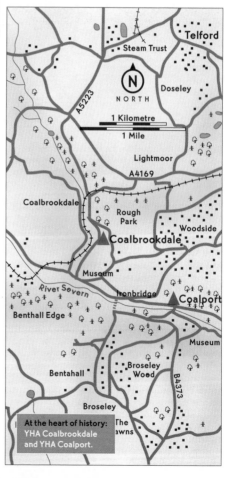

At the heart of history: YHA Coalbrookdale and YHA Coalport.

● FAMILY ● CITY ● GROUP ● TRADITIONAL ● CAMPING BARN ● COASTAL ● RURAL

Reception open: All day.
Getting there: From Telford, take A442 towards Kidderminster, then follow Ironbridge Museum signs past Blists Hill. Hostel is 1 mile on right at China Museum.
Parking: Museum car park.
Nearest other hostels: Coalbrookdale 3 miles, Wilderhope Manor 14.
Public transport: BUS: Coalport bus stop outside hostel. To Telford, change at Madeley (1.5 miles from hostel). RAIL: Telford 5 miles.

●● COPT OAK ☆

Whitwick Rd, Copt Oak, Markfield, Leicestershire LE67 9QB; reservations@yha.org.uk
Tel: 0870 770 5776 Fax: 0870 770 5776
Bookings more than 7 days ahead: 0870 770 6113

A converted school house in the Leicestershire hills, Copt Oak has basic accommodation and is an ideal base for visiting the National Forest. Charnwood Forest offers good walking and cycling countryside while Donington Race Circuit and the National Watersports Centre at Holme Pierrepont are also nearby.
Location: OS 129, GR 482129.
Great for... cycling and walking.
You need to know... this hostel may close during 2003. Please enquire before planning your stay.
Accommodation: 16 beds: 1x6- and 1x10-bed rooms.
Family rooms: No. **Rent-a-Hostel:** Yes.
Classroom: No. **Education packages:** No.
Facilities: Lounge/self-catering kitchen, showers, cycle store, lockers and shop. **Daytime access:** Restricted. ⊗
Meals: Self-catering only.
Reception open: 17.00hrs.
Getting there: Leave M1 at J22 and take A50 towards Leicester. Take first left (250 metres) and follow signs for Copt Oak. Hostel is on the right, 50 metres past the Copt Oak pub before traffic lights.
Parking: Yes.
Nearest other hostels: Matlock 35 miles, Badby 42, Stratford 45.
Public transport: BUS: Arriva Fox/Barton/Kinchbus 121 Leicester–Loughborough, otherwise Arriva Fox 117/9, 217/8 Leicester–Coalville (pass close to Leicester station), alight Flying Horse roundabout, 1 mile. RAIL: Loughborough 10 miles.
NATIONALEXPRESS» Coalville, Memorial Square 4.5 miles.

●● IVINGHOE ☆

High Street, Ivinghoe, Leighton Buzzard, Bedfordshire LU7 9EP; ivinghoe@yha.org.uk
Tel: 0870 770 5884 Fax: 0870 770 5885

The former home of a brewer, this Georgian mansion stands in the picturesque Bedfordshire village of Ivinghoe. It is an ideal base for walkers with the Ridgeway and Chilterns both nearby. Whipsnade Zoo is also in the area.
Location: OS 165, GR 945161.
Great for... walking, cycling and visiting London.

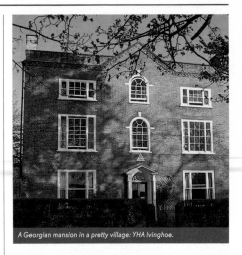
A Georgian mansion in a pretty village: YHA Ivinghoe.

Accommodation: 50 beds: 2x5-, 2x6-, 1x8- and 2x10-bed rooms.
Family rooms: No. **Rent-a-Hostel:** No.
Classroom: No. **Education packages:** Yes.
Facilities: Lounge, TV, self-catering kitchen, showers, drying room and cycle store. **Daytime access:** Restricted.
Meals: Breakfast, picnic lunch, evening meal.
Reception open: 17.00hrs.
Getting there: The hostel is in the village centre, next to the church and opposite the village green on the B489.
Parking: Yes.
Nearest other hostels: Jordans 19 miles, Bradwell Village 19, Windsor 28.
Public transport: BUS: Arriva The Shires 61 Aylesbury–Luton (passes close to Aylesbury and Luton stations).
RAIL: Cheddington 2.5 miles. AIRPORT: Luton 15 miles.
NATIONALEXPRESS» Tring 4 miles.

● LEOMINSTER ☆☆☆☆

The Old Priory, Leominster, Herefordshire HR6 8EQ
Tel: 0870 770 5916 Fax: 0870 770 5916

This new hostel is in a section of the Old Priory monastic complex, part of the Benedictine monastery that dates back to 1123. It was enlarged to form a workhouse in 1836 and now offers small, comfortable rooms from where you can wander the town's narrow streets and wonder at its medieval, Tudor and Georgian houses. The Lindlow and Kington Mortimer trails are close by.
Location: OS 149, GR 499593.
Great for... families in search of history.
You need to know... the hostel has self-catering facilities only.
Accommodation: 30 beds: 4x2-, 2x3- and 4x4-bed rooms.
Family rooms: Yes. **Rent-a-Hostel:** Yes.
Classroom: No. **Education packages:** No.
Facilities: Lounge, kitchen, toilets, showers, laundry and drying

● FAMILY   ● CITY   ● GROUP   ● TRADITIONAL   ● CAMPING BARN   ● COASTAL   ● RURAL

Tudor houses in the historic town of Leominster.

room. Facilities for people with disabilities.
Daytime access: Restricted.   ✍
Meals: Self-catering only.
Reception open: 17.00 hrs.
Getting there: From all directions, enter town centre one-way system. At end of Burgess St, go straight across junction into Church St and follow road round left side of the church to end. From rail station, pedestrian access via Pinsley Road, park and churchyard.
Parking: Yes.
Nearest other hostels: Clun Mill 32 miles, Malvern Hills 24, Wilderhope Manor 25.
Public transport: BUS: Frequent. RAIL: Leominster 0.25 miles.

● MALVERN HILLS ☆☆

18 Peachfield Road, Malvern Wells,
Worcestershire WR14 4AP; malvern@yha.org.uk
Tel: 0870 770 5948 Fax: 0870 770 5949

In Victorian times, wealthy socialites would visit the spa town of Great Malvern to take the water cure. Book a break here today and you'll still get a healthy holiday. This hostel, a fine Edwardian house, is adjacent to the Malvern commons, from where the Malvern Hills

YHA Malvern Hills: a fine Edwardian house near the Malvern commons.

●● OXFORD ☆☆☆☆

2a Botley Road, Oxford, Oxfordshire OX2 0AB;
oxford@yha.org.uk
Tel: 0870 770 5970 Fax: 0870 770 5971

This new, purpose-built Youth Hostel is located next to the railway station, close to the River Thames and only a few minutes' stroll from the historic city centre. It's the perfect base for exploring the multitude of attractions in the city or touring the Cotswolds, Ridgeway and the Chilterns. And staying here is all too easy – internet access is available and breakfast is included in the overnight price.
Location: OS 164, GR 486063.
Great for... a base to explore the Oxford area.
You need to know... there's no parking but park and ride nearby.
Accommodation: 184 beds: 8x2- (2 with wheelchair access), 12x4- and 20x6-bed rooms.
Family rooms: Yes. **Rent-a-Hostel:** No.
Classroom: Yes. **Education packages:** Yes.
Facilities: Common room, lounge, TV room, café with table licence, wheelchair access, gardens, internet access, games room, laundry facilities, luggage store, payphone, smoking room.
Daytime access: All areas.
Meals: Breakfast, evening meal.
Reception open: 24hrs (night security).

Getting there: From the station turn right and go under bridge. Hostel is on the right immediately behind the railway station (see map on page 175).
Parking: None except for disabled badge holders.
Nearest other hostels: Ridgeway 17 miles, Streatley 19.
Public transport: BUS: Frequent from surrounding areas.
RAIL: Oxford Station adjacent to hostel.
NATIONAL EXPRESS ≫ Gloucester Green 0.25 miles.

Make the most of the varied facilities at YHA Oxford.

For offers and discounts visit www.yha.org.uk

FAMILY   CITY   GROUP   TRADITIONAL   CAMPING BARN   COASTAL   RURAL

HOSTEL MANAGERS CHOOSE...

THE TOP 10 ATTRACTIONS IN...
OXFORD

1. THE ASHMOLEAN MUSEUM
"The first museum to open to the public in England. See treasures from a human skull from 6000BC to 20th century works of art. Don't miss Guy Fawkes's lantern."

2. PITT RIVERS MUSEUM
"Children will love the shrunken heads and witch in a bottle at this ethnological museum."

3. BODLEAN LIBRARY
"One of the world's great libraries, it houses more than 6 million books. Impressive architecture too."

4. CURIOXITY
"All the family will enjoy this hands-on science exhibition, designed with children in mind."

5. OXFORD UNIVERSITY
"Many of the university's 39 colleges are open to the public, so take advantage."

6. THE UNIVERSITY MUSEUM OF NATURAL HISTORY
"See dinosaur skeletons and stuffed animals. People always remember seeing the remains of a dodo."

7. BOOKSHOPS
"The city of Oxford is paradise for book lovers. There are many second-hand bookshops and the Norrington Room in Blackwells' main store has more books for sale in one room than anywhere else in the world."

8. HARRY POTTER
"If you loved the films, see where some scenes were set. The Great Hall at Christ Church College doubled as Hogwarts Hall and the Duke Humfrey's Library in the Bodlean was Hogwarts Library."

9. THE OXFORD STORY
"A witty insight into the city's past with all the sights, sounds (and smells!) of old Oxford."

10. BOTANIC GARDENS
"The oldest in England. There are over 8,000 plant species. Don't miss the new bog garden or the tropical plants in the riverside glasshouses."

(Recommended by YHA Oxford)

Area of Outstanding Natural Beauty stretches in a 10-mile ridge with views to 15 counties from the top. And of course, there are still opportunities to sample the famous spring water.

Location: OS 150, GR 774440.

Great for... walkers wanting a relaxed break.

Accommodation: 58 beds: 2x2- and 5x4–6-bed rooms, plus 3 larger rooms.

Family rooms: No. **Rent-a-Hostel:** No.

Classroom: No. **Education packages:** No.

Facilities: Lounge, TV, dining room, self-catering kitchen, games room, showers, drying room, cycle store, shop and garden.

Daytime access: Restricted. 🚭

Meals: Breakfast, picnic lunch, evening meal.

Reception open: 17.00hrs.

Getting there: The hostel is 1.5 miles south of Great Malvern on the Wells Road (A449). Turn opposite the Railway Inn into Peachfield Road and the hostel is 400 metres on the right.

Parking: Yes.

Nearest other hostels: Leominster 24 miles, Welsh Bicknor 28, Stow-on-the-Wold 33, Slimbridge 35.

Public transport: BUS: Frequent from surrounding areas.
RAIL: Great Malvern 1 mile.

NATIONAL EXPRESS Rosebank Gdns, Great Malvern, 1.25 miles.

●● SLIMBRIDGE ☆☆☆
Shepherd's Patch, Slimbridge, Gloucestershire GL2 7BP; slimbridge@yha.org.uk
Tel: 0870 770 6036 Fax: 0870 770 6037

Birdwatchers will be in their element here, as a wide variety of wildfowl flocks to this area. The world famous WWT Wildfowl and Wetlands Centre is nearby and the hostel has an observation lounge so you can keep an eye on feathered visitors to the duck pond. Walkers will find plenty to do too, with long-distance footpath The Severn Way running past the hostel and the Cotswold Way four miles away. The National Water Museum and Berkeley Castle are also nearby.

Location: OS 162, GR 730043.

Great for... outdoor folk with an interest in wildfowl.

Accommodation: 56 beds: 5x2-, 4x4–8-, 1x8- and 1x10-bed rooms.

Family rooms: Yes. **Rent-a-Hostel:** No.

Classroom: Yes. **Education packages:** Yes.

Facilities: Lounge, games room, self-catering kitchen, showers, drying room, cycle store, shop and laundry facilities.

Daytime access: Restricted.

Meals: Breakfast, picnic lunch, evening meal.

Reception open: 17.00hrs.

Getting there: From M5 going south, exit at J13. Going north, exit

Heart of England & The Wye Valley

● FAMILY ● CITY ● GROUP ● TRADITIONAL ● CAMPING BARN ● COASTAL ● RURAL

J14. Follow signs to WWT Wetlands Centre from motorway and on A38. At Slimbridge roundabout on A38, follow signs to hostel. Continue through village of Slimbridge to Tudor Arms. The hostel is 250 metres down the lane to the right.
Parking: Yes.
Nearest other hostels: Bristol 25 miles, Bath 30, St Briavels Castle 30, Malvern Hills 35.
Public transport: BUS: Stagecoach in the Cotswolds 20 Stroud–Dursley, Stagecoach in Gloucester 91 Gloucester–Dursley (passes close to Gloucester station). On both, alight Slimbridge roundabout 1.5 miles. RAIL: Cam and Dursley 3 miles, Stonehouse 8.5.

A listed 16th century townhouse: YHA Stow-on-the-Wold.

●● STOW-ON-THE-WOLD ☆☆☆☆
The Square, Stow-on-the-Wold GL54 1AF;
stow@yha.org.uk
Tel: 0870 770 6050 Fax: 0870 770 6051

Stay in a listed 16th century townhouse in the market square of the Cotswold stone-built market town of Stow-on-the-Wold. Thanks to a

Stay in a moated Norman castle: YHA St Briavels Castle.

●● ST BRIAVELS CASTLE ☆☆☆☆
St Briavels, Lydney, Gloucestershire
GL15 6RG; stbriavels@yha.org.uk
Tel: 0870 770 6040 Fax: 0870 770 6041

You'll have no trouble thinking what to write on your postcards if you stay in this Youth Hostel, housed in a moated Norman castle. Originally built as a hunting lodge for King John in 1205 on the site of an earlier stronghold, its towers were added in 1293 as part of the Ring of Stone around Wales. It's a unique experience, especially when you enter into the ancient spirit with medieval banquets on Wednesdays and Saturdays in August.
Location: OS 162, GR 558045.
Great for... a unique experience for wannabe Norman knights.
You need to know... the building has no disabled access.
Accommodation: 70 beds: 1x4-, 3x6- and 2x8-bed rooms, plus 3 larger rooms.
Family rooms: No. **Rent-a-Hostel:** No.
Classroom: Yes. **Education packages:** Yes.
Facilities: Lounges, self-catering kitchen, dining room, showers, drying room, cycle store, shop and grounds. Medieval banquets on Wednesday and Saturday nights in August.
Daytime access: Restricted. ⊗
Meals: Breakfast, picnic lunch, evening meal.
Reception open: 17.00hrs.
Getting there: From Chepstow take A466 towards Monmouth. After 6 miles, when the road crosses the River Wye, immediately take the right turn signposted St Briavels. After 0.5 miles, turn right again and follow St Briavels signs up the hill. The castle is right in front of you at the top of the hill. From Monmouth turn left before the bridge.
Parking: Yes.
Nearest other hostels: Welsh Bicknor 12 miles, Slimbridge 30.
Public transport: BUS: Stagecoach 69 from Chepstow, alight Bigsweir Bridge, 2 miles. RAIL: Lydney 7 miles.

For current prices visit www.yha.org.uk

● FAMILY ● CITY ● GROUP ● TRADITIONAL ● CAMPING BARN ● COASTAL ● RURAL

●● STRATFORD-UPON-AVON ☆☆☆

Hemmingford House, Alveston, Stratford-upon-Avon, Warwickshire, CV37 7RG;
stratford@yha.org.uk
Tel: 0870 770 6052 Fax: 0870 770 6053

This splendidly refurbished Georgian mansion house is set in over three acres of grounds in a quiet village, just under two miles from Stratford-upon-Avon. It's a convenient place to stay if you're seeking a cultural weekend, visiting Shakespeare's birthplace and catching performances by the world renowned Royal Shakespeare Company at one of the town's three theatres. Warwick and Kenilworth Castles are also nearby.

Location: OS 151, GR 231562.
Great for... those who know Othello from Macbeth.
Accommodation: 132 beds: 11x2-, 2x3-, 5x4-, 7x6-, 2x7-, 1x8- and 2x10-bed rooms, some en-suite.
Family rooms: Yes. **Rent-a-Hostel:** No.
Classroom: Yes. **Education packages:** Yes.
Facilities: TV lounge, games room, self-catering kitchen, showers, cycle store, laundry facilities, internet access, extensive grounds and foreign exchange. **Daytime access:** All areas.
Meals: Breakfast, picnic lunch, evening meal.
Reception open: 24hrs.
Getting there: From Stratford-upon-Avon, at Clopton Bridge take B4086 Wellesbourne Road. Follow hostel signs and hostel is 1.5 miles on left. From M40, exit J15 and take A429 south, follow signs to Charlecote Park. Then turn right onto the B4086 and hostel is 1.5 miles on right (see map on page 175).

Parking: Large car park.
Nearest other hostels: Stow-on-the-Wold 20 miles, Badby 24.
Public transport: BUS: Stagecoach Red X18 or 77 Leamington Spa–Stratford–Coventry (passes close to Leamington Spa station). RAIL: Stratford-upon-Avon 2.5 miles.
NATIONALEXPRESS» Riverside Bus Station 1.5 miles.

Set in three acres of grounds: YHA Stratford-upon-Avon.

Heritage Lottery grant, the hostel has been comfortably refurbished, with sympathetic restoration of the 17th century staircase. Despite the house's auspicious history, children are welcome here and you'll find swings, a climbing frame and picnic tables in the garden.
Location: OS 163, GR 191258.
Great for... a family break in picturesque surroundings.
You need to know... parking in the square is restricted between 9.00hrs and 17.00hrs.
Accommodation: 48 beds: 2x4-, 4x6- and 2x8-bed rooms, most en-suite.
Family rooms: Yes. **Rent-a-Hostel:** No.
Classroom: No. **Education packages:** Yes.
Facilities: Lounge, self-catering kitchen, TV, dining room, laundry facilities and cycle store. **Daytime access:** Restricted. ⊗
Meals: Breakfast, picnic lunch, evening meal.
Reception open: 17.00hrs.
Getting there: The hostel sits between the White Hart and the Old Stocks Hotel in Market Square.
Parking: Car park at rear of hostel.
Nearest other hostels: Stratford-upon-Avon 20 miles, Oxford 30.
Public transport: BUS: Pulhams P1 Cheltenham Spa–Moreton-in-Marsh, Stagecoach in the Cotswolds 55 Moreton-in-Marsh–Cirencester. Both pass close to Moreton-in-Marsh station. RAIL: Moreton-in-Marsh 4 miles, Kingham 4.

●● WELSH BICKNOR ☆☆☆

near Goodrich, Ross-on-Wye, Herefordshire HR9 6JJ; welshbicknor@yha.org.uk
Tel: 0870 770 6086 Fax: 0870 770 6087

Outdoor folk will be spoiled for choice at this former Victorian rectory, set in 25 acres of relaxing riverside grounds with splendid views of the Royal Forest of Dean and Symonds Yat rock. Hire a canoe and take in the picturesque valley from the River Wye or choose pedal power to explore the Forest of Dean. Walkers will find miles of footpaths to follow – we recommend you start with the Wye Valley Walk which runs past the hostel.
Location: OS 162, GR 591177.
Great for... outdoor folk and families with plenty of energy.
Accommodation: 76 beds: 1x2-, 6x4-, 4x6-, 2x8- and 1x10-bed rooms.
Family rooms: Yes. **Rent-a-Hostel:** No.
Classroom: Yes. **Education packages:** No.
Facilities: Lounges, TV, games room, dining room, self-catering kitchen, showers, drying room, cycle store, laundry facilities, grounds, canoe landing stage and camping.
Daytime access: All areas.
Meals: Breakfast, picnic lunch, evening meal.
Reception open: Staff available before 10.00hrs and after 17.00hrs.

To make a booking visit www.yha.org.uk

125

● FAMILY   ● CITY   ● GROUP   ● TRADITIONAL   ● CAMPING BARN   ● COASTAL   ● RURAL

Explore the Forest of Dean by foot or bike from YHA Welsh Bicknor.

Getting there: Leave A40 midway between Ross-on-Wye and Monmouth, follow signs to Goodrich/Goodrich Castle. From village, follow lane signed hostel 1.5 miles. Take second lane right after crossing cattle grid. It's a narrow, single track drive with sharp bend.
Parking: Yes.
Nearest other hostels: St Briavels Castle 12 miles, Slimbridge 24.
Public transport: BUS: Stagecoach in Wye and Dean 34 Monmouth–Ross-on-Wye, with connections from Gloucester and Hereford, alight Goodrich 1.5 miles. RAIL: Lydney 12 miles, Gloucester 19.

●● WILDERHOPE MANOR ☆☆

Longville-in-the-Dale, Shropshire TF13 6EG;
wilderhope@yha.org.uk
Tel: 0870 770 6090 Fax: 0870 770 6091

Arrive along this hostel's sweeping drive and you may wonder if you've come to the wrong place. But this 16th century National Trust-owned manor house, with oak spiral staircases, timber-framed walls and grand dining hall, really can be your base. On Wenlock Edge in the Welsh Marches, you'll find plenty of walking in the Shropshire Hills. Sit awhile in its extensive grounds with views across the Hope Valley and you may not want to go home.
Location: OS 137, GR 544928.
Great for... history lovers who want to live it up.
You need to know... for safety reasons, Wilderhope Manor is not suitable for children under five.
Accommodation: 70 beds: 4x4-, 1x6-, 2x10- and 2x14-bed rooms.
Family rooms: Yes. **Rent-a-Hostel:** No.
Classroom: No. **Education packages:** No.

HOSTEL MANAGERS CHOOSE...
THE BEST CYCLE TRAILS IN THE REGION

West of Hills Route 25 YHA Malvern Hills: "This is very steep and 25 miles long but the views are stunning. I always tell families to try the Upton route - 10 miles, flat country lanes and good pubs."

Forest of Dean YHA Welsh Bicknor: "It's got biking for everyone on traffic-free trails. There are great views, peaceful woodland and plenty of pubs and picnic places. Hire bikes, including some special needs bikes, from the cycle centre."

Aston Hill YHA Ivinghoe: "A mountain bike course that has everything from basic trails for youngsters to more exhilarating challenges for experienced riders."

Silkin Way YHA Coalport: "This is easy pedalling along dry canal beds and abandoned railway lines. Best of all, it passes right outside the hostel."

Milton Keynes YHA Bradwell: "With 200 miles of dedicated routes, cyclists can explore every corner of Milton Keynes via parkland and country trails. The Millennium Circular Route also passes the hostel doorstep."

Stratford Greenway YHA Stratford-upon-Avon: "I like the old Honeybourne railway line. It's a haven of wildlife with two picnic sites en route. Very family friendly."

Facilities: Lounge, games room, self-catering kitchen, showers, drying room, cycle store and camping.
Daytime access: Restricted. ⊗
Meals: Breakfast, picnic lunch, evening meal.
Reception open: 17.00hrs.
Getting there: From Much Wenlock, take B4371 towards Church Stretton for approx 7 miles to Longville-in-the-Dale. Take first left in village, after 0.75 miles turn into the drive on the left.
Parking: Yes.
Nearest other hostels: Bridges 13 miles, Coalbrookdale 13, Coalport 13.
Public transport: BUS: A shuttle bus runs from Beaumont Road (near Church Stretton station) and drops off at hostel; Choice Travel 712 from Ludlow (Mon–Fri only), otherwise more frequent services from Ludlow or Bridgnorth to Shipton, then 0.5-mile walk (footpath). RAIL: Church Stretton 8 miles.

GET INVOLVED WITH YHA

Lending a hand at a Heart of England Youth Hostel is just one way to help the YHA which depends on its members' support. See details on page 30.

The Youth Hostels of...
East of England

Relaxing: unspoilt landscapes and quaint villages are typical of eastern England.

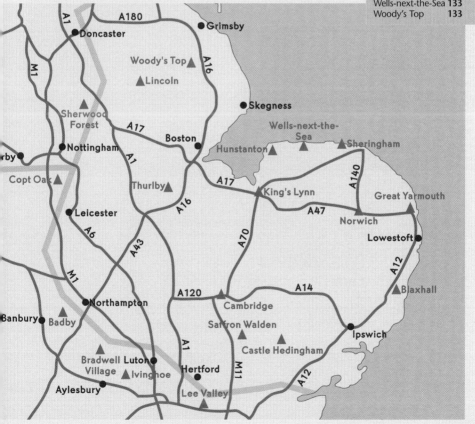

For further information visit www.yha.org.uk

○ FAMILY ● CITY ● GROUP ● TRADITIONAL ● CAMPING BARN ● COASTAL ● RURAL

○● BLAXHALL ☆☆☆

Heath Walk, Blaxhall, Woodbridge, Suffolk
IP12 2EA
Tel: 0870 770 5702 Fax: 0870 770 5703

This redbrick hostel has recently been refurbished to provide comfortable accommodation in what was once the village school. It now offers good disabled access on the edge of the Suffolk Sandlings, an Area of Outstanding Natural Beauty, with easy walking and flat cycling routes as well as the nearby bird reserves of Minsmere and Orfordness.
Location: OS 156, GR 369570.
Great for... weekend walkers and birdwatchers.
You need to know... the nearest shop is 2 miles away.
Accommodation: 40 beds: 1x2-, 2x4- and 5x6-bed rooms.
Family Rooms: Yes. **Rent-a-Hostel:** Yes.
Classroom: Yes. **Education packages:** Yes.
Facilities: Dining room, lounge, self-catering kitchen, showers, drying room, cycle store and lockers. **Daytime access:** All areas. ⊗

Sunset over the canal at Snape Maltings near YHA Blaxhall.

Meals: Breakfast, picnic lunch, evening meal.
Reception open: Staff available before 10.00hrs and after 17.00hrs.
Getting there: Leave A12 at Wickham Market, follow signs to Tunstall (B1078) and then to hostel.
Parking: Yes.
Nearest other hostels: Norwich 39 miles, Great Yarmouth 41.
Public transport: BUS: First Eastern Counties 81 Ipswich–

HOSTEL MANAGERS CHOOSE...

THE TOP 10 ATTRACTIONS IN...
CAMBRIDGE

1. BRIDGE OF SIGHS
"The University of Cambridge has over 30 colleges. This is part of St John's College and probably the most photographed. It's a city must-see."

2. CORN EXCHANGE
"All the biggest acts come to this venue – theatre, art exhibitions, ballets, concerts by chart-toppers: you name it, it's here."

3. KING'S COLLEGE CHAPEL
"Simply the most beautiful building in Cambridge. The best view is from across the river but venture closer and you'll hear the choir singing."

4. RIVER CAM
"Stroll along the riverbanks (known locally as the Backs). They're covered with daffodils in spring. Or hire a punt to see the sights in style."

5. CASTLE MOUND
"William the Conqueror's castle used to stand on the top of this grassy motte. That's long gone, but the great views of town and country are still there."

6. CAMBRIDGE AND COUNTY FOLK MUSEUM
"A fascinating place. Climb winding staircases to rooms full of domestic bits and bobs from the past 300 years."

7. CAMBRIDGE MARKET
"Buy all sorts of fruit and vegetables, flowers, books and clothes between Monday and Saturday. Go on Sunday for arts, crafts and antiques."

8. BOTANIC GARDENS
"You can easily wander an afternoon away in these gardens. There's an amazing variety of plants. Great for a picnic too."

9. THE FITZWILLIAM MUSEUM
"One of Britain's first public galleries. Entry is free and it now houses a world famous collection of art and antiquities. Great for a rainy day."

10. FESTIVALS
"We love our festivals! Cambridge has more than its fair share – don't miss Strawberry Fair with live music and theatre, held on the first Saturday in June."
(Recommended by YHA Cambridge)

For further information visit www.yha.org.uk

FAMILY CITY ● GROUP ● TRADITIONAL ● CAMPING BARN COASTAL ● RURAL

Aldeburgh. RAIL: Alight Woodbridge then bus 81, Saxmundham 5 miles. FERRY: Harwich to Hook of Holland.

●● CAMBRIDGE ☆

97 Tenison Road, Cambridge, Cambridgeshire CB1 2DN; cambridge@yha.org.uk
Tel: 0870 770 5742 Fax: 0870 770 5743

This busy international hostel is just minutes from the railway station and 15 minutes' walk from the city centre. The Victorian townhouse makes a great base for an English city break where you can relax by the river and visit colleges, museums and art galleries galore.
Location: OS 154, GR 460575.
Great for... a city break.
You need to know... breakfast is included in the overnight price; it's on-street parking only – metered and maximum stay two hours between 9.00hrs and 17.00hrs.
Accommodation: 99 beds: 2-, 3-, 4-, 6- and 8-bed rooms.
Family rooms: No. **Rent-a-Hostel:** No.
Classroom: No. **Education packages:** No.
Facilities: Reception, lounges, games room, self-catering kitchen, showers, luggage store, laundry facilities, cycle store and garden.
Daytime access: All areas.
Meals: Breakfast, picnic lunch, evening meal.
Reception open: 24hrs.
Getting there: From city centre, follow signs to railway station. Take last left turning (at hostel sign) before the railway station (see map on page 174).
Parking: Free parking for cars on roadside from 17.00hrs to 09.00hrs (metered at other times).
Nearest other hostels: Saffron Walden 15 miles, Castle Hedingham 29, London 60.
Public transport: BUS: Frequent from surrounding areas. RAIL: Cambridge 0.25 miles.
NATIONALEXPRESS Drummer Street coach stop 1 mile.

●● CASTLE HEDINGHAM ☆☆

7 Falcon Square, Castle Hedingham, Essex CO9 3BU; castlehed@yha.org.uk
Tel: 0870 770 5756 Fax: 0870 770 5757

If your idea of hostelling is basic bed and board, think again. Stay in this 16th century building and you'll enjoy substantial meals with the emphasis on home-cooked dishes and vegetarian fare. There are plenty of attractions to help you work up an appetite, and the hostel has a large lawned garden in which to relax afterwards. Bon appetit!
Location: OS 155, GR 786355.
Great for... home-cooked food.
Accommodation: 50 beds: 1x2-, 1x4-, 1x8-, 2x6- and 2x10+-bed rooms.
Family rooms: Yes. **Rent-a-Hostel:** No.
Classroom: Yes. **Education packages:** Yes.
Facilities: Lounge, self-catering kitchen, showers, drying room, cycle store and garden with BBQ. **Daytime access:** Restricted. ⊗
Meals: Breakfast, picnic lunch, evening meal.

Reception open: 17.00hrs.
Getting there: Follow signs for Hedingham Castle. Opposite castle entrance, turn down Castle Lane. Hostel is on left at bottom of hill.
Parking: Nearby.
Nearest other hostels: Saffron Walden 20 miles, Cambridge 29.
Public transport: BUS: Hedingham Omnibuses 89 from Braintree except Sun (passes close to Braintree station).
RAIL: Sudbury (not Sun, except June–Sept) 7 miles, Braintree 8.
FERRY: Harwich 25 miles.

●● GREAT YARMOUTH ☆

2 Sandown Road, Great Yarmouth, Norfolk NR30 1EY
Tel: 0870 770 5840 Fax: 0870 770 5841

Once an Edwardian family hotel, this hostel makes a convenient base for that long-lost art – the traditional seaside holiday. The huge sandy shore of Great Yarmouth is minutes away and the town centre offers endless amusements for children. Visit the Maritime Museum of East Anglia or follow miles of coastal trails and cycle paths.
Location: OS 134, GR 529083.

All the fun of the fair on seaside amusements: YHA Great Yarmouth.

Great for... families looking for a beach-based holiday.
Accommodation: 40 beds: 1x2-, 2x4-, 2x6-, 1x8- and 1x10-bed rooms.
Family rooms: No. **Rent-a-Hostel:** Yes.
Classroom: No. **Education packages:** No.
Facilities: TV lounge, self-catering kitchen, dining room, showers and cycle store. **Daytime access:** Restricted. ⊗
Meals: Self-catering only.
Reception open: 17.00hrs.
Getting there: Enter Yarmouth from A12/A47 roundabout. Follow road to lights, with Sainsbury's left. Bear left into Nicholas Rd. Turn left at next lights (Nelson Rd), then first right after coach station.
Parking: On roadside by hostel.
Nearest other hostels: Norwich 21 miles, Sheringham 39, Blaxhall 41.
Public transport: BUS: Frequent from surrounding areas, also local services. RAIL: Great Yarmouth 0.75 miles. FERRY: Harwich 60 miles.
NATIONALEXPRESS Market Gates 0.5 miles.

East of England

● FAMILY　● CITY　● GROUP　● TRADITIONAL　● CAMPING BARN　● COASTAL　● RURAL

●● HUNSTANTON ☆

15 Avenue Road, Hunstanton, Norfolk PE36 5BW;
hunstanton@yha.org.uk
Tel: 0870 770 5872 Fax: 0870 770 5873

For the past eight years, Hunstanton has won seaside awards for its cleanliness and amenities that are just two minutes' walk from this hostel, a pair of Victorian townhouses built of warm red sandstone. But don't spend all your time swimming and sunbathing – put on your walking boots and explore further afield for miles of easy striding. The Norfolk Coast Path will lead you along the famous striped chalk cliffs, while Peddars Way follows an ancient route.

Location: OS 132, GR 674406.

Great for... quiet days spent walking, cycling, birdwatching and lazing on the beach.

Accommodation: 44 beds: 1x2-, 2x3-, 5x4- and 2x8-bed rooms.

Family rooms: Yes. **Rent-a-Hostel:** Yes.

Classroom: Yes. **Education packages:** Yes.

Facilities: Lounge/TV room, self-catering kitchen, dining room, showers, drying room and cycle store. **Daytime access:** Restricted.

Meals: Breakfast, picnic lunch, evening meal.

Reception open: 17.00hrs.

Getting there: From coast road (A149) turn on to Park Road, then second left into Avenue Road.

Parking: Roadside parking outside hostel.

Nearest other hostels: King's Lynn 16 miles, Wells-next-the-Sea 16, Sheringham 38, Norwich 40.

Public transport: BUS: From King's Lynn, First Eastern Counties 410/411 to Hunstanton, Coast Hopper (Sheringham–King's Lynn) stops at Hunstanton. RAIL: King's Lynn 16 miles. FERRY: Harwich 70 miles.

● KING'S LYNN ☆

Thoresby College, College Lane, King's Lynn,
Norfolk PE30 1JB
Tel: 0870 770 5902 Fax: 0870 770 5903

This traditional hostel is in a wing of the 500-year-old Chantry College building in the historic part of King's Lynn. Discover the

YHA evening meals: a choice of dishes, suitable for all the family.

HOSTEL MANAGERS CHOOSE...

THE BEST CYCLE TRAILS IN EAST ENGLAND

Suffolk coastal road tour YHA Blaxhall: "A 75-mile circuit of signposted lanes through classic English countryside. Pick up the tour at either Woodbridge or Snape."

The National Cycle Network YHA Wells-next-the-Sea: "Route 30 stretches from Wells to Great Yarmouth. You can hire mountain bikes in Wells and Great Yarmouth – ask at the hostel for more details."

Thetford Forest YHA Sheringham: "I think this is East Anglia's best off-road venue, with a huge choice of open riding among the pines."

Holkham Hall YHA Wells-next-the-Sea: "Great for children. Welcomes cyclists on the estate's tracks close to the deer park and lake. The hall tour is excellent value if you want to make a day of it."

Marriotts Way rail trail YHA Norwich: "A gentle route between Norwich and Aylsham. You can combine your ride with a trip on the Bure Valley steam railway at the Aylsham end. All the family will manage a section of this."

heritage buildings and museums, as well as other local attractions such as the Queen's country residence at Sandringham, Houghton Hall and the Norman ruins of Castle Rising and Castle Acre. Walkers and cyclists will also enjoy the varied west Norfolk countryside.

Location: OS 132, GR 616199.

Great for... walking and cycling.

Accommodation: 35 beds: 1x1-, 1x3-, 2x6-, 1x9- and 1x10-bed rooms.

Family rooms: No. **Rent-a-Hostel:** Yes.

Classroom: No. **Education packages:** No.

Facilities: Lounge, self-catering kitchen, dining room, showers, drying room and cycle store. **Daytime access:** Restricted. ⊗

Meals: Breakfast only; full meal service available for pre-booked groups of 10 or more.

Reception open: 17.00hrs.

Getting there: Follow signs to the Old Town. College Lane is opposite The Guildhall.

Parking: Follow signs to Old Town/South Quay. Free parking is on left of South Quay, north of College Lane, 50 metres from hostel.

Nearest other hostels: Hunstanton 16 miles, Thurlby 38, Sheringham 39, Norwich 44, Cambridge 45.

Public transport: BUS: Frequent from surrounding areas. RAIL: King's Lynn 0.75 miles. NATIONALEXPRESS» Vancouver Centre Bus Station 0.5 miles.

To make a booking visit www.yha.org.uk

● FAMILY ● CITY ● GROUP ● TRADITIONAL ● CAMPING BARN ● COASTAL ● RURAL

●● LINCOLN ☆

77 South Park, Lincoln, Lincolnshire LN5 8ES;
lincoln@yha.org.uk
Tel: 0870 770 5918 Fax: 0870 770 5919

Lincoln has often been described as York in miniature, with its cathedral, castle, steep medieval streets and ancient Roman walls. With a range of modern shops and a cosmopolitan cluster of cafés, it's every bit as busy too. This hostel, a Victorian villa in a traffic-free area, has fine views from the dining room and conservatory across an open common, making it a suitably elegant base for rest and recuperation. It's also well-known for its home-cooked food using mainly local and organic produce.
Location: OS 121, GR 980700.

www.britainonview.com

Discover Lincoln's medieval streets and historic buildings.

Great for... exploring Lincoln's city centre.
Accommodation: 46 beds: 2x2-, 1x3-, 1x4-, 1x5-, 1x6- and 3x8-bed rooms.
Family rooms: Yes. **Rent-a-Hostel:** Yes.
Classroom: Yes. **Education packages:** Yes.
Facilities: Lounge, TV room, self-catering kitchen, showers, drying room, cycle store, laundry facilities and grounds.
Daytime access: Restricted. ☺
Meals: Breakfast, picnic lunch, evening meal.
Reception open: 15.00hrs.
Getting there: From the train station turn right onto St Mary's Street. Continue down road to Oxford Street. Go under flyover and up steps on the right. Go along Canwick Road and over traffic lights. When the cemetery is on your left, South Park is on your right (see map on page 174).
Parking: On site and additional parking opposite hostel.
Nearest other hostels: Woody's Top 25 miles, Sherwood Forest 30, Thurlby 35, Beverley Friary 54.
Public transport: BUS: Frequent from surrounding areas.
RAIL: Lincoln 1 mile.
NATIONAL EXPRESS» Lincoln City bus station 1 mile.

●● NORWICH ☆

112 Turner Road, Norwich, Norfolk NR2 4HB;
norwich@yha.org.uk
Tel: 0870 770 5976 Fax: 0870 770 5977

A former children's home, this hostel now provides comfortable rooms in an attractive building close to the River Wensum. There's plenty to do in the historic city of Norwich with its city walls, Norman castle, medieval buildings and colourful market. It's also a good base for visiting the Norfolk Broads and countryside.
Location: OS 134, GR 213095.
Great for... a relaxed city break.
You need to know... this hostel may close during 2003. Please enquire before planning your stay.
Accommodation: 57 beds: all 2–6-bed rooms.
Family rooms: Yes. **Rent-a-Hostel:** Yes.
Classroom: Yes. **Education packages:** No.
Facilities: Lounge, TV room, self-catering kitchen, showers, drying room, internet access, games room and cycle store.
Daytime access: Restricted. ☺
Meals: Breakfast, picnic lunch, evening meal (1900hrs-2000hrs).
Reception open: 17.00hrs.
Getting there: From A11 north, turn left at roundabout with A140 (signed University), go straight over first roundabout and turn right at second roundabout. Then follow signs to hostel.
Parking: Yes.
Nearest other hostels: Great Yarmouth 21 miles, Sheringham 25, Wells-next-the-Sea 32, Hunstanton 40.
Public transport: BUS: Frequent from surrounding areas.
RAIL: Norwich 2 miles. AIRPORT: 5 miles.
NATIONAL EXPRESS» Norwich bus station 1.25 miles.

● SAFFRON WALDEN ☆

1 Myddylton Place, Saffron Walden, Essex CB10 1BB; saffron@yha.org.uk
Tel: 0870 770 6014 Fax: 0870 770 6015

Stay in the oldest inhabited building in Saffron Walden, a 600-year-old former maltings with oak beams, uneven floors and a walled garden. Saffron Walden is an ancient town with a rich heritage of old buildings set in rolling countryside, good for walking and cycling. It's also close to the Imperial War Museum's aviation collection at Duxford and Thaxted Windmill.
Location: OS 154, GR 535386.
Great for... walkers and cyclists — it makes an excellent base for exploring the area.
You need to know... there's no parking at the hostel.
Accommodation: 40 beds: 4x2–6- and 2x10–12-bed rooms.
Family rooms: No. **Rent-a-Hostel:** Yes.
Classroom: No. **Education packages:** No.
Facilities: Lounge, dining room, showers, self-catering kitchen, drying room, cycle store and garden.
Daytime access: Restricted. ☺
Meals: Breakfast, picnic lunch, evening meal.
Reception open: 17.00hrs.

● FAMILY ● CITY ● GROUP ● TRADITIONAL ● CAMPING BARN ● COASTAL ● RURAL

Getting there: From the town centre follow High Street past the Saffron Hotel. The hostel is on the corner opposite Castle Street. From the south take M11 J9 and from the north take M11 J10, and follow signs to Saffron Walden on B184. The hostel is on the right just past the Eight Bells pub as you come into the town.
Parking: 800 metres to free car park.
Nearest other hostels: Cambridge 15 miles, Castle Hedingham 20.
Public transport: BUS: Frequent local services, including link with Audley End station and Stansted Airport (10 miles), two-hourly service. RAIL: Audley End 2.5 miles.

●● SHERINGHAM ☆

**1 Cremer's Drift, Sheringham, Norfolk
NR26 8HX; sheringham@yha.org.uk
Tel: 0870 770 6024 Fax: 0870 770 6025**

This large, rambling Victorian building is set in an Area of Outstanding Natural Beauty on the heritage coastline of Norfolk. Sheringham is a fascinating example of a Victorian seaside resort where shellfishing remains an important industry. The hostel is ideally positioned for visiting beaches, the steam railway and the heavy horse centre.
Location: OS 133, GR 159428.
Great for... a traditional seaside holiday with lots of fresh air; activities without a car.
You need to know... the self-catering kitchen is very small and can be busy during school holidays.
Accommodation: 100 beds: mostly 2-, 3-, 3x4- and a few 6–8-bed rooms. Ground floor accommodation for six wheelchair users.
Family rooms: Yes. **Rent-a-Hostel:** Yes.
Classroom: Yes. **Education packages:** Yes.
Facilities: Lounge/dining room, TV room, games room, self-catering

www.britainonview.com

The spectacular cliffs of the north Norfolk coast near YHA Sheringham.

kitchen, drying room and cycle store. **Daytime access:** All areas.
Meals: Breakfast, picnic lunch, evening meal.
Reception open: 13.00hrs.
Getting there: The hostel is off the main A149 behind St Joseph's Roman Catholic Church, only five minutes on foot from the railway and bus stations.
Parking: Yes.
Nearest other hostels: Wells-next-the-Sea 18 miles, Norwich 25, Hunstanton 38, Great Yarmouth 39.
Public transport: BUS: First Eastern Counties/Sanders 50/50A, Norwich–Holt, X98 King's Lynn–Cromer.
RAIL: Sheringham 0.25 miles.
NATIONAL EXPRESS Station Approach bus shelter 0.25 miles.

●● THURLBY ☆

**16 High St, Thurlby, Bourne, Lincolnshire
PE10 0EE
Tel: 0870 770 6066 Fax: 0870 770 6066**

This homely hostel and its lovely garden enjoy a peaceful setting in an unspoilt Lincolnshire village. A 15th century forge and annexe, it offers a quiet haven to those seeking a tranquil base. Attractions in the area include the Wool Churches built by local sheep farmers, while cycling, fishing and watersports are on hand at Rutland Water.
Location: OS 130, GR 097168.
Great for... cycling, birdwatching and visiting Rutland Water.
You need to know... this hostel may close during 2003. Please enquire before planning your stay.

HOSTEL MANAGERS CHOOSE...
THE BEST SEASIDE SPOTS

Blakeney Point YHA Wells-next-the-Sea: "A holiday highpoint for kids and adults alike. Take a boat from Blakeney harbour to see the seal colony."

Holkham YHA Sheringham: "A great beach and very clean. Film buffs can walk where Gwyneth Paltrow did in the film Shakespeare in Love."

Winterton-on-Sea YHA Great Yarmouth: "A well-kept secret. It's backed by miles of sand dunes and has a conservation area to the north – a quiet place to explore on foot."

Wells beach YHA Wells-next-the-Sea: "Superb sand, very clean and great for families. The sea almost disappears out of sight at low tide!"

Cromer pier YHA Sheringham: "Go crabbing off the pier at Cromer. It doesn't take very long to catch a bucketful."

Burnham Overy Staithe and Morston YHA Wells-next-the-Sea: "Two lovely harbours a short drive from the hostel. There's a boat to Blakeney Point from the latter."

For offers and discounts visit www.yha.org.uk

○ FAMILY ● CITY ◐ GROUP ● TRADITIONAL ● CAMPING BARN ◑ COASTAL ◐ RURAL

Accommodation: 24 beds: 1x3-, 2x4-, 1x5- and 1x8-bed rooms.
Family rooms: No. **Rent-a-Hostel:** Yes.
Classroom: No. **Education packages:** No.
Facilities: Lounge, self-catering kitchen, dining room, showers, drying room, cycle store, shop, grounds and camping.
Daytime access: Restricted.
Meals: Self-catering only.
Reception open: 17.00hrs.
Getting there: On the A15 between Peterborough and Bourne (don't confuse it with Thurlby near Lincoln). From Stamford take the A6121 to Bourne and turn south. The hostel is clearly signed from the road (0.25 miles).
Parking: Yes, but limited.
Nearest other hostels: Lincoln 35 miles, King's Lynn 38, Copt Oak 50.
Public transport: BUS: Delaine's from Peterborough (passes close to Peterborough station). RAIL: Peterborough 15 miles, Grantham 18. **NATIONALEXPRESS** Bourne bus station 2.5 miles.

●● WOODY'S TOP ☆☆☆

Ruckland, Louth, Lincolnshire LN11 8RQ;
woodystop@yha.org.uk
Tel: 0870 770 6098 Fax: 0870 770 6098

This is one of YHA's quietest hostels, hidden well away from civilisation in the Lincolnshire Wolds. The converted farm buildings

are surrounded by open fields so, if you don't want to see a soul, travel by foot or bike to explore the landscape. When you're ready to face the world again, ease yourself gently back into the rat race in the nearby market towns before making the 25-mile trip to Lincoln to ponder the might of its cathedral built on the orders of William the Conqueror.
Location: OS 122, GR 332786.
Great for... those seeking a peaceful rural retreat.
Accommodation: 20 beds: 1x2-, 3x4- and 1x6-bed rooms.
Family rooms: No. **Rent-a-Hostel:** Yes.
Classroom: No. **Education packages:** No.
Facilities: Lounge, self-catering kitchen, dining room, showers, drying room, cycle store and grounds. **Daytime access:** Restricted. ⊗
Meals: Self-catering only.
Reception open: 17.00hrs.
Getting there: From A16 take minor road towards Ruckland, turn left and hostel is 300 metres from junction on right.
Parking: Yes.
Nearest other hostels: Lincoln 25 miles, Beverley 50, Thurlby 55.
Public transport: BUS: Post Bus from Louth, Translink 6C Horncastle to Louth with connections for Grimsby, Skegness and Lincoln stations. RAIL: Thorpe Culvert (not Sun) 18 miles, Grimsby Town 22, Lincoln Central 25. FERRY: Hull to Zeebrugge (Rotterdam) 45 miles.
NATIONALEXPRESS Louth and Horncastle.

◑● WELLS-NEXT-THE-SEA ☆☆☆☆

Church Plain, Wells, Norfolk NR23 1EQ;
wellsnorfolk@yha.org.uk
Tel: 0870 770 6084 Fax: 0870 770 6085

The quays still teem with yachts and fishing boats in the port of Wells, where you'll find this newly-opened hostel in the heart of the town. It's a fine base from which to indulge in flora and fauna forays into the surrounding countryside. Follow creeks and salt marshes busy with birdlife, enjoy miles of empty beaches or take a boat at high tide to see seals. Explore the network of footpaths leading inland and you'll discover ancient churches, flint villages and welcoming pubs. For the fit, the North Norfolk Coast Path is temptingly close.
Location: OS 132, GR 917433.
Great for... those with an interest in wildlife.
Accommodation: 32 beds: 3x2-3-bed rooms (double bed with bunk over; one is on the ground floor with disabled access and en-suite facilities), 1x3- and 5x4-bed rooms.
Family rooms: Yes. **Rent-a-Hostel:** Yes.
Classroom: No. **Education packages:** No.
Facilities: Lounges, TV, dining room, self-catering kitchen, meeting room and laundry. **Daytime access:** Restricted. ⊗
Meals: Self-catering only.
Reception open: 17.00 hrs.
Getting there: On south side of town opposite church tower.

From Hunstanton or Sheringham keep on A149 and turn into Church Plain next to church. From Fakenham (B1105), take first right on entering the town and turn left after 350 metres into Church Plain. By foot from waterfront take Staithe Street then High Street to Church Plain.
Parking: Yes, behind hostel.
Nearest other hostels: Hunstanton 16 miles, Sheringham 18, King's Lynn 24, Norwich 32.
Public transport: BUS: Coasthopper from King's Lynn, Sheringham and Fakenham (hourly July–Aug, otherwise two-hourly, tel: 0845 602 0121), First 56/A, 56, 431 from Norwich. RAIL: Sheringham 16 miles, King's Lynn 24.
NATIONALEXPRESS Fakenham 8 miles.

The timeless village of Cley near YHA Wells-next-the-Sea.

www.britainonview.com

The Youth Hostels of...
South West England

Historic: the South West is full of reminders of the past.

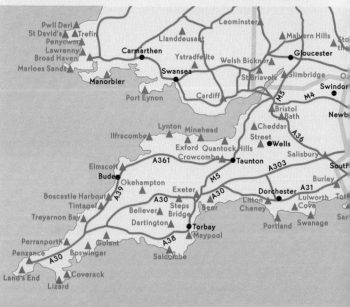

For further information visit www.yha.org.uk

●● BATH ☆

Bathwick Hill, Bath BA2 6JZ; bath@yha.org.uk
Tel: 0870 770 5688 Fax: 0870 770 5689

A beautiful Italianate mansion in its own gardens, YHA Bath offers a comfortable base for exploring this elegant city. Buzzing with cosmopolitan energy, it enjoys all the facilities you would expect of such a prestigious location. Bath is a World Heritage City and famous for its hot springs, Roman Baths and Georgian architecture. Whatever time of year you choose to visit, you'll be sure to find a variety of festivals, theatre shows and exhibitions to keep you entertained.

Location: OS 172, GR 766644.

Great for... theatre, exhibition and festival goers.

You need to know... some beds are in an annexe; it's on-street parking with drop-off at hostel.

Accommodation: 122 beds: 3x2-, 12x4-, 2x5-, 5x6-, 1x8- and 2x10-bed rooms.

Family rooms: No. **Rent-a-Hostel:** No.

Classroom: No. **Education packages:** Yes.

Facilities: Lounge with TV, self-catering kitchen, showers, cycle store, small shop, laundry facilities, internet access and foreign exchange. **Daytime access:** All areas.

Meals: Breakfast, picnic lunch, evening meal.

Reception open: 24hrs.

Getting there: From London Road, follow signs to university and American Museum. From southwest, follow A36 to roundabout on

Pulteney Road (see map on page 173).

Parking: On Bathwick Hill.

Nearest other hostels: Bristol 14 miles, Cheddar 27, Slimbridge 30.

Public transport: BUS: First Badgerline 18 from bus station. RAIL: Bath Spa 1.25 miles.

NATIONALEXPRESS» Manvers St bus station 1.25 miles.

Bath's historic Pump Room, near YHA Bath.

●● BELLEVER (awaiting classification)

Bellever, Postbridge, Devon PL20 6TU;
bellever@yha.org.uk
Tel: 0870 770 5692 Fax: 0870 770 5693

Escape the modern world at this hostel in the centre of Dartmoor National Park surrounded by open moorland with a network of off-road walking and cycling routes. Once part of a Duchy farm, this hostel makes a comfortable, child-friendly retreat.

Location: OS 191, GR 654773.

Great for... keen walkers and cyclists.

You need to know... parking is limited.

Accommodation: 38 beds: 4x4-, 1x6- and 2x8-bed rooms.

Family rooms: Yes. **Rent-a-Hostel:** Yes.

Classroom: No. **Education packages:** Yes.

Facilities: Dining room/self-catering kitchen, showers, drying room and cycle store. **Daytime access:** Restricted. ⊗

Meals: Breakfast, picnic lunch, evening meal.

Reception open: 17.00hrs.

Getting there: From Postbridge (B3212) take road marked Bellever.

Parking: Limited.

Nearest other hostels: Steps Bridge 18 miles, Dartington 19, Exeter 25, Okehampton 25.

Public transport: BUS: Plymouth City Bus 98 from Tavistock (stops at hostel), otherwise 82 Exeter–Plymouth, alight Postbridge 1 mile. RAIL: Plymouth 23 miles. FERRY: Plymouth to France/Spain 24 miles.

●● BOSCASTLE HARBOUR

Palace Stables, Boscastle, Cornwall PL35 0HD
Tel: 0870 770 5710 Fax: 0870 770 5711

Experience the unique character of this cosy retreat. Originally a stable for the horses that pulled the boats ashore in the National Trust-protected harbour, the hostel is now popular with walkers on the South West Coast Path that runs right past its door. Superb coastal scenery ensures excellent walking country while lovers of literature will appreciate the local Thomas Hardy connections.

Location: OS 190, GR 096915.

Great for... walkers on the South West Coast Path.

You need to know... it's self-catering, except for pre-booked parties of 10 or more.

Accommodation: 25 beds: 4x4–9-bed rooms.

Family rooms: No. **Rent-a-Hostel:** Yes.

Classroom: No. **Education packages:** No.

Facilities: Lounge/dining area, self-catering kitchen, showers, drying room and cycle store. **Daytime access:** Restricted. ⊗

Meals: Self-catering only although meals are available for pre-booked parties of 10 or more.

Reception open: 17.00hrs.

Getting there: Walk from bridge on the B3263 towards harbour alongside river. Hostel is last building on right at top of slipway.

Parking: Public car park for cars and coaches, 250 metres (overnight free).

Nearest other hostels: Tintagel 5 miles, Elmscott 28, Golant 30.

● FAMILY　● CITY　● GROUP　● TRADITIONAL　● CAMPING BARN　● COASTAL　● RURAL

www.britainonview.com

The South West Coast Path near YHA Boscastle Harbour.

Public transport: BUS: First Western National X10 from Exeter St David's Station, 55 and 122/5 from Bodmin Parkway station. **RAIL:** Bodmin Parkway 24 miles, Exeter 65.

●● BOSWINGER ☆☆

Boswinger, Gorran, St Austell, Cornwall PL26 6LL
Tel: 0870 770 5712 Fax: 0870 770 5712

If you're planning on visiting the Eden Project and the Lost Gardens of Heligan this year, then YHA Boswinger makes a convenient base. A cosy mix of old farm buildings with a courtyard and veranda, it enjoys excellent sea views and is surrounded by a wide choice of beaches. On the Coast Path, walkers will find a multitude of routes and cyclists will enjoy the Cornish Trail.

Location: OS 204, GR 991411.
Great for... a convenient base with sea views.
You need to know... only breakfast is available unless a group has pre-booked.
Accommodation: 40 beds: 3x2-, 4x4- and 3x6-bed rooms.
Family rooms: Yes. **Rent-a-Hostel:** Yes.
Classroom: No. **Education packages:** No.
Facilities: Lounge, dining room, self-catering kitchen, showers, drying room, cycle store and BBQ. **Daytime access:** All areas.
Meals: Breakfast only.
Reception open: Staff available before 10.00hrs and after 17.00hrs.
Getting there: From St Austell take B3273 towards Mevagissey. After 5 miles turn right at top of hill and follow signs for Gorran, passing Heligan Gardens on left. Fork right just before Gorran to follow brown hostel signs. The hostel is situated in Boswinger

●● BEER ☆☆

Bovey Combe, Beer, Seaton, Devon EX12 3LL;
beer@yha.org.uk
Tel: 0870 770 5690 Fax: 0870 770 5691

On the edge of the fishing village of Beer, this light and airy country house, once a smugglers' haunt, has a large lawned garden. It's a relaxing hostel with child-friendly facilities. Activities nearby include mackerel fishing, a visit to the Quarry Caves or a ride on the steam train at Pecorama. Take a stroll along the South West Coast Path or head a little further to hunt for fossils on Charmouth Beach.

Location: OS 192, GR 223896.
Great for... quiet family holidays.
You need to know... the hostel's access road is steep and narrow.
Accommodation: 40 beds: 5x4-, 1x5-, 1x6- and 1x9-bed rooms.
Family rooms: Yes. **Rent-a-Hostel:** Yes.
Classroom: No. **Education packages:** No.
Facilities: Dining room, lounge, self-catering kitchen, showers, drying room, cycle store and grounds.
Daytime access: All areas. ⊗
Meals: Breakfast, picnic lunch, evening meal.
Reception open: Staff available before 10.00 and after 17.00hrs.

Getting there: From Beer village go up Fore Street to Townsend and turn off to track on right, signposted.
Parking: Cars only (steep narrow access).
Nearest other hostels: Exeter 24 miles, Litton Cheney 28, Portland 44.
Public transport: BUS: Axe Valley from Seaton with connections from Axminster Station, First Southern National X53 Weymouth–Exeter (bus stop at end of Bovey Lane). **RAIL:** Axminster 7 miles.

Once a smugglers' haunt, now a relaxing hostel: YHA Beer.

● FAMILY ● CITY ● GROUP ● TRADITIONAL ● CAMPING BARN ● COASTAL ● RURAL

hamlet near Seaview international campsite.

Parking: Yes.

Nearest other hostels: Golant 17 miles, Perranporth 25.

Public transport: BUS: First Western National 26/ABR St Austell–Gorran Churchtown, then 1 mile. RAIL: St Austell 10 miles. FERRY: Plymouth to France/Spain 50 miles.

●● BRISTOL ☆☆

14 Narrow Quay, Bristol BS1 4QA;
bristol@yha.org.uk
Tel: 0870 770 5726 Fax: 0870 770 5727

This hostel makes the perfect base to explore the vibrant city of Bristol. With views over the waterways, it has been sympathetically restored to create a relaxing yet cosmopolitan atmosphere. Visit the magnificent Avon Gorge, Brunel's suspension bridge or one of

Well-sited: YHA Bristol is the ideal base to explore the city's attractions.

the many theatres, museums and art galleries in the city.

Location: OS 172, GR 586725.

Great for... city activities.

You need to know... breakfast is included in the overnight price.

Accommodation: 92 beds: mostly 2–4-bed rooms, plus 1x5- and 2x6-bed rooms.

Family rooms: Yes. **Rent-a-Hostel:** No.

Classroom: Yes. **Education packages:** Yes.

Facilities: Lounge, TV room, games room, self-catering kitchen, showers, cycle store, luggage store and laundry facilities.

Daytime access: All areas.

Meals: Breakfast only. Full meal service available to pre-booked groups of 10+.

Reception open: 24 hrs.

Getting there: From London or South Wales, exit M4 at J19, then take M32. From Birmingham or South West, exit M5 at J18, then A4 (see map on page 173).

Parking: At NCP Prince Street. Meter parking behind hostel.

Nearest other hostels: Bath 14 miles, Cheddar 20, Slimbridge 25.

Public transport: BUS: Frequent from surrounding areas. RAIL: Bristol Temple Meads 1 mile.

NATIONAL EXPRESS» Marlborough St bus station 1 mile.

● BURLEY ☆☆☆

Cott Lane, Burley, Ringwood, Hampshire BH24 4BB
Tel: 0870 770 5734 Fax: 0870 770 5735

A former family home, this hostel stands in extensive grounds with immediate access to the New Forest and within easy reach of the Beaulieu Motor Museum and the beaches of Bournemouth. With cycling, pony trekking and watersports all possible to arrange locally, it's the ideal base for a get-away-from-it-all break close to the seaside.

Location: OS 195, GR 220028.

Great for... cyclists, horseriders and nature lovers.

You need to know... the hostel is at the end of an unsurfaced track and can be hard to find in the dark. Watch out for cattle and ponies.

Accommodation: 36 beds: 1x4-, 1x6-, 2x8- and 1x10-bed rooms.

Family rooms: No. **Rent-a-Hostel:** Yes.

Classroom: No. **Education packages:** No.

Facilities: Lounge, dining room, self-catering kitchen, showers, drying room, grounds and camping. **Daytime access:** Restricted. 🚭

Meals: Breakfast, picnic lunch, evening meal.

Reception open: 17.00hrs.

Getting there: Follow Lyndhurst Road past Burley School on left and past golf course for 0.5 miles to a crossroads. Follow signpost to White Buck Inn and turn left into Cott Lane. Follow signs for hostel.

Parking: Yes.

Nearest other hostels: Totland Bay 17 miles (via ferry), Salisbury 21, Winchester 23.

Public transport: BUS: Wilts and Dorset X34/5 Bournemouth–Southampton (passes Ashurst and Southampton stations), alight Durmast Corner 0.25 miles or 105, 126 from Christchurch, alight Burley 0.25 miles. RAIL: Sway 5.5 miles, New Milton 6.

● FAMILY   ● CITY   ● GROUP   ● TRADITIONAL   ● CAMPING BARN   ● COASTAL   ● RURAL

●● CHEDDAR ☆

Hillfield, Cheddar, Somerset BS27 3HN;
cheddar@yha.org.uk
Tel: 0870 770 5760 Fax: 0870 770 5761

Cheddar Gorge is an adventure playground for all and this hostel is in the thick of the action. The modernised Victorian house sits in the village below the dramatic gorge that has the highest limestone cliffs in England. There's an exciting underground world to discover in Cheddar's incredible caves and Wookey Hole, just six miles away. The Mendip Hills and Somerset Levels will keep walkers busy while families will want to travel the 12 miles to the traditional seaside resort of Weston-super-Mare.

www.britainonview.com

The incredible underworld of Goughs Cave, near YHA Cheddar.

HOSTEL MANAGERS CHOOSE...
THE BEST WEST COUNTRY BEACHES

Treyarnon Bay, Cornwall YHA Treyarnon Bay: "The surfing beach right on our doorstep is perfect for all standards. Learn in safety with expert tuition on our tailored surf breaks."

Mill Bay, Devon YHA Salcombe: "Sheltered and sandy, it's the best in the area for sun worshippers."

Porthuney Cove, Cornwall YHA Boswinger: "Safe swimming and great for beach games."

Vault Beach, Cornwall YHA Boswinger: "It's sandy, secluded and ideal for sun seekers."

Beer Beach, Devon YHA Beer: "A pebble beach 10 minutes' walk from our door."

Studland Bay, Dorset YHA Swanage: "Four miles of golden sand and dunes."

Sennon Cove & Whitesands Bay, Cornwall YHA Land's End: "Both are around four miles away and offer good surfing and swimming. Sennon Cove is a Blue Flag beach and boasts two surf schools."

Hemmick, Cornwall YHA Boswinger: "A sandy beach close to the hostel with safe, sheltered swimming in most conditions and even the occasional surfable wave!"

Thurlstone, Devon YHA Salcombe: "Good for rock pools and windsurfing."

Location: OS 182, GR 455534.

Great for... an action-packed family holiday.

Accommodation: 51 beds: mostly 2-, 4- and 6-bed rooms.

Family rooms: Yes. **Rent-a-Hostel:** No.

Classroom: No. **Education packages:** No.

Facilities: Lounge, self-catering kitchen, conservatory, showers, drying room, cycle store and laundry. **Daytime access:** All areas. ⊗

Meals: Breakfast, picnic lunch, evening meal.

Reception open: Staff available before 10.00hrs and after 17.00hrs.

Getting there: From M5 exit at J22. Take A38 and A371 to Cheddar. In village turn left at war memorial into The Hayes. Just beyond school, turn left into Hillfield to hostel. From Wells follow A371, turning right into The Hayes in village.

Parking: Yes.

Nearest other hostels: Street 17 miles, Bristol 20, Bath 27.

Public transport: BUS: First Badgerline 126, 826 Weston-super-Mare–Wells (passes close to Weston Milton and Weston-super-Mare stations). RAIL: Weston-super-Mare 11 miles.

● CHENSON

campingbarns@yha.org.uk
Booking: 0870 770 6113
Arrival time: Mr & Mrs Chandler, 01363 83236

This cob and timber camping barn, formerly used for cider pressing, is on a working farm in the beautiful Taw Valley. It's just half a mile from the Tarka Trail and close to the Forestry Commission's Eggesford Forest with its many walks and mountain bike routes. And when you return from a full day's workout, you'll be pleased to know that cream teas are available to order.

Accommodation: Sleeps 8 in two areas.

Facilities: Cooking facilities, sitting area, wood-burning stove, showers (hot water included), electric light and metered electricity. Breakfast and cream teas available to order.

Nearest pub: 2 miles. **Nearest shop:** 2 miles.

Location: OS 191, GR 705099.

For offers and discounts visit www.yha.org.uk

FAMILY CITY GROUP TRADITIONAL CAMPING BARN ● COASTAL ● RURAL

●● COVERACK ☆☆

Parc Behan, School Hill, Coverack, Helston,
Cornwall TR12 6SA; coverack@yha.org.uk
Tel: 0870 770 5780 Fax: 0870 770 5781

The Lizard Peninsula will fascinate all outdoor lovers. Amateur geologists will be fascinated by rocks forced up from under the earth's crust. Walkers will delight in the ever-changing scenery of the South West Coast Path. Fishermen will take to the sea and adrenalin junkies will try their hands at new watersports. This hostel is ideally placed to explore it all with panoramic views of dramatic cliffs and deserted coves. A Victorian country house, it also boasts spacious grounds for games and camping.

Location: OS 204, GR 782184.
Great for... families willing to try their hands at new sports.
Accommodation: 37 beds: 1x3-, 3x4-, 1x6- and 2x8-bed rooms.
Family rooms: Yes. **Rent-a-Hostel:** Yes.
Classroom: No. **Education packages:** No.
Facilities: Dining room, games room, self-catering kitchen, lounge, showers, camping and grounds. **Daytime access:** Restricted. ⊗
Meals: Breakfast, picnic lunch, evening meal.
Reception open: 17.00hrs.
Getting there: From Helston, follow signs to St Keverne and Coverack. At Zoar garage turn right and follow signs to hostel and Coverack village.
Parking: Yes.
Nearest other hostels: Penzance 25 miles, Land's End 31.
Public transport: BUS: Truronian T3 from Helston with connections from Redruth station. RAIL: Redruth (for bus connection at Helston Tesco) 18 miles. FERRY: Penzance to Scilly Isles 25 miles.

●● CROWCOMBE ☆

Crowcombe Heathfield, Taunton, Somerset
TA4 4BT
Tel: 0870 770 5782 Fax: 0870 770 5782

If you have young children and want a relaxing break, come to Crowcombe. It's on a quiet country lane with high earth banks and fences surrounding the garden, so you can let the kids play safely. Families will find plenty to do – easy walking on the Quantock Hills, mountain biking, the West Somerset Steam Railway and the coast are all nearby.

Location: OS 181, GR 138339.
Great for... families who enjoy countryside activities.
Accommodation: 47 beds: all 4–6-bed rooms, plus 1x2-bed rooms
Family rooms: Yes. **Rent-a-Hostel:** Yes.
Classroom: Yes. **Education packages:** Yes.
Facilities: Lounge, TV room, large self-catering kitchen and dining room, showers, drying room, central heating, laundry facilities, cycle store, shop, garden, games field and camping.
Daytime access: All areas.
Meals: Breakfast, picnic lunch, evening meal.
Reception open: Staff available before 10.00hrs and after 17.00hrs.
Getting there: Follow A358 from Taunton for 10 miles. Turn left at Triscombe Cross (Red Post Cottage), signposted Crowcombe

Station. The hostel is 0.75 miles on right after the railway bridge.
Parking: Yes.
Nearest other hostels: Quantock Hills 10 miles (7 by path), Minehead 16.
Public transport: BUS: First Southern National 28/C, 928 Taunton–Minehead (passes Taunton station), alight Red Post 0.75 miles. RAIL: Taunton 10 miles, Crowcombe (West Somerset Railway) 0.5.

●● DARTINGTON ☆

Lownard, Dartington, Totnes, Devon TQ9 6JJ
Tel: 0870 770 5788 Fax: 0870 770 5789

This traditional 16th century cottage hostel comes complete with exposed beams, log-burning stove and its own babbling brook. It's an ideal base for exploring the River Dart and South Hams countryside. The historic town of Totnes, with a Norman castle and medieval guildhall, is a couple of miles away. Dartmoor National Park and the south Devon coastal resorts are all within easy reach.

Location: OS 202, GR 782622.
Great for... a quiet countryside break.
You need to know... parking is limited and the toilets are outside.
Accommodation: 30 beds: 5x6-bed rooms.
Family rooms: Yes. **Rent-a-Hostel:** Yes.
Classroom: No. **Education packages:** No.
Facilities: Sitting/dining area, two self-catering kitchens, showers, cycle store, drying room and garden. **Daytime access:** All areas. ⊗
Meals: Self-catering only.
Reception open: Staff available before 10.00hrs and after 17.00hrs.
Getting there: Take A385 from Shinner's Bridge roundabout in centre of Dartington. Turn right after 0.25 miles into a narrow lane unsuitable for coaches. The hostel is 200 metres on right.
Parking: Limited. Please park cars in car park and not in lane.
Nearest other hostels: Maypool 11 miles, Bellever 19.
Public transport: BUS: First Western X80 Torquay–Plymouth (passes Paignton and Totnes Stations), alight Shinner's Bridge 0.5 miles. RAIL: Totnes 2 miles.
NATIONALEXPRESS Royal Seven Stars Hotel 2 miles.

Charming: YHA Dartington is a 16th century cottage with its own brook.

For further information visit www.yha.org.uk

South West England

●● ELMSCOTT ☆

Elmscott, Hartland, Bideford, Devon EX39 6ES;
reservations@yha.org.uk
Tel: 0870 770 5814 Fax: 0870 770 5815
Bookings more than 7 days ahead: 0870 770 6113

Expect a windswept but warm welcome at the remote YHA Elmscott. This newly renovated Victorian school is in a wild, next-to-nature location close to Clovelly with sea views of Lundy Island. You'll find amazing rock formations, a profusion of wild flowers and many lanes on this unspoilt section of coastline plus easy access to the South West Coast Path. And, after exhilarating walks, a well-equipped kitchen and comfortable lounge will restore your spirits.
Location: OS 190, GR 231217.
Great for... walkers wanting a remote retreat.
You need to know... it's self-catering accommodation only.
Accommodation: 32 beds: all 2-, 4- and 6-bed rooms, most in an annexe.
Family rooms: No. **Rent-a-Hostel:** Yes.
Classroom: No. **Education packages:** No.
Facilities: Self-catering kitchen, sitting room, dining room, showers, washrooms and cycle store. **Daytime access:** Restricted.
Meals: Self-catering only.
Reception open: 17.00hrs.
Getting there: Leave A39 just north of West Country Inn and follow signs. On foot from Hartland, continue to far west end of Fore Street and pick up footpath to Elmscott through The Vale (3.5 miles).
Parking: Yes.
Nearest other hostels: Boscastle 28 miles, Tintagel 32.
Public transport: BUS: First Red Bus 319 Barnstaple–Hartland (passes close to Barnstaple station), alight Hartland 3.5 miles. RAIL: Barnstaple 25 miles.

●● EXETER ☆☆

Mount Wear House, 47 Countess Wear Road, Exeter, Devon EX2 6LR; exeter@yha.org.uk
Tel: 0870 770 5826 Fax: 0870 770 5827

This spacious 17th century building is tucked away on the edge of the city and is surrounded by tranquil grounds. A walk along the historic ship canal or expansive River Exe (where herons and kingfishers sometimes linger) will lead you towards the Quay and the beautiful cathedral in the heart of the city. The centre is only a 10-minute bus ride away and has many intriguing attractions to explore – the Royal Albert Memorial Museum to name just one. Safe cycle routes, Powderham Castle, the east and south Devon coasts and rugged Dartmoor are all within easy visiting distance.
Location: OS 192, GR 941897.
Great for... a family break close to both city and countryside.
Accommodation: 66 beds: 1x2-, 6x4-, 2x5-, 1x6- and 3x8-bed rooms.
Family rooms: Yes. **Rent-a-Hostel:** Yes.
Classroom: No. **Education packages:** No.
Facilities: Lounge, TV, self-catering kitchen, showers, drying room, cycle store, lockers, laundry, garden and camping.
Daytime access: Restricted.
Meals: Breakfast, picnic lunch, evening meal.

Impressive: Exeter Cathedral is just one of the sights near YHA Exeter.

Reception open: Staff available before 10.00hrs and after 17.00hrs.
Getting there: From M5, J30, follow signs for city centre. Turn right at Countess Wear roundabout, then first left into School Lane. From A30, join M5 at J29 southbound and follow instructions above. From A379, follow signs for Topsham, turn left at Countess Wear roundabout then left into School Lane. From Exeter city centre follow signs for Topsham (see map on page 174).
Parking: Yes.
Nearest other hostels: Steps Bridge 10 miles, Beer 24, Dartington 27.
Public transport: BUS: K or T from High Street, 57 or 85 from bus station, alight Countess Wear post office, 0.75 miles. RAIL: Exeter Central 3 miles, Exeter St David's 4.
NATIONALEXPRESS» Paris St bus station 3 miles.

●● EXFORD (EXMOOR) ☆

Exe Mead, Exford, Minehead, Somerset TA24 7PU
Tel: 0870 770 5828 Fax: 0870 770 5829

This Victorian house stands in its own grounds on the bank of the River Exe in Exford village. In the centre of Exmoor National Park, it's the ideal base to explore the open hills and wooded valleys all around. You may even be lucky enough to spot a red deer. Dunkery Beacon, Porlock Weir and Dunster Castle are all nearby while Exmoor and the Somerset coast are on the doorstep.
Location: OS 181, GR 853383.
Great for... a central base to explore Exmoor.
Accommodation: 51 beds: some 2x2-bed rooms, mostly 4-6-bed

FAMILY CITY GROUP TRADITIONAL CAMPING BARN COASTAL RURAL

options (3 en-suite).
Family rooms: Yes. **Rent-a-Hostel:** Yes.
Classroom: No. **Education packages:** No.
Facilities: Lounge, self-catering kitchen, dining room, drying room and cycle store. **Daytime access:** All areas.
Meals: Breakfast, picnic lunch, evening meal. In winter, meals are only available if booked in advance.
Reception open: Staff available before 10.00hrs and after 17.00hrs.
Getting there: The hostel is in the centre of the village by the bridge over the river.
Parking: Yes.
Nearest other hostels: Minehead 13 miles, Lynton 15, Crowcombe 22.
Public transport: BUS: Exmoor Community Bus 178 from Minehead (Fri only), Exmoor Bus 285 from Minehead (Sun only) or Southern National 38 from Minehead, alight Porlock 7 miles.
RAIL: Taunton 28 miles, Minehead (West Somerset Railway) 13.

● FOX AND HOUNDS
campingbarns@yha.org.uk
Booking: 0870 770 6113
Arrival time: Mr Ward, 01822 820206

This camping barn, close to the village of Lydford, has direct access onto the western edge of Dartmoor.
You need to know... this barn has no catering area.
Accommodation: Sleeps 12 in two areas, each with six bunk beds.
Facilities: Electric light. No catering area but adjacent pub serves breakfast and other meals. Some facilities shared with campers.
Nearest pub: Next door. **Nearest shop:** 0.5 miles.
Location: OS 191, GR 525866.

●● GOLANT ☆
Penquite House, Golant, Fowey, Cornwall PL23 1LA; golant@yha.org.uk
Tel: 0870 770 5832 Fax: 0870 770 5833

Set in three acres of grounds with a further 14 acres of woodland to explore, YHA Golant is ideally suited to children. Overlooking the Fowey Estuary, it's just four miles from the sea and an excellent base for discovering the Cornish coastline. There's plenty of good walking on Bodmin Moor where you can't miss the ancient standing stones and circles. The Lost Gardens of Heligan and the Eden Project are both nearby, as is Dobwalls Family Adventure Park.
Location: OS 200, GR 116556.
Great for... an active family holiday.
You need to know... the approach is down a long single-track lane.
Accommodation: 94 beds: 1x2-, 4x4-, 7x6-bed rooms, plus two larger dormitories.
Family rooms: Yes. **Rent-a-Hostel:** No.
Classroom: Yes. **Education packages:** Yes.
Facilities: TV lounge, games room, self-catering kitchen, dining room, drying room, cycle store, dinner licence, laundry and shop.
Daytime access: All areas.
Meals: Breakfast, picnic lunch, evening meal.

Local wonder: Cornwall's Eden Project is not far from YHA Golant.

Reception open: Staff available before 10.00hrs and after 17.00hrs.
Getting there: Leave A30 at Bodmin and follow signs for B3268 (Lostwithiel) until signs for B3269 (Fowey). Take B3269 (Fowey) from A390 1.5 miles west of Lostwithiel. The hostel is signposted from Castle Dore Crossroads after 2 miles.
Parking: Yes.
Nearest other hostels: Boswinger 17 miles, Boscastle Harbour 28, Tintagel 28, Treyarnon Bay 28.
Public transport: BUS: First Western National 24 St Austell–Fowey (passes Par station), alight Castle Dore Crossroads 1.5 miles.
RAIL: Par 3 miles. FERRY: Plymouth to Roscoff/Santander 40 miles.
NATIONAL EXPRESS St Blazey 4.5 miles.

● GREAT HOUNDTOR
campingbarns@yha.org.uk
Booking: 0870 770 6113
Arrival time: Mr & Mrs Moreton, 01647 221202

On the eastern edge of Dartmoor near the village of Manaton, this camping barn stands in the shadow of Houndtor and close to Haytor, Saddle Tor and Widecombe in the Moor.
You need to know... dogs are not allowed.
Accommodation: Sleeps 14 in two upstairs sleeping galleries.

Hiking in the Dartmoor National Park near YHA Bellever.

● FAMILY   ● CITY   ● GROUP   ● TRADITIONAL   ● CAMPING BARN   ● COASTAL   ● RURAL

Facilities: Electric light, shower (both on meter), cooking area with two gas rings and open fire (wood available).
Nearest pub: 1.5 miles.
Location: OS 191, GR 749795.

●● ILFRACOMBE ☆

1 Hillsborough Terrace, Ilfracombe, Devon EX34 9NR; ilfracombe@yha.org.uk
Tel: 0870 770 5878 Fax: 0870 770 5879

A sea captain built this Georgian house 200 years ago so he could keep a close watch on his boats in the harbour below. The hostel now makes a great base for exploring the north Devon coast. There are rocky coves to discover, a sandy Blue Flag beach at Woolacombe and plenty of nautical bustle to watch all around. Walkers and cyclists are well catered for with routes including the Coast Path and Tarka Trail, while birdwatchers will enjoy a trip to Lundy Island.
Location: OS 180, GR 524476.
Great for... outdoor people who like to keep busy.
You need to know... parking is limited at the hostel.
Accommodation: 50 beds: mostly 2-, 3- and 4-bed rooms, plus a few 5- and 6-bed rooms.
Family rooms: No. **Rent-a-Hostel:** No.
Classroom: No. **Education packages:** Yes.
Facilities: Lounge, TV, self-catering kitchen, showers, cycle storage and drying facilities. **Daytime access:** Restricted.
Meals: Breakfast, picnic lunch. Evening meals only available to pre-booked groups of 10+.
Reception open: 17.00hrs.
Getting there: Follow Combe Martin road signs out of Ilfracombe High Street. The hostel is opposite the Cliffe Hydro Hotel.
Parking: Limited at hostel, plenty on roadside (20 metres).
Nearest other hostels: Lynton 18 miles, Exford 25.
Public transport: BUS: First Red Bus 1, 2, 30 from Barnstaple (passing close to Barnstaple station). RAIL: Barnstaple 13 miles. FERRY: Lundy Island service 600 metres.
NATIONAL EXPRESS» Ilfracombe bus station 0.5 miles.

●● LAND'S END ☆

Letcha Vean, St Just-in-Penwith, Penzance, Cornwall TR19 7NT
Tel: 0870 770 5906 Fax: 0870 770 5907

The closest hostel to Land's End with more than half of the rooms commanding fine views of the sea. This peaceful location provides a haven for rare migratory birds in spring and autumn and, in summer, visitors should make the four-mile trip to the fine surfing and swimming beach at Sennan Cove. The South West Coast Path is just five minutes away or, for a day out with a difference, take a flight to the Isles of Scilly from the airport that's just 10 minutes' drive away. A pint and live music at the local pub will round off your stay.
Location: OS 203, GR 364305.
Great for... active families with older children.
You need to know... parking is limited.

Accommodation: 38 beds: 2x2-, 1x3-, 2x4-, 1x5- and 3x6-bed rooms.
Family rooms: Yes. **Rent-a-Hostel:** Yes.
Classroom: No. **Education packages:** No.
Facilities: Lounge, self-catering kitchen, cycle store, grounds and camping. **Daytime access:** Restricted. ⊗
Meals: Breakfast, picnic lunch, evening meal.
Reception open: 17.00hrs.
Getting there: By car from B3306, turn right at Kelynack through farmyard and down lane marked No Access For Motors. By foot from St Just bus station, walk past library and turn left to follow a surfaced road past the chapel to the end. Cross a stile, go through field following hedge and through gate at bottom. Path comes out on road above hostel. Bring a torch.
Parking: Limited.
Nearest other hostels: Penzance 8 miles, Coverack 31.
Public transport: BUS: First Western 10/A/B, 11/A from Penzance (Penzance station), alight St Just 0.75 miles; 15 from St Ives (not Sat), June–Sept only, alight Kelynack, 0.5 miles; or Sunset Bus 345 from YHA Penzance, alight Kelynack. RAIL: Penzance 8 miles.

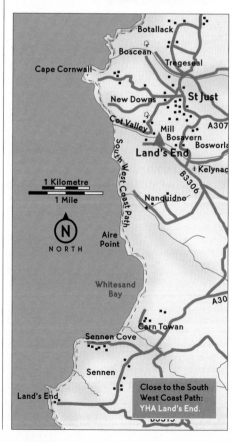

Close to the South West Coast Path: YHA Land's End.

For all the latest YHA news visit www.yha.org.uk

FAMILY   CITY   GROUP   TRADITIONAL   CAMPING BARN   COASTAL   RURAL

● LITTON CHENEY ☆☆☆

Litton Cheney, Dorchester, Dorset DT2 9AT;
reservations@yha.org.uk
Tel: 0870 770 5922 Fax: 0870 770 5923
Bookings more than 7 days ahead: 0870 770 6113

In a traditional Dorset village in an Area of Outstanding Natural Beauty, YHA Litton Cheney is surrounded by excellent walking and cycling country. This comfortable Dutch barn, once a cheese factory, makes a good family base and is close to Chesil Beach, Abbotsbury Swannery and subtropical gardens.

Location: OS 194, GR 548900.
Great for... walkers and cyclists keen to explore Dorset.
You need to know... only self-catering accommodation is offered.
Accommodation: 22 beds: 2x2-, 3x4- and 1x6-bed rooms.
Family rooms: Yes. **Rent-a-Hostel:** Yes.
Classroom: No. **Education packages:** No.
Facilities: Self-catering kitchen, lounge/diner, showers, cycle store and drying room. **Daytime access:** Restricted. ✆
Meals: Self-catering only.
Reception open: 17.00hrs.
Getting there: From A35 into village, follow hostel signs. The hostel is next door to White Horse pub.
Parking: Limited.
Nearest other hostels: Portland 19 miles, Lulworth Cove 25, Beer 28, Street 40.
Public transport: BUS: First Southern National 31 Weymouth–Axminster (passes Axminster, Dorchester South and close to Dorchester West stations), alight Whiteway 1.5 miles. RAIL: Dorchester South or West, both 10 miles.

South West England offers miles of cycling for everyone.

●● LIZARD ☆☆☆☆

Lizard Point, Cornwall, TR12 7NT
Tel: 0870 770 6120 Fax: 0870 770 6121

Formerly a Victorian hotel acquired by the National Trust to preserve and protect this most unique location, this newly restored building now offers first-class facilities and has stunning views out to sea over Lizard Point. Almost the most southerly building in England, it provides a superb base for exploring the spectacular coastline of this historic peninsula. This hostel is also within easy reach of all the exciting attractions west Cornwall has to offer.
Location: OS 204, GR 051495.
Great for... families and walkers.
You need to know... this hostel opens in April 2003.
Accommodation: 32 beds: 2x3- (en-suite, suitable for disabled), 1x4-, 2x5- and 2x6-bed rooms.
Family rooms: Yes. **Rent-a-Hostel:** Yes.
Classroom: Yes. **Education packages:** No.
Facilities: Lounge, TV, self-catering kitchen, dining room, showers, toilets, cycle store, parking. **Daytime access:** Restricted. ✆
Meals: Self-catering only.
Reception open: 17.00hrs.
Getting there: From Helston, take the A3083, signposted to Lizard. When you arrive at Lizard Point, follow the signs for the National Trust car park and the hostel is next to the lighthouse.
Parking: Yes.
Nearest other hostels: Coverack 8 miles, Penzance 20, Land's End 22.

South West England

● FAMILY ● CITY ● GROUP ● TRADITIONAL ● CAMPING BARN ● COASTAL ● RURAL

Public transport: BUS: From Helston T1 runs 6.30hrs to 22.40hrs.
RAIL: Penzance 20 miles.
NATIONALEXPRESS Request stop at Helston.

● LOPWELL
campingbarns@yha.org.uk
Booking: 0870 770 6113 (Owners will contact guests to arrange key collection.)

This camping barn sits on the banks of the River Tavy in an Area of Outstanding Natural Beauty. On the edge of Dartmoor, it's an ideal location for walking, cycling, canoeing and birdwatching. The Tamar Valley Discovery Trail runs close by.
You need to know... you cannot hire the barn for celebrations; dogs are allowed downstairs if you book sole usage; also book sole usage if you have children under five years of age.
Accommodation: Sleeps 16 on first floor.
Facilities: Shower, toilets adjacent, cooking area with microwave and fridge, sitting areas, hot water and metered electricity.
Nearest pub: 1.5 miles. **Nearest shop:** 2.5 miles.
Location: OS 201, GR 475650.

●● LULWORTH COVE ☆☆
School Lane, West Lulworth, Wareham, Dorset BH20 5SA; lulworth@yha.org.uk
Tel: 0870 770 5940 Fax: 0870 770 5941

YHA Lulworth Cove is a single storey purpose-built timber building on the edge of the tranquil fishing village of West Lulworth. Surrounded by fields and wonderful views of the Dorset hills, it's a mile's walk to the oyster-shaped Lulworth Cove and dramatic coastline. Children will enjoy a day out at the largest entertainment centre in the south, Tower Park Leisure Centre.
Location: OS 194, GR 832806.
Great for... families looking for a mix of coast and countryside.
Accommodation: 34 beds: 1x4- and 6x5-bed rooms.

Dramatic: Durdle Door is near YHA Lulworth Cove.

Family rooms: Yes. **Rent-a-Hostel:** Yes.
Classroom: No. **Education packages:** No.
Facilities: Lounge/diner, self-catering kitchen, showers, drying room, cycle store and grounds. **Daytime access:** Restricted.
Meals: Breakfast, picnic lunch, evening meal.
Reception open: 17.00hrs.
Getting there: 100 metres east of B3070, turn opposite Castle Inn into School Lane.
Parking: Yes.
Nearest other hostels: Swanage 17 miles, Portland 23, Litton Cheney 25.
Public transport: BUS: First Southern National 103 Dorchester–Bovington, Dorset Linkrider from Weymouth (both pass Wool station). RAIL: Wool 5 miles.

●● LYNTON ☆☆
Lynbridge, Lynton, Devon EX35 6AZ
Tel: 0870 770 5942 Fax: 0870 770 5943

This tranquil hostel, a former country house, sits on the side of a steep wooded gorge and is a good base for discovering Exmoor. Close to the sea and the National Trust estate of Watersmeet, there are plenty of child-friendly attractions nearby. A wildlife park, dinosaur park and the Big Sheep Theme Park are all a short drive away. For quieter days out, there are also lots of riverside and cliff walks leading from the hostel.
Location: OS 180, GR 720487.

Why not take advantage of the South West's coastline and learn to sail?

Great for... an energetic family holiday.
You need to know... parking is limited.
Accommodation: 36 beds: 2x2-, 2x4- and 4x6-bed rooms.
Family rooms: Yes. **Rent-a-Hostel:** Yes.
Classroom: No. **Education packages:** Yes.
Facilities: Lounge, self-catering kitchen, dining room, drying room, cycle store, shop and laundry. **Daytime access:** All areas.
Meals: Breakfast, picnic lunch, evening meal.
Reception open: Staff available before 10.00hrs and after 17.00hrs.
Getting there: From A39 at Lynmouth, follow Lynton sign right up steep hill (B3234), turn left to Lynbridge and right at the Bridge Inn. From Barbrook, turn off A39 at petrol station and follow B3234 (Lynmouth Road) for 1 mile (do not turn off). In Lynbridge, turn left

● FAMILY　● CITY　● GROUP　● TRADITIONAL　● CAMPING BARN　● COASTAL　● RURAL

---

at The Bridge Inn up a steep, narrow road.
Parking: Limited.
Nearest other hostels: Exford 15 miles, Ilfracombe 18, Minehead 21.
Public transport: BUS: First Red Bus 309/310 from Barnstaple
(passes close to Barnstaple station), 300 Barnstaple–Minehead (Sat
and Sun all year and daily June–Sept only). RAIL: Barnstaple 20 miles.

●● MAYPOOL ☆

Galmpton, Brixham, Devon TQ5 0ET;
maypool@yha.org.uk
Tel: 0870 770 5962 Fax: 0870 770 5963

With 20 beaches within easy travelling distance of this hostel, you'll
be spoilt for choice for where to build your sandcastles. The area is
also popular for watersports and other outdoor activities so, by the
time you return to this hostel, you're likely to be exhausted. Just as
well then that this Victorian house is in a quiet setting above the Dart
Valley, where you can sit back and watch the Paignton to Kingswear
steam train chuff through the hostel grounds.
Location: OS 202, GR 877546.
Great for... active family breaks.
Accommodation: 65 beds: all 4–12-bed rooms.
Family rooms: Yes. **Rent-a-Hostel:** Yes.
Classroom: Yes. **Education packages:** No.
Facilities: Lounges, TV room, dining room, games room,
self-catering kitchen, showers, drying room and cycle store.

●● OKEHAMPTON (DARTMOOR) ☆☆☆

Klondyke Road, Okehampton EX20 1EW;
okehampton@yha.org.uk
Tel: 0870 770 5978 Fax: 0870 770 5979

Prepare for serious fun in this uniquely preserved Victorian
railway goods shed, now offering modern accommodation.
On the edge of Dartmoor National Park, this licensed adventure
centre specialises in providing outdoor holidays. Have a go at rock
climbing, gorge scrambling, pony trekking, archery, treasure hunts
and lots more. Or opt for a more relaxed pace and put on your
walking boots to explore the surrounding moors.
Location: OS 191, GR 591942.
Great for... improving your skills in a fun-filled atmosphere.
Accommodation: 124 beds: all 2-, 4-, 6- and 8-bed rooms.
Family rooms: Yes. **Rent-a-Hostel:** Yes.
Classroom: Yes. **Education packages:** No.
Facilities: Lounge, dining room, self-catering kitchen, laundry,
showers, toilets and camping. Outdoor activities (book in
advance). **Daytime access:** All areas. ✪
Meals: Breakfast, picnic lunch, evening meal.
Reception open: Staff available before 10.00 and after 17.00hrs.
Getting there: From A30, head into Okehampton. In town centre
at traffic lights turn into George Street and then right into Station
Road. Bear left at monument and continue under bridge. The
hostel is on the left.

Daytime access: All areas.
Meals: Breakfast, picnic lunch, evening meal.
Reception open: Staff available before 10.00hrs and after 17.00hrs.
Getting there: At A38, A380 and A3022 intersection with A379,
take second turning on right (Manor Vale Road) and follow
Greenway Road through the village, turning left at YHA sign.
Parking: Yes.
Nearest other hostels: Dartington 11 miles, Salcombe 26,
Exeter 32.
Public transport: BUS: Stagecoach Devon 12 Paignton station–
Brixham, alight Churston School 2 miles. RAIL: Paignton 5 miles,
Churston (Dart Valley Railway) 2.
FERRY: Plymouth to France and Spain 36 miles.
NATIONALEXPRESS Brixham, Bank Lane 4 miles.

●● MINEHEAD ☆☆☆

Alcombe Combe, Minehead, Somerset
TA24 6EW
Tel: 0870 770 5968 Fax: 0870 770 5969

Combine a traditional seaside holiday with a blast of outdoor
activity at Minehead. This attractive country house sits high in the
Exmoor hills of Somerset, just two miles from sandy beaches where
children will love the funfair and swimming pools. Plenty of easy
walking routes leave from the hostel's back door (with the South
West Coast Path nearby), leading you to spectacular hill views that
inspired the hymn, All Things Bright and Beautiful. Mountain bikers

Parking: Yes.
Nearest other hostels: Steps Bridge 18 miles, Bellever 20
(13 over moors), Exeter 24.
Public transport: BUS: First Western X9/10 Exeter–Bude (Exeter
St David's station), alight Okehampton, then 0.75 miles or 187
Gunnislake Station–Okehampton station (Sun, June–Sept only).
RAIL: Okehampton (adjacent), Sun, June–Sept, otherwise
Copplestone 13 miles, Exeter St David's 22.
NATIONALEXPRESS West Street 0.5 miles.

www.britainonview.com

Prepare for a fun-filled activity holiday at YHA Okehampton.

⬤ FAMILY   ⬤ CITY   ⬤ GROUP   ⬤ TRADITIONAL   ⬤ CAMPING BARN   ⬤ COASTAL   ⬤ RURAL

YHA Minehead has easy walking routes right from its door.

will also find exciting trails.

Location: OS 181, GR 973442.

Great for... walking and seaside fun.

You need to know... the hostel is at the end of a private track with limited parking.

Accommodation: 35 beds: 1x3- (double bed with single over), 5x4- and 2x6-bed rooms.

Family rooms: Yes. **Rent-a-Hostel:** Yes.

Classroom: No. **Education packages:** No.

Facilities: Lounge, self-catering kitchen, dining room, drying room, cycle store and grounds. **Daytime access:** All areas. ⊗

Meals: Breakfast, picnic lunch, evening meal.

Reception open: Staff available before 10.00hrs and after 17.00hrs.

Getting there: Turn off the A39 at Alcombe into Brook Street or Church Street and follow this road to Britannia Inn on Manor Road, continuing when it becomes a private track for the last 0.5 miles. Turn sharp left up to the hostel. The hostel can be difficult to find after dark.

Parking: Limited.

Nearest other hostels: Exford 13 miles (10 on foot), Quantock Hills 14, Crowcombe Heathfield 16, Lynton 21.

Public transport: BUS: First Southern National 28, 928 Taunton–Minehead (Taunton station), alight Alcombe 0.75 mile. RAIL: Taunton 25 miles, Minehead or Dunster (both West Somerset Railway) 2 miles.

⬤ MULLACOTT FARM

campingbarns@yha.org.uk

Booking: 0870 770 6113

Arrival time: Mrs Homa, 01271 866877

These former stables are on a small working farm in an Area of Outstanding Natural Beauty in Exmoor. Free-range eggs and sausages are available from the farm.

Great for... exploring north Devon, Tarka country, Exmoor and nearby beaches.

You need to know... the main sleeping area is an above-ground platform, not bunkbeds.

Accommodation: Sleeps 10 in one large area, plus small stalls each

sleeping 2.

Facilities: Electric light, dining area, kitchen area with full-size oven, hob, fridge-freezer, microwave, toaster, kettle, sinks with hot water (all on coin-operated meters), basic cooking equipment and cutlery. Separate toilets and shower (coin operated) adjacent, covered storage area, picnic area and car parking. Dogs welcome.

Nearest pub: 0.25 mile. **Nearest shop:** 0.25 miles.

Location: OS 180, GR 514455.

⬤ NORTHCOMBE

campingbarns@yha.org.uk

Booking: 0870 770 6113

This attractive camping barn has been converted from a watermill. Just a mile from Dulverton, a network of footpaths and bridleways leads onto Exmoor and to the Barle River valley where you'll find good canoeing.

Great for... riding, canoeing, cycling and walking.

Accommodation: Sleeps 15 in bunk beds in two areas.

Facilities: Fully equipped cooking area, hot water, fridge, shower, electric light (all on meter), wood-burning stove. Stabling available.

Nearest pub: 1 mile. **Nearest shop:** 1 mile.

Location: OS 181, GR 915292.

⬤⬤ PENZANCE ☆

Castle Horneck, Alverton, Penzance, Cornwall TR20 8TF; penzance@yha.org.uk

Tel: 0870 770 5992 Fax: 0870 770 5993

This early Georgian manor stands in landscaped gardens and commands sweeping views of Mounts Bay and the Lizard Peninsula. Visit St Michael's Mount and the home of the Tate Gallery (St Ives), or take a boat to the Isles of Scilly. Enjoy a wide choice of meals, from speciality fresh-baked pizzas to Cornish clotted cream ice cream.

Location: OS 203, GR 457302.

Great for... coastal views and lovely beaches.

You need to know... this hostel has facilities for camping.

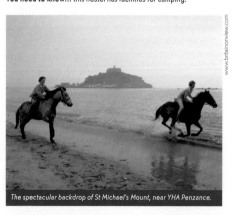

The spectacular backdrop of St Michael's Mount, near YHA Penzance.

www.britainonview.com

● FAMILY   ● CITY   ● GROUP   ● TRADITIONAL   ● CAMPING BARN   ● COASTAL   ● RURAL

Accommodation: 80 beds: mostly 4–10-bed rooms.
Family rooms: No. **Rent-a-Hostel:** No.
Classroom: No. **Education packages:** Yes.
Facilities: Lounge, TV room, showers, drying room, cycle store, lockers, grounds and camping with dedicated facilities.
Daytime access: All areas.
Meals: Breakfast, picnic lunch, evening meal.
Reception open: Staff available before 10.00hrs and after 17.00hrs.
Getting there: Drivers, follow A30 around Penzance by-pass and turn at Castle Horneck sign to avoid town centre. Walkers/cyclists, go through town centre and past YMCA. Turn right onto Castle Horneck Road and cross A30. Continue through trees, hostel on left.
Parking: Yes.
Nearest other hostels: Land's End 8 miles, Coverack 19, Perranporth 29.
Public transport: BUS: Sunset coaches to all points of the coastal footpath and beaches; First Western 5B to Penzance station and St Ives; 5B, 6B, 10B to YMCA then follow signs.
RAIL: Penzance 1.5 miles. FERRY: Isles of Scilly 1.5 miles.
NATIONAL EXPRESS» Penzance bus station 1 mile.

●● PERRANPORTH ☆

Droskyn Point, Perranporth, Cornwall TR6 0GS
Tel: 0870 770 5994 Fax: 0870 770 5994

Once a coastguard station, this hostel is perched in a clifftop location on the rugged north coast of Cornwall, a surfer's paradise. Expect spectacular views of untamed Atlantic seas and three miles of lifeguarded sandy beaches. Walkers will want to follow the South West Coast Path, while nature lovers should look out for seals and dolphins in the St Agnes Marine Conservation Area.
Location: OS 204, GR 752544.
Great for... active people in need of an adrenalin rush.
You need to know... there's a charge for daytime parking between June and September.
Accommodation: 24 beds: 2x4- and 2x8-bed rooms.
Family rooms: No. **Rent-a-Hostel:** Yes.
Classroom: No. **Education packages:** No.
Facilities: Lounge/dining room, self-catering kitchen, garden, cycle and surfboard store and drying room (suitable for wetsuits).
Daytime access: Restricted.
Meals: Self-catering only.

●● PORTLAND ☆☆☆

Hardy House, Castle Road, Portland, Dorset
DT5 1AU; portland@yha.org.uk
Tel: 0870 770 6000 Fax: 0870 770 6001

During the heyday of the Royal Navy's presence in Portland, this early Edwardian building belonged to the First Admiral and was later used as the headquarters for the MOD police. It benefits from extensive views over Lyme Bay and is a good base to explore the island's heritage, including Portland Castle and Portland Lighthouse. The Round Island Coastal Footpath will give you a good look at the flora and fauna, or visit Chesil beach or nearby Weymouth to enjoy its award-winning beaches.
Location: OS 194, GR 685741.
Great for... a look into Portland's past, exploring the Jurassic Coast and Thomas Hardy country, walking and watersports.
Accommodation: 28 beds: 1x4- and 4x6-bed rooms.
Family rooms: Yes. **Rent-a-Hostel:** Yes.
Classroom: No. **Education packages:** Yes.
Facilities: Day room, self-catering kitchen, shower, toilet and camping. Tourist information centre.
Daytime access: Restricted. 🚭
Meals: Self-catering only. Meals available for pre-booked groups of 10+.
Reception open: 17.00 hrs.
Getting there: On arriving at Portland, from Victoria Square turn left into Victory Road, then left again into Castle Road. The hostel is on the right-hand side.
Parking: Yes.
Nearest other hostels: Litton Cheney 19 miles, Lulworth Cove 23, Beer 44.
Public transport: BUS: First 1 from Weymouth and Sureline X10.

RAIL: Weymouth 5.5 miles. FERRY: White Boat services from Weymouth Quay to Portland Castle (May to October), Condor Ferries (tickets available from hostel) to and from Channel Islands (March to October).
NATIONAL EXPRESS» Weymouth 4 miles.

www.britainonview.com

Try your hand at windsurfing on the beaches near YHA Portland.

● FAMILY   ● CITY   ● GROUP   ● TRADITIONAL   ● CAMPING BARN   ● COASTAL   ● RURAL

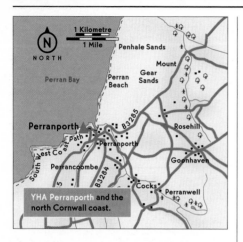

YHA Perranporth and the north Cornwall coast.

Reception open: 17.00hrs.
Getting there: From A30 turn right onto B3285 signposted Perranporth. Continue into Perranporth centre and turn right then immediately left on to St George's Hill signposted St Agnes. Turn right into Tywarnhayle Road at hostel sign. Turn left on to Tregundy Lane at car park following hostel sign. Continue on Droskyn Point beyond Cellar Cove Hotel. On South West Coast Path from St Agnes, fork left at trail marker to Perranporth and hostel is 100 metres down footpath.
Parking: Free overnight parking 250 metres (charge for daytime parking June–Sept).
Nearest other hostels: Treyarnon Bay 22 miles, Boswinger 25.
Public transport: BUS: First Western National 57 St Ives–Newquay, 87A/B/C Truro–Newquay (pass close to Truro and Newquay stations), Truronian T1 Lizard–Perranporth. RAIL: Truro 9 miles.
NATIONAL EXPRESS Beach Road 0.25 miles.

●● QUANTOCK HILLS ☆

Sevenacres, Holford, Bridgwater, Somerset TA5 1SQ; reservations@yha.org.uk
Tel: 0870 770 6006 Fax: 0870 770 6006
Bookings more than 7 days ahead: 0870 770 6113

Head off the beaten track to this traditional country house high on the Quantock Hills with views across the Bristol Channel to Wales. Walk straight from the hostel onto the hills to see a wealth of wildlife or venture down to Kilve beach to hunt for fossils. History lovers will enjoy exploring the nearby town of Dunster, dominated by the towers and turrets of a Victorian castle.
Location: OS 181, GR 146416.
Great for... keen walkers wanting a country retreat.
You need to know... it's self-catering accommodation only.
Accommodation: 24 beds: 1x2-, 1x4- and 3x6-bed rooms.
Family rooms: No. **Rent-a-Hostel:** Yes.
Classroom: No. **Education packages:** No.
Facilities: Lounge, dining room, self-catering kitchen, showers,

central heating, wood-burning stove, drying room, grounds and camping. **Daytime access:** Restricted.
Meals: Self-catering only.
Reception open: 17.00hrs.
Getting there: From Kilve, take Lane opposite post office and, after 1 mile, follow a rough track. From Holford, take road through Hotel (1.5 miles), cross second cattle grid, go uphill to a sharp bend and take rough track on right to hostel.
Parking: Limited.
Nearest other hostels: Crowcombe 10 miles (7 on foot), Minehead 14.
Public transport: BUS: First Southern National 15, 915, 927 Bridgwater–Minehead (passes close to Bridgwater station). RAIL: Bridgwater 13 miles.

● RUNNAGE

campingbarns@yha.org.uk
Booking: 0870 770 6113
Arrival time: Christine Coaker, 01822 880222

A former hay loft and stable block has been converted to form this camping barn. It stands on a working farm in the centre of Dartmoor, close to Bellever Forest and the River Dart. This is a good location for walking, cycling, climbing, letterboxing and canoeing.
You need to know... it's a minimum of 12 people for weekend bookings; minimum two nights on Bank Holidays; bike hire available.
Accommodation: Sleeps 15x2.
Facilities: Hot water, fridge, shower and electric light. Electricity for cooking and heating extra. Breakfast is available by prior arrangement.
Nearest pub: 0.25 miles. **Nearest shop:** 0.25 miles.
Location: OS 191, GR 667792.

●● SALCOMBE ☆

Sharpitor, Salcombe, Devon TQ8 8LW
Tel: 0870 770 6016 Fax: 0870 770 6017

If you love the sea, Salcombe is the place for you. Test out your sea legs on one of the sailing packages available at the hostel or be brave and try your hand at a range of watersports. Safe sandy

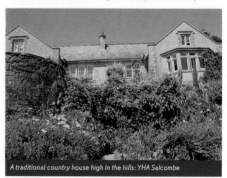

A traditional country house high in the hills: YHA Salcombe

○ FAMILY ● CITY ● GROUP ● TRADITIONAL ● CAMPING BARN ○ COASTAL ● RURAL

beaches are just a few minutes away, or venture further on the coastal path to Bolthead, Hope Cove and beyond. After a busy day, this Edwardian National Trust property set in six acres of semi-tropical gardens makes an elegant spot in which to recuperate.
Location: OS 202, GR 728374.
Great for... groups with a passion for the sea and the outdoors.
You need to know... there's no parking at the hostel between 10.00hrs and 17.00hrs.
Accommodation: 50 beds: 1x2-, 5x4-, 2x6- and 2x8-bed rooms.
Family rooms: Yes. **Rent-a-Hostel:** No.
Classroom: Yes. **Education packages:** No.
Facilities: Lounge, TV room, dining room, self-catering kitchen, showers, drying room and cycle store.
Daytime access: Restricted. ⊗
Meals: Breakfast, picnic lunch, evening meal.
Reception open: 17.00hrs.
Getting there: From Kingsbridge, follow A381 to Salcombe, then follow brown YHA and Overbecks signs to hostel.
Parking: Convenient National Trust car park available between 17.00hrs and 10.00hrs. During the day, please park at South Sands Hotel (15 minutes by foot) or North Sands (20 minutes).
Nearest other hostels: Dartington 21 miles, Maypool 26 (via Dart Ferry or Totnes).
Public transport: BUS: Tally Ho! from Kingsbridge (connects from Plymouth, Dartmouth and for rail connections from Totnes, through buses from Totnes on Sundays), alight Salcombe 2 miles. RAIL: Totnes 20 miles. FERRY: From Salcombe town centre to South Sands, then 15-minute walk uphill to Overbecks.

●● SALISBURY ☆

Milford Hill, Salisbury, Wiltshire SP1 2QW;
salisbury@yha.org.uk
Tel: 0870 770 6018 Fax: 0870 770 6019

This is a 200-year-old building in secluded grounds. It's just a short walk into the heart of the historic city of Salisbury and makes a good base for groups seeking to explore the multitude of attractions throughout Wiltshire. It's just minutes from Salisbury Cathedral and nine miles from Stonehenge.
Location: OS 184, GR 149299.
Great for... off-road cycling; history enthusiasts.
You need to know... the main building has 50 beds with a 20-bedded lodge available for private hire.
Accommodation: 70 beds. Main house: 1x1-, 1x2-, 3x4-bed rooms, plus larger rooms; Lodge: 2x3-, 4x4-bed rooms including lounge, showers and toilets.
Family rooms: Yes. **Rent-a-Hostel:** No.
Classroom: No. **Education packages:** Yes.
Facilities: TV room, lounge, showers, self-catering kitchen, coin-operated laundry, cycle store and garden.
Daytime access: All areas.
Meals: Bed and breakfast package only. Full meals service only available to pre-booked groups.
Reception open: 7.30hrs–22.30hrs.
Getting there: Motorists, follow A36 signposts. Follow brown signs

Salisbury Cathedral dominates this city near YHA Salisbury.

www.britainonview.com

on A36 by Salisbury college roundabout. On foot, walk east from tourist information centre following black footpath signs, leading into Milford Street and up hill (see map on page 175).
Parking: Yes.
Nearest other hostels: Burley 21 miles, Winchester 24, Bath 39.
Public transport: BUS: Frequent from surrounding areas, bus station 5 minutes' walk. RAIL: Salisbury 1 mile.
FERRY: Portsmouth to France (Caen, Cherbourg, St Malo, Le Havre) and Spain (Santander) 40 miles.
NATIONAL EXPRESS Endless Street, Salisbury 1.2 miles.

●● STEPS BRIDGE ☆

Steps Bridge, near Dunsford, Exeter,
Devon EX6 7EQ; bellever@yha.org.uk
Tel: 0870 770 6048 Fax: 0870 770 6049
Bookings over 7 days ahead: 0870 770 5692

If you feel the need for peace and tranquillity, this unpretentious chalet is a quiet haven in a secluded woodland location on the edge of East Dartmoor. From this steep hillside overlooking the Teign Valley, there are endless walks leading across the rugged Dartmoor

● FAMILY ● CITY ● GROUP ● TRADITIONAL ● CAMPING BARN ● COASTAL ● RURAL

A quiet haven in secluded woodland: YHA Steps Bridge.

Tors and onto the lower slopes where you'll discover rare wildflowers, birds and butterflies. Although facilities are basic, the bunkrooms are comfortable.

Location: OS 191, GR 802882.

Great for... active walkers who want to avoid the crowds.

You need to know... the toilets, showers and some bunkrooms are outside the main building.

Accommodation: 24 beds: 1x2-, 2x4-, 1x6- and 1x8-bed rooms.

Family rooms: No. **Rent-a-Hostel:** Yes.

Classroom: No. **Education packages:** No.

Facilities: Sitting/dining area, self-catering kitchen, showers, drying room and cycle store. **Daytime access:** All areas. 🚭

Meals: Self-catering only.

Reception open: Staff available before 10.00hrs and after 17.00hrs.

Getting there: On the B3212 Exeter to Moretonhampstead road, turn left 200 metres after Steps Bridge. The hostel drive is very steep so please take care.

Parking: Please park in the public car park opposite end of hostel drive; no parking on drive.

Nearest other hostels: Exeter 11 miles, Bellever 18, Okehampton 18, Dartington 26.

Public transport: BUS: Stagecoach 359 from Exeter Central station. RAIL: Exeter Central 9 miles, Exeter St David's 9.

●● STREET ☆

The Chalet, Ivythorn Hill, Street, Somerset BA16 0TZ

Tel: 0870 770 6056 Fax: 0870 770 6057

Overlooking Glastonbury Tor, this basic Swiss-style chalet is surrounded by National Trust land and feels like a quiet retreat. However, it's within easy reach of the Mendip Hills, Somerset Levels, mystical Glastonbury and historic Wells. The amenities of the town of Street are also close by.

Location: OS 182, GR 480345.

Great for... a quiet base for touring Somerset.

Accommodation: 28 beds: 2x3-, 4x4- and 1x6-bed rooms.

Family rooms: Yes. **Rent-a-Hostel:** Yes.

Classroom: No. **Education packages:** No.

Facilities: Lounge/diner, self-catering kitchen, showers, drying

Quiet: YHA Street is a Swiss-style chalet surrounded by NT land.

room, cycle store and camping ground.

Daytime access: All areas.

Meals: Self-catering only.

Reception open: Staff available before 10.00hrs and after 17.00hrs.

Getting there: From Street, take the B3151 towards Somerton for 2 miles. Turn right at Marshalls Elm crossroads and follow signs to hostel which is 500 metres on your right.

Parking: Yes.

Nearest other hostels: Cheddar 17 miles, Quantock Hills 28, Bristol 33.

Public transport: BUS: First Badgerline/First Southern National 376, 377, 976/7 Bristol–Yeovil (passes Bristol Temple Meads station), alight Marshalls Elm then walk 500 metres (hostel signposted). RAIL: Castle Cary 11 miles, Bridgwater 13. **NATIONALEXPRESS»** Leigh Road 1.25 miles.

●● SWANAGE ☆☆☆

Cluny, Cluny Crescent, Swanage, Dorset BH19 2BS; swanage@yha.org.uk

Tel: 0870 770 6058 Fax: 0870 770 6059

For an activity-packed seaside holiday, Swanage is the place to be. The town boasts safe, sandy beaches, spectacular coastal scenery, high sunshine ratings and festivals galore. And just a few minutes' walk from the town centre is this elegant Victorian house offering fine views across the bay. Don't miss exploring the Jurassic Coast,

● FAMILY   ● CITY   ● GROUP   ● TRADITIONAL   ● CAMPING BARN   ● COASTAL   ● RURAL

a newly designated World Heritage Site that tells a geological story covering 200 million years.

Location: OS 195, GR 031785.

Great for... sunbathers and swimmers.

Accommodation: 102 beds: a few 2–4-, mostly 5–9-bed rooms, plus 1x12-bed room.

Family rooms: Yes. **Rent-a-Hostel:** No.

Classroom: Yes. **Education packages:** Yes.

Facilities: Lounge, TV, games room, self-catering kitchen, showers, drying room, laundry facilities and cycle store.

Daytime access: All areas.

Meals: Breakfast, picnic lunch, evening meal.

Reception open: All day.

The hilltop ruins of Corfe Castle near YHA Swanage.

Getting there: From Bournemouth, take Sandbanks ferry, then travel on to Swanage via Studland village. From Wareham, take A351 to Swanage via Corfe Castle. From Swanage town centre, go up Stafford Road (next to White Swan Inn in High Street) which runs into Cluny Crescent. The hostel is at the top of the hill on the right.

Parking: Yes.

Nearest other hostels: Lulworth Cove 17 miles, Burley 29.

Public transport: BUS: Wilts & Dorset 150 from Bournemouth (passes Branksome station), 142–4 from Poole, all services alight Swanage bus station 0.25 miles. RAIL: Wareham 10 miles. FERRY: Poole to Cherbourg 15 miles.

NATIONALEXPRESS» Swanage bus station 0.25 miles.

●● TINTAGEL ☆

Dunderhole Point, Tintagel, Cornwall PL34 0DW;
reservations@yha.org.uk
Tel: 0870 770 6068 Fax: 0870 770 6069
Bookings more than 7 days ahead: 0870 770 6113

Have you had enough of 21st century Britain? Then stay in this well-equipped and comfortable hostel, perched on Glebe Cliff with stunning coastal views over Dunderhole Point. Walk the South West Coast Path, explore the 13th century remains of Tintagel Castle or just watch the wild seas crash over the rocks below.

Location: OS 200, GR 047881.

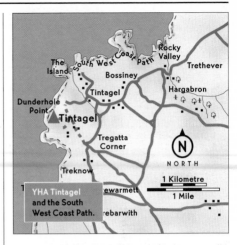

YHA Tintagel and the South West Coast Path.

Great for... Arthurian legend lovers, walkers and families.

You need to know... access to the hostel is along a narrow, rough and unlit track and parking is limited.

Accommodation: 22 beds, 1x2-, 2x4- and 2x6-bed rooms.

Family rooms: No. **Rent-a-Hostel:** Yes.

Classroom: No. **Education packages:** No.

Facilities: Self-catering kitchen, sitting/dining area, showers and cycle store. **Daytime access:** Restricted. ☺

Meals: Self-catering only.

Reception open: 17.00hrs.

Getting there: By car, from Tintagel village take B3263 to Tregatta (0.75 miles). Turn right along a narrow lane, then a very rough, unlit

Brave the steep descent to Tintagel Cove near YHA Tintagel.

● FAMILY ● CITY ● GROUP ● TRADITIONAL ● CAMPING BARN ● COASTAL ● RURAL

---

track to the hostel. On foot, follow road to Tintagel church, then path for 300 metres to hostel.

Parking: Limited.

Nearest other hostels: Boscastle Harbour 5 miles, Treyarnon Bay 23 (18 by ferry), Golant 28.

Public transport: BUS: First Western National X10 from Exeter St David's Station, 55 or 122/5 from Bodmin Parkway station. On all, alight Tintagel, 0.75 miles. RAIL: Bodmin Parkway 20 miles.

●● TREYARNON BAY ☆

**Tregonnan, Treyarnon, Padstow, Cornwall
PL28 8JR; treyarnon@yha.org.uk
Tel: 0870 770 6076 Fax: 0870 770 6077**

Enjoy a traditional seaside break at this hostel situated above a beautiful sandy bay. Formerly a 1930s summer residence, the hostel is virtually on the beach so you can build sandcastles, surf and watch sunsets to your heart's content. Beach games and the obligatory buckets and spades are available for hire at the hostel. Walkers and cyclists will find plenty to do or, if you're feeling energetic, try the all-inclusive surf package offered by the hostel.

Location: OS 200, GR 859741.

Great for... a quiet seaside break.

Accommodation: 39 beds: 1x3-, 1x4-, 4x6- and 1x8-bed rooms.

Family rooms: Yes. **Rent-a-Hostel:** Yes.

Classroom: Yes. **Education packages:** Yes.

Facilities: Dining/sitting room, self-catering kitchen, drying room, showers, cycle store and garden. **Daytime access:** All areas. Ⓢ

Meals: Breakfast, picnic lunch, evening meal.

Reception open: Staff available before 10.00hrs and after 17.00hrs.

Getting there: From A30 southbound, take A389 to Padstow, then B3276 to St Merryn and on towards Newquay. Then turn off at third right turn to Treyarnon. From Newquay, take B3276 towards Padstow and, after Porthcuthan, follow hostel signs. From Treyarnon

Tarr Steps in the Exmoor National Park, near Woodadvent.

beach follow lane marked Private Residents Only. Hostel is on right.

Parking: Yes.

Nearest other hostels: Perranporth 22 miles, Tintagel 23, Boscastle Harbour 24.

Public transport: BUS: First Western National 55 Bodmin Parkway station–Padstow, then 555/6 to Constantine (0.5 miles). From Newquay 555/6 to Constantine. RAIL: Newquay (not Sun, except June–Sept) 12 miles, Bodmin Parkway 25 (best bus links).

● WOODADVENT

**campingbarns@yha.org.uk
Booking: 0870 770 6113
Arrival time: Mrs Brewer, 01984 640920**

You'll find this camping barn in a quiet, unspoilt corner of Exmoor National Park. In the farmyard a mile outside Roadwater village, the former cider barn still has the original cider press in situ.

Great for... walking, pony riding and the nearby steam railway.

Accommodation: Sleeps 12 in two areas.

Facilities: Electric light and shower (both metered), heating, cooking and recreation area and BBQ area. Breakfast available.

Nearest pub: 1 mile. **Nearest shop:** 1 mile.

Location: OS 181, GR 037374.

All the family will enjoy the South West's mild climate and clean seas.

ENJOY A YHA FAMILY HOLIDAY

Many of the hostels in the South West boast family-friendly facilities. For details on how YHA caters for families, turn to page 14.

The Youth Hostels of...
South East England

Coves and beaches: part of the South's classic coastline.

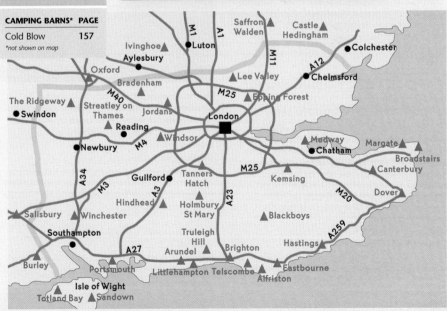

● FAMILY   ● CITY   ● GROUP   ● TRADITIONAL   ● CAMPING BARN   ● COASTAL   ● RURAL

● ALFRISTON ☆

**Frog Firle, Alfriston, Polegate, East Sussex
BN26 5TT; alfriston@yha.org.uk
Tel: 0870 770 5666 Fax: 0870 770 5667**

This Sussex flint house, partly dating from 1530 with a Tudor beamed
lounge, is just a mile from the picturesque village of Alfriston.
Norman and medieval sites are within easy reach, as is
the Herstmonceux Science Centre, Drusilla's Zoo Park and the
Seven Sisters spectacular sea cliffs. Set in a large garden
overlooking the Cuckmere Valley, the hostel is also an ideal base for
exploring the South Downs where walkers and cyclists alike will find
plenty of footpaths and bridleways to explore.

Location: OS 199, GR 518019.

Great for... walking.

You need to know... the hostel is on a busy road with limited parking.

Accommodation: 66 beds: 6x2–4-, 6x6–8- and 1x10-bed rooms.

Family rooms: No. **Rent-a-Hostel:** No.

Classroom: Yes. **Education packages:** Yes.

Facilities: Two common rooms, self-catering kitchen, showers,
drying room, cycle store and garden. **Daytime access:** Restricted.

Meals: Breakfast, picnic lunch, evening meal.

Reception open: 17.00hrs.

Getting there: On foot, follow river to Litlington footbridge, take
bridlepath west for 400 metres. By road, the hostel is 0.75 miles
south of Alfriston on east side where road narrows.

Parking: Yes.

Nearest other hostels: Eastbourne 8 miles, Telscombe 11,
Blackboys 17.

Public transport: BUS: Renown 126 Seaford–Alfriston–Eastbourne
(passes close to Seaford and Polegate stations), RDH 125 from Lewes
to within 0.5 miles. RAIL: Berwick 3 miles, Seaford 3.
FERRY: Newhaven to Dieppe 6 miles.

●● ARUNDEL ☆☆☆

**Warningcamp, Arundel, West Sussex BN18 9QY;
arundel@yha.org.uk
Tel: 0870 770 5676 Fax: 0870 770 5677**

Enjoy the best of both worlds in this handsome Georgian mansion.
Situated at the end of a private road with a spacious front lawn, it's
well away from the busy traffic of Arundel yet just over a mile from
the town centre. If you're bringing the family, you'll be pleased to
know the sandy beaches of Littlehampton and West Wittering are
nearby, where the kids can run riot with buckets and spades. There's
also walking aplenty – the Monarch's Way will lead you onto the
expansive South Downs or, for an evening stroll, follow the
riverside path to Arundel.

Location: OS 197, GR 032076.

Great for... families with young children.

You need to know... this hostel is run by a family for families.

Accommodation: 60 beds: all 4–6-bed rooms, 3 rooms en-suite with
double beds.

Family rooms: Yes. **Rent-a-Hostel:** No.

Classroom: Dining room seats 60. **Education packages:** No.

Expansive views of the South Downs near YHAs Alfriston and Arundel.

Facilities: TV lounge and games room, dining room, two
self-catering kitchens, showers, drying room, pool table, table-tennis
table, internet access and bar football, cycle store, grounds,
camping and BBQ. **Daytime access:** Restricted. ⊛

Meals: Breakfast, picnic lunch, evening meal.

Reception open: 17.00hrs.

Getting there: Follow A27 around Arundel towards Littlehampton.
Turn down small road next to train station, signposted to hostel and
Warningcamp. Continue to first crossroads and turn left. Follow lane
around two right-hand turns.

Parking: Yes.

Nearest other hostels: Littlehampton 4 miles (opens 2003),
Truleigh Hill 16, Brighton 20.

Public transport: BUS: Stagecoach Coastline 702 from Brighton/
Chichester, alight Arundel Station then 1.25 miles.
RAIL: Arundel 1 mile.
FERRY: Portsmouth to Cherbourg, Le Havre, Caen, St Malo 27 miles.
NATIONALEXPRESS A27 Arundel 1.25 miles.

For current prices visit www.yha.org.uk

● FAMILY ● CITY ● GROUP ● TRADITIONAL ● CAMPING BARNS ● COASTAL ● RURAL

● BLACKBOYS ☆

Blackboys, Uckfield, East Sussex TN22 5HU
Tel: 0870 770 5698 Fax: 0870 770 5699

With just 30 beds, this wooden cabin set in woodland is a quiet escape from the hurly-burly of southern England. A walk along the Weald Way will be high on your priority list if you stay here, as will a visit to Batemans at Burwash, a National Trust property and once the home of Rudyard Kipling. It's also ideal for exploring the Bluebell Railway and Cuckoo Trail.

Location: OS 199, GR 521215.
Great for... small groups wanting a quiet weekend away.
You need to know... you should bring provisions — Blackboys only offers self-catering accommodation.
Accommodation: 29 beds: 1x2-, 3x3-, 2x4- and 2x5-bed rooms.
Family rooms: No. **Rent-a-Hostel:** Yes.
Classroom: No. **Education packages:** No.
Facilities: Lounge/dining room, self-catering kitchen, showers, laundry, drying room, cycle store, luggage store, camping and grounds. **Daytime access:** Restricted. ⊗
Meals: Self-catering only.
Reception open: 17.00hrs.
Getting there: From Cross-in-Hand take right fork at Blackboys village then second right following signs to hostel at crossroads. From Uckfield take Heathfield Road B2102. After 4 miles turn left at crossroads, turn down Gun Road and go across stream. Hostel is in woods on right next to farmhouse. From Lewes road fork left at Blackboys Inn. Follow hostel sign and keep straight on.
Parking: Cars and minibuses only.

Take a trip on the Bluebell Steam Railway near YHA Blackboys.

Nearest other hostels: Alfriston 17 miles, Brighton 17, Telscombe 17, Eastbourne 18, Kemsing 30.
Public transport: BUS: Stagecoach 318 Heathfield–Uckfield (passes close to Uckfield and Eastbourne stations), alight Blackboys 0.5 miles. RAIL: Buxted 2.5 miles, Lewes 11.
FERRY: Newhaven to Dieppe 22 miles.
NATIONALEXPRESS» Uckfield bus terminal 4 miles.

● BRADENHAM ☆☆☆

Bradenham, High Wycombe, Buckinghamshire
HP14 4HF; bradenham@yha.org.uk
Tel: 0870 770 5714 Fax: 0870 770 5715

Once the village hall and schoolhouse, Bradenham was previously the central focus of this National Trust village. It now offers modest accommodation to keen walkers and cyclists wanting to explore the surrounding maze of waymarked paths.

Location: OS 165, GR 828972.
Great for... keen walkers who want to explore the Chiltern beechwoods on foot.
You need to know... accommodation is in three large bedrooms.
Accommodation: 16 beds: 2x5- and 1x6-bed rooms.
Family rooms: No. **Rent-a-Hostel:** Yes.
Classroom: No. **Education packages:** No.
Facilities: Lounge/dining room, self-catering kitchen, showers, drying room and cycle store. **Daytime access:** Restricted. ⊗
Meals: Self-catering only.
Reception open: 17.00hrs.
Getting there: Leave M40 at J4, follow A4010 (signed Aylesbury) to Bradenham. Turn off at Red Lion and hostel is opposite church.
Parking: Roadside lay-by.
Nearest other hostels: Jordans 12 miles, Ivinghoe 17, Windsor 18.
Public transport: BUS: Arriva The Shires 323–5, 332, High Wycombe–Princes Risborough, alight Bradenham 0.25 miles or Walter's Ash 1 mile.
RAIL: Saunderton 1.25 miles, High Wycombe 4.5.
NATIONALEXPRESS» High Wycombe bus station 4.25 miles.

●● BRIGHTON ☆

Patcham Place, London Road, Brighton,
East Sussex BN1 8YD; brighton@yha.org.uk
Tel: 0870 770 5724 Fax: 0870 770 5725

With so much to do, Brighton is an exciting city to visit. No one can resist the traditional seaside pursuits at the world-famous pier and pavilion. Then there's a cosmopolitan range of shops to explore before you even contemplate an energetic night on the town. Just as well then, that this 16th century manor house offers a

A quiet parkland retreat on the outskirts of town: YHA Brighton.

retreat from the city in open parkland on the outskirts of Brighton. And, when you're rested, the staff will be only too happy to help plan your activities for tomorrow.

Location: OS 198, GR 300088.

Great for... a base to explore Brighton's bright lights.

You need to know... the hostel is on the outskirts of Brighton, 3 miles from the city centre.

Accommodation: 56 beds: 1x4-, 3x6-, 1x10- and 2x12-bed rooms.

Family rooms: No. **Rent-a-Hostel:** No.

Classroom: No. **Education packages:** Yes.

Facilities: Lounge/TV room, games room, self-catering kitchen, showers, cycle shed, laundry facilities and grounds.

Daytime access: All areas.

Meals: Breakfast included.

Reception open: 13.00hrs–23.00hrs.

Getting there: Public transport from city centre. From train station walk down Queens Road to clock tower, turning right to Churchill Square bus stops. Stage Coach bus 770 stops outside hostel (Patcham–Black Lion) or take 5A bus to Patcham (Co-op). The bus also stops on North Road, pavilion on Old Steine, Preston Park and all stops on London Road. From Patcham village Co-op, follow Old London Road round to left past Post Office to London Road. Hostel is opposite Black Lion pub. By road, hostel is 3 miles north of Brighton city centre on London Road (A23) adjacent to A23/A27 junction (see map on page 173).

Parking: Yes.

Nearest other hostels: Truleigh Hill 6 miles, Telscombe 10, Alfriston 14.

Public transport: BUS: Brighton Centre–Patcham 5/5A, Stagecoach Coastline 107A and Metrobus 87/8 Brighton–Horsham, Stagecoach in East Sussex 770/2 Brighton–Haywards Heath (passes near Preston Park and Haywards Heath stations).

RAIL: Preston Park 2 miles, Brighton 3.5.

NATIONALEXPRESS Opposite hostel outside Black Lion pub.

●● BROADSTAIRS ☆☆

3 Osborne Road, Broadstairs, Kent CT10 2AE;
broadstairs@yha.org.uk
Tel: 0870 770 5730 Fax: 0870 770 5730

If you're always complaining that the world isn't what it used to be, a stay at Broadstairs should restore your faith in old-time Britain. A traditional hostel with a personal atmosphere, it's centrally located in this historic seaside resort. Gentle pursuits are the name of the day and a stroll along the award-winning beach half a mile away is a must. Or, if you're looking for a dash of culture, book during the Charles Dickens week in June or the folk week in August.

Location: OS 179, GR 390679.

Great for... folk seeking a traditional retreat.

You need to know... there are two cats at the hostel.

Accommodation: 34 beds: 2x2-, 1x3-, 1x4-, 1x5- and 3x6-bed rooms.

Family rooms: Yes. **Rent-a-Hostel:** Yes.

Classroom: No. **Education packages:** No.

Facilities: Lounge, dining room with TV and video, self-catering

kitchen, showers, drying room, cycle store, laundry facilities, currency exchange and garden with BBQ.

Daytime access: Restricted. 🚫

Meals: Self-catering only; full meals service available for pre-booked groups of 10 or more.

Reception open: 17.00hrs.

Getting there: From town centre and beach, head uphill along High Street, under railway bridge and left at traffic lights. The hostel is first building after the row of shops (see map on page 173).

Parking: Roadside.

Nearest other hostels: Margate 4 miles (7 along coast), Canterbury 18, Dover 19, Medway 45.

Public transport: BUS: From Sandwich (with connecting bus from Dover), Ramsgate Harbour, Canterbury and surrounding areas.

RAIL: Broadstairs 100 metres. FERRY: Dover 19 miles.

AIRPORT: London (Manston) 3 miles.

NATIONALEXPRESS Pierremont Hall, High Street 0.25 miles.

● CANTERBURY ☆

54 New Dover Road, Canterbury, CT1 3DT;
canterbury@yha.org.uk
Tel: 0870 770 5744 Fax: 0870 770 5745

This splendid Victorian villa is near the centre of the early Christian city of Canterbury, with good access onto the Kent Downs. The hostel is popular with groups and individuals alike, who enjoy the friendly atmosphere. It's within easy reach of the North Downs Way and Pilgrims' Way, while the city itself has a cathedral, St Augustine's Abbey, various museums, guided tours and theatres.

Location: OS 179, GR 157570.

Great for... cathedral lovers and those who want to explore Kent.

You need to know... parking is limited.

Accommodation: 68 beds: 1x1-, 2x2-, 1x3-, 1x4-, 4x5-, 1x6- and 3x10-bed rooms.

Family rooms: No. **Rent-a-Hostel:** No.

Classroom: No. **Education packages:** No.

Facilities: Lounge, TV, cycle shed, laundry, self-catering kitchen,

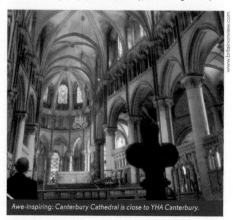
Awe-inspiring: Canterbury Cathedral is close to YHA Canterbury.

● FAMILY   ● CITY   ● GROUP   ● TRADITIONAL   ● CAMPING BARN   ● COASTAL   ● RURAL

showers, bureau de change, National Express and Hoverspeed tickets, internet access and garden. **Daytime access:** All areas. ⊗

Meals: Breakfast only. Full meals service available for pre-booked groups of 10 or more.

Reception open: 15.00hrs.

Getting there: Follow signs for Dover and the hostel is on the A2050, 1.25 miles from the city centre (see map on page 174).

Parking: Yes.

Nearest other hostels: Dover 14 miles, Margate 15, Broadstairs 18, Medway 30, Kemsing 42.

Public transport: BUS: Frequent from surrounding areas. RAIL: Canterbury East 0.75 miles, Canterbury West 1.25. FERRY: Dover to Calais and Ostend 15 miles.

NATIONALEXPRESS>> Canterbury bus station 0.75 miles.

Spend a dramatic day out at Dover Castle near YHA Dover.

www.britainonview.com

● COLD BLOW

campingbarns@yha.org.uk

Booking: 0870 770 6113

Arrival time: Dora Pilkington, 01622 735038

This camping barn, near Thurnham in Kent, is on the North Downs and close to the Pilgrim's Way. It is also near to YHA Kemsing and YHA Medway, making it a convenient stop on a short walking tour.

You need to know... the toilets and shower for the camping barn are in an adjoining barn.

Accommodation: The camping barn sleeps up to 18; there are two bunk barns sleeping up to 10 and 32.

Facilities: Camping barn: fully equipped kitchen, log burner, radiators, BBQ, some sleeping mats provided, showers on 50p meter, drying and laundry in adjacent barn. Bunk barns: both self-contained, though smaller barn shares toilet/showers with camping barn; fully equipped kitchen, toilets, showers; all electricity included but showers are on meters; bring sleeping bag and pillow case.

Nearest pub: 1 mile. **Nearest shop:** 2 mile.

Location: OS 188, GR 822580.

●● DOVER ☆

306 London Road, Dover, Kent CT17 0SY;

dover@yha.org.uk

Tel: 0870 770 5798 Fax: 0870 770 5799

This Georgian listed building is a convenient stop for those hopping across the Channel to France and Belgium. Situated close to the town centre shops, public transport terminals and ferry ports, it offers foreign exchange, some cross-Channel transport ticket sales and internet access should you wish to check sailing times. If you've a few hours to spare before you leave these shores, then a visit to nearby Dover Castle will keep that holiday excitement afloat.

Location: OS 179, GR 311421.

Great for... a stress-free night en-route to the Continent.

You need to know... the hostel is on two sites, 0.5 miles apart.

Accommodation: 122 beds: 6x2-, 1x4-, 5x6-, 9x8–10-bed rooms.

Family rooms: Yes. **Rent-a-Hostel:** Yes.

Classroom: Yes. **Education packages:** Yes.

Facilities: Lounge, TV, games room, self-catering kitchen, showers

and garden, foreign exchange and Hoverspeed tickets.

Daytime access: All areas.

Meals: Breakfast included.

Reception open: All day.

Getting there: From Dover Priory station turn left to roundabout, take first exit and hostel is 0.5 miles on left. From M20/A20, at fourth roundabout, take first exit. At next roundabout, take second exit and hostel is 0.5 miles on left.

Parking: On street nearby.

Nearest other hostels: Canterbury 14 miles, Broadstairs 20,

HOSTEL MANAGERS CHOOSE...

THE REGION'S BEST CYCLE TRAILS

The Ridgeway and Berkshire Downs
YHA The Ridgeway: "Fantastic mountain biking for experienced riders with demanding rutted and loose surfaces. Bike shops are on hand at Marlborough and Wantage to help with any mechanical mishaps."

Seawall route YHA Broadstairs: "A refreshingly flat route from Birchington to Reculver and on to Herne Bay, ideal for families."

The Ridgeway YHA The Ridgeway: "This historic National Trail is a downland classic for mountain bikers. Riders have access from Avebury to Streatley-on-Thames."

South Downs YHA Truleigh Hill: "Family groups on mountain bikes will cope with all bridlepaths in the area. Harder riders will want to take on the real challenge – doing the 100 mile-long South Downs Way in two days!"

Black Park country park, Chilterns YHA Jordans: "Safe cycling for families just eight miles from the hostel."

East Kent YHA Broadstairs: "Very pleasant cycling country, with 20- to 25-mile rides between the four hostels in the area, using quiet back lanes and Sustrans waymarked routes."

● FAMILY ● CITY ● GROUP ● TRADITIONAL ● CAMPING BARN ● COASTAL ● RURAL

Medway 40, Kemsing 50.
Public transport: BUS: Frequent from surrounding areas.
RAIL: Priory 1 mile.
FERRY: P&O Stena (tel: 0990 980980), Hoverspeed (tel: 01304 240241), Le Shuttle Channel Tunnel (tel: 01303 271100).
NATIONALEXPRESS Pencester Road bus station 0.25 miles.

●● EASTBOURNE ☆☆

East Dean Road, Eastbourne, E Sussex BN20 8ES
Tel: 0870 770 5806 Fax: 0870 770 5806

A stay in Eastbourne will leave your family ruddy-cheeked and fighting fit. Maybe it's the sea air, but you won't be able to resist the sea views or the walking routes all around this hostel. The South Downs Way is literally on the doorstep and it's only a short walk to the picture-perfect village of Alfriston and the dramatic coastline at Beachy Head. Or perhaps you will wander into Eastbourne to spend a day on the beach.
Location: OS 199, GR 588990.
Great for... active families who want a comfortable base.

Towering sea cliffs at Seaford near YHAs Brighton and Eastbourne.

Accommodation: 32 beds: 1x3-, 3x4-, 1x5- and 2x6-bed rooms.
Family rooms: Yes. **Rent-a-Hostel:** Yes.
Classroom: No. **Education packages:** No.
Facilities: Lounge, dining room, self-catering kitchen, showers, drying room and cycle store. **Daytime access:** Restricted. ⊗
Meals: Self-catering; breakfast available on request.
Reception open: 17.00hrs.
Getting there: Follow A259 from railway station west for 1.5 miles. Approaching Eastbourne from west on A259, the hostel is 0.25 miles past the golf club.
Parking: Limited.
Nearest other hostels: Alfriston 8 miles, Blackboys 19, Telscombe 20, Brighton 25, Hastings 25.
Public transport: BUS: Brighton & Hove/Stagecoach in East Sussex 712–4 Eastbourne–Brighton (passes close to Eastbourne station). RAIL: Eastbourne 1.5 miles. FERRY: Newhaven to Dieppe 10 miles.
NATIONALEXPRESS Coach station, Cavendish Place 2 miles.

Idyllic: Cuckmere Haven, near YHA Eastbourne.

●● EPPING FOREST ☆

Wellington Hill, High Beach, Loughton, Essex IG10 4AG
Tel: 0870 770 5822 Fax: 0870 770 5823

Combine hectic days in the big city with a generous dose of tranquillity in Epping Forest. With London just 10 miles away on the Central Line, a day trip to the capital is an easy option, made all the better by your return to this woodland retreat. For a more relaxed day out, Waltham Abbey, Connaught Water and Loughton Iron Age Camp are all nearby. Or for ultimate peace, follow the miles of paths that criss-cross the 6,000 acres of uncrowded ancient woodland surrounding the hostel.
Location: OS 167, GR 408983.
Great for... the best of both worlds; and for mixed groups wanting a variety of activities.
You need to know... there's a pub next door.
Accommodation: 36 beds: 6x4- and 2x6-bed rooms.
Family rooms: Yes. **Rent-a-Hostel:** Yes.
Classroom: No. **Education packages:** No.
Facilities: Lounge/dining room, self-catering kitchen, showers, cycle store, garden with BBQ and camping. **Daytime access:** Restricted. ⊗
Meals: Self-catering only; breakfast trolley available.
Reception open: 17.00hrs.
Getting there: From the M25, exit J26 and take the A121 to Loughton. Turn right after Volunteer Inn. Continue on this road for approx 500 metres then turn right, then left up Wellington Hill. The hostel is on the right. From Loughton tube station, take a minicab or walk (40 minutes).
Parking: Car park available (don't park on rough track); not suitable for coaches.
Nearest other hostels: City of London 13 miles, Saffron Walden 29.
Public transport: BUS: Arriva 240, 250 (Waltham Cross station–Loughton Underground), alight Volunteer Inn 1.5 miles.
UNDERGROUND: Loughton 2 miles. RAIL: Chingford 3.5 miles.

For further information visit www.yha.org.uk

● FAMILY   ● CITY   ● GROUP   ● TRADITIONAL   ● CAMPING BARN   ● COASTAL   ● RURAL

●● HASTINGS ☆☆☆

**Rye Road, Guestling, Hastings, East Sussex
TN35 4LP; hasting@yha.org.uk
Tel: 0870 770 5850 Fax: 0870 770 5851**

A great base for exploring this activity-packed area. Children in particular will love it here. With one-and-a-half acres of land and a wood, there's plenty of room for children to run around. Cots and highchairs are available, as is a special menu catering for the tastes of under-10s. A host of attractions will keep the kids entertained by day – Bodiam Castle, Camber Sands, Sealife Centre and Smugglers Adventure, set in a labyrinth of caves, are a few favourites.
Location: OS 199, GR 848133.
Great for... a family holiday.
You need to know... there's a small lake in the grounds so keep a close eye on the children.
Accommodation: 52 beds: 6x4-, 3x6- and 1x10-bed rooms.
Family rooms: Yes. **Rent-a-Hostel:** Yes.
Classroom: No. **Education packages:** No.
Facilities: Lounge, dining room, table-tennis room, self-catering kitchen, showers, drying room, cycle store and grounds. Camping is usually available. **Daytime access:** Restricted.
Meals: Breakfast, picnic lunch, evening meal.
Reception open: 17.00hrs.
Getting there: From Hastings, take A259 Folkestone/Rye for 4 miles and hostel is 200 metres past White Hart on left. From Rye, it is on the right, 300 metres after road changes to double lane.
Parking: Limited to 12 cars.
Nearest other hostels: Blackboys 25 miles, Eastbourne 25, Alfriston 33.
Public transport: BUS: Stagecoach South Coast 711 Brighton–Dover (passes close to Hastings and Rye stations), Coastal Coaches 346. RAIL: Ore 2.5 miles, Hastings 4.
NATIONALEXPRESS» Queen's Parade 4 miles (town centre).

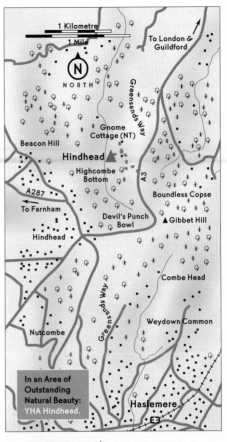

In an Area of Outstanding Natural Beauty: YHA Hindhead.

●● HINDHEAD ☆

**Devil's Punchbowl, off Portsmouth Road, Thursley,
Godalming, Surrey GU8 6NS;
reservations@yha.org.uk
Tel: 0870 770 5864 Fax: 0870 770 5864
Bookings more than 7 days ahead: 0870 770 6113**

A break at Hindhead is an experience all of its own and you'll forget that the rest of the world even exists. You'll be staying in sympathetically restored National Trust cottages that are chock-full of character. They're situated in an Area of Outstanding Natural Beauty so expect an abundance of flora and fauna in among the heath and woodland-rich countryside. Walkers will be in heaven, with trails to the dramatic Devil's Punchbowl, nearby Frenshaw Common and The Pilgrims' Way.
Location: OS 186, GR 892368.
Great for... walkers wanting a rural retreat.
You need to know... you will have to walk 0.5 miles from the car park to the hostel.

The well-preserved might of Bodiam Castle near YHA Hastings.

www.britainonview.com

● FAMILY   ● CITY   ● GROUP   ● TRADITIONAL   ● CAMPING BARN   ● COASTAL   ● RURAL

Accommodation: 12 beds: 2x2-, 2x4-bed rooms.
Family rooms: No. **Rent-a-Hostel:** Yes.
Classroom: No. **Education packages:** No.
Facilities: Lounge/dining area, self-catering kitchen, toilets, shower.
Daytime access: Restricted. ⊛
Meals: Self-catering only.
Reception open: 17.00hrs.
Getting there: Turn off A3 (Portsmouth Road) onto track between Brook turning and Hindhead crossroads.
Parking: National Trust 0.5 miles, no access by car to hostel, unload by arrangement.
Nearest other hostels: Holmbury St Mary 20 miles, Tanners Hatch 25, Portsmouth 29.
Public transport: BUS: Stagecoach 18/9 Aldershot–Haslemere (passes close to Haslemere station), 71 from Guildford (passes close to Godalming and Farnham stations), alight in Hindhead area and walk 0.5–1 mile (according to stops).
RAIL: Haslemere 2.5 miles by path, 4.5 by road.
NATIONALEXPRESS》 A3 lay-by near traffic lights 1.5 miles.

YHA Hindhead is a National Trust cottage chock-full of character.

●● HOLMBURY ST MARY ☆
Radnor Lane, Dorking, Surrey RH5 6NW;
holmbury@yha.org.uk
Tel: 0870 770 5868 Fax: 0870 770 5869

In 4,000 acres of woodland in an Area of Outstanding Natural Beauty, this cosy hostel with small rooms enjoys quiet surroundings. Set in grounds perfect for playing and relaxing, it's also ideally suited as a base to explore the Surrey Hills or walk the North Downs Way and Greensand Way. There's an orienteering course and treasure hunt to try, mountain bikes and guided walks can be arranged locally and National Trust properties such as Polesden Lacey are nearby.
Location: OS 187, GR 104450.

Great for... walking, mountain biking and orienteering.
You need to know... this hostel may close during 2003. Please enquire before planning your stay.
Accommodation: 52 beds: 2x2- and 12x4-bed rooms.
Family rooms: No. **Rent-a-Hostel:** No.
Classroom: No. **Education packages:** No.
Facilities: Lounge, self-catering kitchen, showers, drying room, cycle store, grounds and camping. **Daytime access:** Restricted. ⊛
Meals: Breakfast, picnic lunch, evening meal.
Reception open: 17.00hrs.
Getting there: The hostel is 2 miles south of Abinger Hammer on A25 between Guildford and Dorking. Follow signs to Holmbury St Mary on B2126 and hostel is 1 mile north of village.
Parking: Yes.
Nearest other hostels: Tanners Hatch 6 miles, Hindhead 20, Windsor 27.
Public transport: BUS: Arriva 21. RAIL: Gomshall 3 miles, Dorking 6.

●● JORDANS ☆
Welders Lane, Jordans, Beaconsfield,
Buckinghamshire HP9 2SN; jordans@yha.org.uk
Tel: 0870 770 5886 Fax: 0870 770 5887

Hunt for history in this traditional hostel in a quiet village with an impressive heritage. Closely associated with the early Quaker movement, the village is home to the Mayflower Barn, William Penn's grave and a 17th century meeting house. A trip to Milton's Cottage in the next village is recommended and Windsor is within visiting distance. The hostel enjoys quiet surroundings with a garden and all-day access available for families.
Location: OS 175, GR 975910.
Great for... a quiet break just outside London.
You need to know... the London Underground is 5 miles away.
Accommodation: 22 beds: 2x5- and 2x6-bed rooms.
Family rooms: Yes. **Rent-a-Hostel:** Yes.
Classroom: No. **Education packages:** No.
Facilities: Well equipped self-catering kitchen, lounge/dining area, showers, cycle store, grounds, camping, BBQ and patio area.
Daytime access: Restricted. ⊛
Meals: Self-catering only.
Reception open: 17.00hrs.
Getting there: Leave the M40 at J2 and follow the A355 (signed Beaconsfield). At the A40, head for Gerrard's Cross. Take the first left up Potkiln Lane and, after 1 mile, turn right up Welders Lane, then the second entrance on the left. From Seer Green station turn right onto Long Bolton Lane, left onto Potkiln Lane, then take the first right onto Welders Lane.
Parking: 8 cars maximum.
Nearest other hostels: Bradenham 12 miles, Windsor 13, Ivinghoe 19.
Public transport: BUS: Arriva 305 High Wycombe–Uxbridge, alight Seer Green 0.75 mile, 353 Slough–Berkhamsted, alight Chalfont leisure centre 1 mile. UNDERGROUND: Chalfont and Latimer (Metropolitan Line) 5 miles. RAIL: Seer Green 0.75 mile.
NATIONALEXPRESS》 Beaconsfield.

● FAMILY ● CITY ● GROUP ● TRADITIONAL ● CAMPING BARN ● COASTAL ● RURAL

● KEMSING ☆

**Church Lane, Kemsing, Sevenoaks, Kent
TN15 6LU; kemsing@yha.org.uk
Tel: 0870 770 5890 Fax: 0870 770 5891**

Commanding fine views, this former 19th century vicarage set in its own grounds lies at the foot of the North Downs. There is plenty to do nearby, including the attractions of Knole House, Ightham Mote, Chartwell, Whitbread Hop farm and Lullingstone Park Visitor Centre. It's also handy for the famous Pilgrims' Way.

Location: OS 188, GR 555588.
Great for... a base to explore the North Downs.
Accommodation: 50 beds: 2x4-, 4x6-, 1x8- and 1x10-bed rooms.
Family rooms: No. **Rent-a-Hostel:** No.
Classroom: No. **Education packages:** No.
Facilities: Lounge and quiet room, self-catering kitchen, dining

Enjoy a cultural day at Knole House near YHA Kemsing.

www.britainonview.com

room, TV, showers, cycle store, grounds and camping.
Daytime access: Restricted.
Meals: Breakfast, picnic lunch, evening meal.
Reception open: 17.00hrs.
Getting there: From Otford station turn right, take first right to junction with Childsbridge Lane and turn right again. Turn left at crossroads into West End and continue to Church Lane (2 miles).
Parking: Yes.
Nearest other hostels: London 26 miles, Medway 26, Canterbury 42, Dover 60.
Public transport: BUS: Arriva 425/6, 433 from Sevenoaks (close to Sevenoaks station), alight Kemsing PO 250 metres. RAIL: Kemsing (not Sun) 1.5 miles, Otford 1.75. FERRY: Dover 60 miles.

●● LITTLEHAMPTON

**Littlehampton, West Sussex;
littlehampton@yha.org.uk
Tel: 0870 770 6114 Fax: 0870 770 6115**

This new hostel is part of a redevelopment of Fisherman's Wharf on the east bank of the River Arun. Set in a traditional seaside resort just five minutes from the beach, it's a great base for all the family to explore the south coast, with family rooms throughout. Although the hostel offers self-catering accommodation, the complex includes a cafeteria, as well as a tourist information centre and the Littlehampton Experience.
Location: OS 176, GR 249797.
Great for... sandy beaches and traditional seaside fun.
You need to know... Littlehampton is due to open in 2003.
Accommodation: 30 beds: all 4- and 5-bed rooms, some en-suite.

●● LEE VALLEY

**Windmill Lane, Cheshunt, Hertfordshire,
EN8 9AJ; lonres@yha.org.uk
Tel: 0870 770 6118 Fax: 0870 770 6119**

Close to London, these six log cabins are situated on the shore of a lake in the 10,000 acres of Lee Valley Country Park. There are plenty of activities on offer – take your pick from sailing, kayaking, caving, climbing and canoeing to name but a few.
Location: OS 166, GR 368024.
Great for... outdoor enthusiasts.
You need to know... this hostel is due to open in 2003; breakfast is included in the price.
Accommodation: 112 beds: 2-, 4- and 6-bed rooms, facilities for the disabled.
Family rooms: Yes. **Rent-a-Hostel:** No.
Classroom: Yes. **Education packages:** Yes.
Facilities: Self-catering kitchens, meeting rooms, laundry, showers and restaurant. **Daytime access:** All areas.
Meals: Breakfast, picnic lunch, evening meal.
Reception open: 7.00hrs to 23.00hrs.
Getting there: By train, travel from Liverpool Street station.

By road, leave the M25 at J25.
Parking: Public car park.
Nearest other hostels: Epping Forest 10 miles, London 16, Ivinghoe 36, Jordans 36.
Public transport: BUS: Frequent from surrounding areas to within 0.5 miles. RAIL: Cheshunt adjacent to hostel.

Canoeing is just one of the many activities on offer at Lee Valley.

● FAMILY ● CITY ● GROUP ● TRADITIONAL ● CAMPING BARN ● COASTAL ● RURAL

Family rooms: Yes. Rent-a-Hostel: Yes.
Classroom: No. Education packages: No.
Facilities: Lounge, dining room, self-catering kitchen, showers, disabled access by lift, cycle shed, laundry, TV room.
Daytime access: Restricted. ⊗
Meals: Self-catering only.
Reception open: 17.00hrs.
Getting there: Follow signs for Littlehampton Experience public car park.
Parking: Nearby.
Nearest other hostels: Arundel 5 miles, Truleigh Hill 18, Brighton 22.
Public transport: BUS: 700 service every 30 minutes from Worthing–Portsmouth. RAIL: Littlehampton 0.5 miles.
FERRY: Portsmouth to Newhaven 27 miles.
NATIONALEXPRESS London–Chichester service 027.

●● MARGATE ☆☆☆

3-4 Royal Esplanade, Westbrook Bay, Margate, Kent CT9 5DL; margate@yha.org.uk
Tel: 0870 770 5956 Fax: 0870 770 5956

Pack your bucket and spade because traditional seaside holidays don't get better than this. The hostel, converted from a hotel, is on the beachfront at Westbrook Bay, which boasts a gently shelving sandy beach. A five-minute stroll along the promenade takes you to to Margate's main beach with its lively attractions and arcades.

HOSTEL MANAGERS CHOOSE...

THE BEST COASTAL EXPERIENCES

Sandown (watersports) YHA Sandown: "Surfboards, jetskis and pedalos can be all hired at this lively beach. The swimming is safe too, although watch out for wash from passing ships."
Hastings (heritage) YHA Hastings: "Attractions include the Shipwreck Heritage Centre, a wreck preserved in the sands of Hastings beach and, for the children, the Smugglers Adventure in the cave system of the West Hill."
West Wight (scenery) YHA Sandown: "Mainly National Trust-owned and designated an Area of Outstanding Natural Beauty."
Portsmouth (maritime) YHA Portsmouth: The finest maritime history in Britain! The historic naval base is home to HMS Victory, HMS Warrior and the Mary Rose. Attractions include the Action Stations interactive experience and boat tours to see modern warships. We sell all-inclusive passes at the hostel."
Colwell Bay (peace) YHA Totland Bay: "On the west coast of the Isle of Wight, this small, quiet sand-and-shingle beach offers panoramic views of the Solent. Backed with cliffs, it's a sheltered spot for sunbathing."

Be warned – with Dreamland Fun-Park and arcades galore, you'll have trouble dragging the kids away from their candyfloss.
Location: OS 179, GR 342706.
Great for... traditional family holidays by the sea.
You need to know... it's self-catering accommodation only.
Accommodation: 55 beds: 2x6- and 2-, 3-, 4- and 5-bed rooms.
Family rooms: Yes. Rent-a-Hostel: Yes.
Classroom: No. Education packages: No.
Facilities: Lounge, dining room, quiet room, self-catering kitchen, cycle store, limited laundry facilities and currency exchange.
Daytime access: Restricted. ⊗
Meals: Self-catering; meals available to pre-booked parties of 10+.
Reception open: 17.00hrs.
Getting there: From Main Beach and railway station take A28 Canterbury Road, passing Royal Sea Bathing Hospital, and turn right into Westbrook Gardens after the Dog and Duck pub. Hostel is third building along Royal Esplanade seafront.
Parking: No.
Nearest other hostels: Broadstairs 4 miles (7 along coast), Canterbury 15, Dover 20, Medway 42.
Public transport: BUS: Frequent from Dover, Canterbury and surrounding areas. RAIL: Margate 500 metres. FERRY: Dover 19 miles. AIRPORT: London (Manston) 3 miles.
NATIONALEXPRESS Clock Tower, Marine Parade 0.5 miles.

●● MEDWAY ☆☆☆

Capstone Road, Gillingham, Kent ME7 3JE; medway@yha.org.uk
Tel: 0870 770 5964 Fax: 0870 770 5965

Make this beautiful Kentish oast house your base for a busy break that will appeal to all the family. The area is rich with history and you'll find everything from a Napoleonic fort to a Norman castle in the area. The nearby towns of Rochester and Chatham are both worth a day's wander or, for more rural entertainment, Capstone Country Park is opposite the hostel and has nature trails, picnic areas and a fishing lake. And, for the energetic, the nearby ski slope, toboggan run and rink offers icy excitement.
Location: OS 178, GR 783653.
Great for... all the family.

Different: YHA Medway is a Kentish oast house in a history-rich area.

For offers and discounts visit www.yha.org.uk

● FAMILY ● CITY ● GROUP ● TRADITIONAL ● CAMPING BARN ● COASTAL ● RURAL

You need to know... there's a country park on the doorstep.
Accommodation: 40 beds: 4x2-, 1x3-, 6x4- and 1x5-bed rooms.
Family rooms: Yes. **Rent-a-Hostel:** Yes.
Classroom: Yes. **Education packages:** Yes.
Facilities: TV lounge, self-catering kitchen, dining room, showers, drying room, cycle store, lockers and laundry facilities.
Daytime access: Restricted. 🚭
Meals: Breakfast, picnic lunch, evening meal.
Reception open: 17.00hrs.
Getting there: Exit M2 at J4 and take A278 to Gillingham. Turn left at first roundabout signed to hostel, Capstone Country Park and Ski

Centre. From Chatham railway station, take taxi or walk to Pentagon Shopping Centre for regular services to the Wheatsheaf pub or 114 to Waggon at Hale pub. All services alight on Capstone Road and follow hostel signs.
Parking: Yes.
Nearest other hostels: Kemsing 23 miles, Canterbury 25, Broadstairs 40, Dover 40.
Public transport: BUS: Nu-Venture 114 from the Pentagon Shopping Centre, alight Luton Recreation Ground. RAIL: Chatham 2 miles. FERRY: Dover to Folkestone 40 miles.
NATIONAL EXPRESS Hempstead Valley Shopping Centre 2 miles.

●● THE RIDGEWAY ☆
Court Hill, Wantage, Oxfordshire OX12 9NE;
ridgeway@yha.org.uk
Tel: 0870 770 6064 Fax: 0870 770 6065

Set on the edge of the Berkshire Downs with views over the Vale of the White Horse, this is a heaven-sent base for walkers with Britain's oldest route, the Ridgeway National Trail, just 500 metres away. The well-maintained hostel is a collection of converted timber barns built around a courtyard. If you appreciate a hefty dose of peace then you'll also enjoy spending time in the extensive grounds that include a beech wood conservation area.
Location: OS 174, GR 393851.
Great for... walkers and cyclists looking for a comfortable base.
You need to know... the disabled toilet is separate from the sleeping accommodation.
Accommodation: 59 beds: 7x4-, 1x8-, 1x10- and 1x13-bed rooms.
Family rooms: Yes. **Rent-a-Hostel:** No.
Classroom: Yes. **Education packages:** Yes.
Facilities: Lounge, TV, self-catering kitchen, dining room, showers, drying room, cycle store, laundry facilities, grounds and camping. **Daytime access:** Restricted. 🚭
Meals: Breakfast, picnic lunch, evening meal.
Reception open: 17.00hrs.
Getting there: From the M4, exit at J14, take the A338 towards

Wantage for 9 miles and the hostel is signposted and on the left. From Wantage, take A338 towards Hungerford — the hostel is signposted and on the right at the brow of the hill. From Ridgeway National Trail east, follow signs. From Ridgeway west, follow A338 (left from trail) and then take first left.
Parking: Yes.
Nearest other hostels: Streatley 14 miles, Oxford 17.
Public transport: BUS: Stagecoach Oxford 32/A/B, X35, 36 from Didcot Parkway station, alight Wantage 2 miles.
RAIL: Didcot Parkway 10 miles.

Extensive grounds and a conservation area: YHA The Ridgeway.

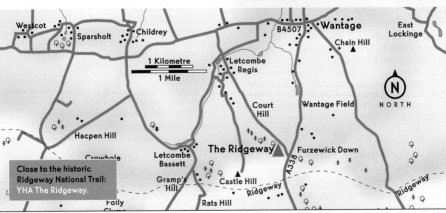

Close to the historic Ridgeway National Trail: YHA The Ridgeway.

⬤ FAMILY ⬤ CITY ⬤ GROUP ⬤ TRADITIONAL ⬤ CAMPING BARN ⬤ COASTAL ⬤ RURAL

● PORTSMOUTH ☆

Old Wymering Lane, Cosham, Portsmouth, Hampshire PO6 3NL; portsmouth@yha.org.uk
Tel: 0870 770 6002 Fax: 0870 770 6003

Step back in time at this hostel with a history dating back to the 11th century. This old manor house has a homely atmosphere, encouraging you to relax in the wood-panelled hall at the end of a day exploring the historic dockyards where you can visit the Mary Rose and stand on the deck of The Victory, Nelson's flagship.
Location: OS 196, GR 640955.
Great for... history aplenty.
Accommodation: 48 beds, 3x6-, 2x8- and 1x14-bed rooms.
Family rooms: No. **Rent-a-Hostel:** No.
Classroom: No. **Education packages:** No.
Facilities: Lounge, self-catering kitchen, showers, drying room and cycle store. **Daytime access:** Restricted.
Meals: Breakfast, picnic lunch, evening meal.
Reception open: 17.00hrs.
Getting there: From Cosham police station, take Medina Road, then seventh turning on the right, Old Wymering Lane. The hostel is opposite the church entrance (see map on page 175).

Impressive: the remains of the Mary Rose near YHA Portsmouth.

Parking: Yes.
Nearest other hostels: Sandown 10 miles (via ferry), Winchester 25, Arundel 26.
Public transport: BUS: Frequent from surrounding areas.
RAIL: Cosham 0.5 miles. FERRY: Portsmouth to Caen/Cherbourg/St Malo/Le Havre/Santander/Bilbao/Isle of Wight.
 The Hard Interchange, Portsmouth 2.5 miles.

●● SANDOWN ☆☆

The Firs, Fitzroy Street, Sandown, Isle of Wight PO36 8JH; sandown@yha.org.uk
Tel: 0870 770 6020 Fax: 0870 770 6021

This hostel is ideally placed to explore the Isle of Wight, an adventure playground for children and adults alike. With a spacious

Sandcastles on Shanklin Beach near YHAs Sandown and Totland Bay.

sandy beach and the bustling town centre of Sandown both a few minutes away, it won't be long before your holiday begins in earnest. You'll find plenty to do, with well-maintained trails to explore on foot or by bike, as well as a range of watersports. The hostel even offers free loans of buckets and spades!
Location: OS 196, GR 597843.
Great for... action-packed family breaks.
You need to know... there's street parking only.
Accommodation: 47 beds: 3x2-, 6x4-, 1x5- and 2x6-bed rooms.
Family rooms: Yes. **Rent-a-Hostel:** Yes.
Classroom: No. **Education packages:** Yes.
Facilities: Lounge/dining area with TV, self-catering kitchen, showers, drying room, cycle store and small garden.
Daytime access: Restricted. ⊗
Meals: Breakfast, picnic lunch, evening meal.
Reception open: 17.00hrs.
Getting there: By car, follow A3055 to Sandown and turn down Melville Street then Fitzroy Street. The hostel is signed from A3055. On foot, the hostel is signposted from the railway station.
Parking: Small car park.
Nearest other hostels: Portsmouth 10 miles (via ferry), Totland Bay 24.
Public transport: BUS: Frequent from surrounding areas.
RAIL: Sandown 0.5 miles. FERRY: Ryde Pierhead 6 miles (Wightlink, tel: 0870 5827744), East Cowes 12 miles (Red Funnel, tel: 023 8033 4010), Ryde 5 miles (Hovertravel, tel: 01983 811000).
NATIONALEXPRESS High St 0.5 miles.

For current prices visit www.yha.org.uk

● FAMILY ● CITY ● GROUP ● TRADITIONAL ● CAMPING BARN ● COASTAL ● RURAL

●● STREATLEY-ON-THAMES ☆

Reading Road, Streatley, Berkshire RG8 9JJ;
streatley@yha.org.uk
Tel: 0870 770 6054 Fax: 0870 770 6055

If you're coming to Streatley-on-Thames with the children, you'd better make sure you book a long break. There are so many kid-friendly attractions to squeeze into your stay, including Legoland (Windsor), Beale Adventure Park and Wyld Court Rainforest Centre. At the end of each day frazzled parents will be glad to return to this comfortable Victorian house, close to one of the prettiest stretches of the River Thames, with plenty of walking on the nearby Ridgeway and Thames paths.

Location: OS 174, GR 591806.
Great for... energetic children.
Accommodation: 49 beds: 1x2-, 1x3-, 3x4-, 4x6- and 1x8-bed rooms.
Family rooms: Yes. **Rent-a-Hostel:** No.
Classroom: Yes. **Education packages:** No.
Facilities: TV room, self-catering kitchen, dining room, showers, drying room and grounds. **Daytime access:** Restricted.

●● TANNERS HATCH ☆

off Ranmore Road, Dorking, Surrey RH5 6BE;
tanners@yha.org.uk
Tel: 0870 770 6060 Fax: 0870 770 6060

If you're looking for an archetypal country cottage to stay in, easily accessible from London, you've found it at Tanners Hatch. Within its ancient whitewashed walls, you'll relax in front of an open fire with a handful of other guests. If you're a walker, you won't have to wait long to stretch your legs as the hostel is only accessible on foot through National Trust woods. There's an extensive network of footpaths that explore the Surrey Hills Area of Outstanding Natural Beauty – don't miss a stroll to Polesden Lacey, a National Trust Regency mansion.

Location: OS 187, GR 140515.
Great for... getting away from it all.
You need to know... Tanners Hatch has outside toilet and showering facilities; there is no access for cars to the hostel; it's a good idea to bring a torch.
Accommodation: 25 beds: 1x7- and 2x9-bed rooms.
Family rooms: No. **Rent-a-Hostel:** No.
Classroom: No. **Education packages:** No.
Facilities: Lounge, self-catering kitchen, shower, cycle store and camping. **Daytime access:** Restricted. ⊗

Meals: Self-catering only.
Reception open: 17.00hrs.
Getting there: From Box Hill station turn left and follow road for 2 miles before turning left at Bagden Farm. Turn right past barn and follow signs along the pedestrian route. By car from A24, take Ashcombe Road straight over mini-roundabout and turn right at T-junction. There is no car access, so from National Trust car park, turn left, take third drive on right to Fox Cottages and follow signs.
Parking: Park at NT car park (charge).
Nearest other hostels: Holmbury St Mary 6 miles, London 23, Hindhead 25.
Public transport: BUS: Surrey Explorer 465 Teddington–Dorking (weekends only, June–Nov), alight West Humble 2.25 miles. RAIL: Box Hill and Westhumble 1.75 miles.

An archetypal country cottage with open fires: YHA Tanners Hatch.

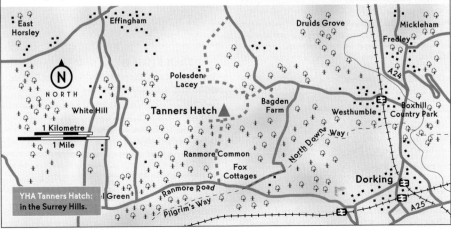

YHA Tanners Hatch: in the Surrey Hills.

● FAMILY　● CITY　● GROUP　● TRADITIONAL　● CAMPING BARN　● COASTAL　● RURAL

Meals: Breakfast, picnic lunch, evening meal.
Reception open: 17.00hrs.
Getting there: Hostel is on A329 north of M4 (exit J12), 50 metres south of traffic lights in village.
Parking: Limited.
Nearest other hostels: Ridgeway 14 miles, Oxford 19, Windsor 25.
Public transport: BUS: Thames Travel 132 Reading–Wallingford. RAIL: Goring and Streatley 1 mile.

●● TELSCOMBE ☆

Bank Cottages, Telscombe, Lewes, East Sussex BN7 3HZ; reservations@yha.org.uk
Tel: 0870 770 6062 Fax: 0870 770 6062
Bookings more than 7 days ahead: 0870 770 6113

The South Downs offer countryside lovers miles of well-drained chalk paths with uninterrupted views over rolling grassland. These 18th century cottages in the minuscule village of Telscombe are ideally placed for exploring the area. If you're looking for a few days of quiet wandering around picturesque villages, then this hostel is for you. If you feel like venturing further afield, then Virginia Woolf's house, Rodmell, is nearby.
Location: OS 198, GR 405033.
Great for... a quiet retreat into the countryside.
You need to know... parking in the village is not permitted.
Accommodation: 22 beds: 1x2- and 5x4-bed rooms.
Family rooms: No. **Rent-a-Hostel:** Yes.
Classroom: No. **Education packages:** No.
Facilities: Lounge/dining area, reading room, self-catering kitchen, showers, drying room, cycle store and grounds.
Daytime access: Restricted. ⊗
Meals: Self-catering only.
Reception open: 17.00hrs.
Getting there: On foot, the South Downs Way footpath passes 1.5 miles north of Telscombe village.
Parking: By arrangement with warden.
Nearest other hostels: Brighton 10 miles, Alfriston 11, Blackboys 17.
Public transport: BUS: Metrobus 123 Lewes Station–Newhaven (goes to hostel if booked by 16.00hrs the day before), otherwise Brighton and Hove 14/A (passes close to Brighton station), alight Telscombe Road, Peacehaven 0.75 miles. RAIL: Southease 2.5 miles, Lewes 6.5, Brighton 7. FERRY: Newhaven to Dieppe 5 miles.
NATIONALEXPRESS Newhaven 5 miles.

●● TOTLAND BAY ☆☆

Hurst Hill, Totland Bay, Isle of Wight PO39 0HD; totland@yha.org.uk
Tel: 0870 770 6070 Fax: 0870 770 6071

Lord Mountbatten opened this Youth Hostel in 1975, once a large private Victorian house. It is situated in West Wight, an Area of Outstanding Natural Beauty much of which is owned by the National Trust. You'll find a wealth of wildlife all around whether you choose to walk on the downs or along the impressive chalk cliffs. Search for sealife in rock pools, brave the chairlift to explore Alum Bay, take the obligatory snapshot of the Needles or head inland on foot to escape the summer crowds.
Location: OS 196, GR 324865.
Great for... wildlife lovers and beach bathers.
You need to know... parking is limited, although there is additional on-street parking.
Accommodation: 56 beds: 1x2-, 7x4-, 3x6- and 1x8-bed rooms.
Family rooms: Yes. **Rent-a-Hostel:** Yes.
Classroom: No. **Education packages:** No.
Facilities: Lounge, TV room, dining room, self-catering kitchen, showers, drying room, cycle store and shop.
Daytime access: Restricted. ⊗
Meals: Breakfast, picnic lunch, evening meal.
Reception open: 17.00hrs.

The multicoloured cliffs of Alum Bay, near YHA Totland Bay.

www.britainonview.com

Getting there: From roundabout in centre of Totland, take left fork past garage up Weston Road. At the end, turn left up Hurst Hill and hostel is at top of a short hill on the left.
Parking: Yes.
Nearest other hostels: Burley 17 miles (by ferry), Sandown 24.
Public transport: BUS: Southern Vectis 7/A Newport–Yarmouth–Ryde, 7B from Newport via Brighstone, 42 from Yarmouth, alight Totland War Memorial 0.25 miles.
FERRY: Yarmouth 3 miles (Wightlink, tel: 0870 582 7744), West Cowes 15 miles (Red Funnel, tel: 02380 333811).

●● TRULEIGH HILL ☆☆☆

Tottington Barn, Shoreham-by-Sea, West Sussex BN43 5FB; truleighhill@yha.org.uk
Tel: 0870 770 6078 Fax: 0870 770 6079

This hostel sits within the boundaries of the newly designated South Downs National Park and so offers a good base for walkers and cyclists. There are a variety of routes to choose from, but one of guests' favourites is the Devil's Dyke walk that leads you to an Iron Age fort. Families with youngsters will also be comfortable here, as cots, highchairs and a child-oriented menu are available.
Location: OS 198, GR 220105.
Great for... walkers wanting to explore the South Downs.
Accommodation: 56 beds: some 2–4-, mostly 6-bed rooms.
Family rooms: Yes. **Rent-a-Hostel:** Yes.

Classroom: No. **Education packages:** No.
Facilities: Lounge, self-catering kitchen, dining room, showers, drying room, cycle store, shop and grounds.
Daytime access: Restricted. 🚫
Meals: Breakfast, picnic lunch, evening meal.
Reception open: 17.00hrs.
Getting there: From the A27, take the A283 Shoreham exit and turn left at the Red Lion pub. Look for the first hostel sign on the left-hand side after approx 300 metres. From here, it's 3 miles to hostel.
Parking: Yes.
Nearest other hostels: Brighton 6 miles (by path), Arundel 16, Littlehampton 18, Holmbury 35.
Public transport: BUS: Compass 100 Pulborough Station–Henfield, alight junction of the Edburton Road then 1 mile or Brighton and Hove/Stagecoach Coastline 20/X from Shoreham-by-Sea station, alight 0.5 miles south of Upper Beeding, then 1.75 miles by bridlepath. RAIL: Shoreham-by-Sea 4 miles.
NATIONAL EXPRESS ≫ Shoreham 5 miles.

●● WINCHESTER ☆
1 Water Lane, Winchester, Hampshire SO23 0EJ;
Tel: 0870 770 6092 Fax: 0870 770 6093

This 18th century water mill is a National Trust property spanning the River Itchen. A hostel since 1931, it offers simple, unusual accommodation. Its low beams, mill machinery and an impressive lofty hall make this a unique hostel, from where you can enjoy relaxing riverside walks. It's also close to Winchester's impressive guildhall, cathedral and King Arthur's Round Table, while it's close

Charming: YHA Winchester is a former watermill.

enough to London for a day trip to the capital.
Location: OS 185, GR 486293.
Great for... sites of historic interest; day trips to London.
You need to know... the hostel offers modest facilities, a small price to pay for such historic charm.
Accommodation: 31 beds: 1x4-, 1x9- and 1x18-bed rooms.
Family rooms: No. **Rent-a-Hostel:** No.
Classroom: No. **Education packages:** No.
Facilities: Lounge/dining area, self-catering kitchen, showers, cycle store and garden. **Daytime access:** Restricted. 🚫
Meals: Breakfast only.
Reception open: 17.00hrs.
Getting there: From guildhall, walk over the Eastgate Bridge and take the first left into Water Lane (no vehicle entry). The hostel is the third door on the left.
Parking: Chesil Street car park 0.25 miles.
Nearest other hostels: Burley 23 miles, Salisbury 24, Portsmouth 25.
Public transport: BUS: Frequent from surrounding areas.
RAIL: Winchester 1 mile.
NATIONAL EXPRESS ≫ King Alfred's Statue 150 metres.

● WINDSOR ☆
Edgeworth House, Mill Lane, Windsor, Berkshire
SL4 5JE; windsor@yha.org.uk
Tel: 0870 770 6096 Fax: 0870 770 6097

Edgeworth House is set on a tranquil stretch of the Thames within easy access of the town centre. You will find plenty to keep you entertained in the historic towns of Windsor and Eton with many attractions including Windsor Castle and Eton College. Or take a day trip to central London, just 18 miles away.
Location: OS 175, GR 955770.
Great for... history enthusiasts; easy access to London.
You need to know... this hostel may close during 2003. Please enquire before planning your stay.
Accommodation: 67 beds: 1x2-, 3x4-, 1x5-, 3x6-, 1x8- and 1x22-bed rooms.
Family rooms: No. **Rent-a-Hostel:** No.
Classroom: No. **Education packages:** No.
Facilities: Lounge, TV room, self-catering kitchen, showers, drying room, cycle store, luggage store, laundry facilities, internet access and grounds. **Daytime access:** All areas.
Meals: Packed breakfast and lunch only.
Reception open: Before 10.00hrs and after 13.00hrs.
Getting there: From M4, J6 take first turning to Windsor. Take exit for Windsor/Maidenhead and at roundabout take third exit to Maidenhead. At mini-roundabout turn right into Mill Lane - no through access on Stovell Road (see map on page 175).
Parking: Cars only – it is illegal for coaches to enter Mill Lane.
Nearest other hostels: Jordans 13 miles, Bradenham 18, London 18.
Public transport: BUS: Frequent from surrounding areas.
RAIL: Windsor & Eton Central 0.75 miles, Windsor and Eton Riverside 1 mile. AIRPORT: Heathrow 10 miles.
NATIONAL EXPRESS ≫ Windsor Parish Church 0.75 miles.

The Youth Hostels of...

London

Bustling: London is one of the busiest, most exhilirating cities in the world.

Hostel Index

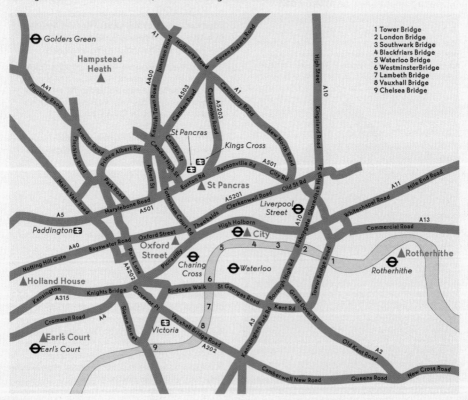

1 Tower Bridge
2 London Bridge
3 Southwark Bridge
4 Blackfriars Bridge
5 Waterloo Bridge
6 WestminsterBridge
7 Lambeth Bridge
8 Vauxhall Bridge
9 Chelsea Bridge

Golders Green
Hampstead Heath
St Pancras
Kings Cross
St Pancras
Liverpool Street
Paddington
Oxford Street
City
Charing Cross
Waterloo
Rotherhithe
Rotherhithe
Holland House
Victoria
Earl's Court
Earl's Court

For further information visit www.yha.org.uk

● FAMILY ● CITY ● GROUP ● TRADITIONAL ● CAMPING BARN ● COASTAL ● RURAL

●● CITY OF LONDON ☆

36 Carter Lane, London EC4V 5AB;
city@yha.org.uk
Tel: 0870 770 5764 Fax: 0870 770 5765

Just 100 metres from St Paul's Cathedral, this hostel is centrally located for exploring London. Formerly the choir boys' school for the Cathedral, it's in London's business area, which is both safer and quieter than many city parts. With plenty of public transport nearby, internet access and lockers, it makes a practical base for sightseers.
Location: OS 176, GR 319811.
Great for... exploring the city from a central location.
You need to know... no self-catering kitchen; no groups accepted; breakfast is included in the overnight fee.
Accommodation: 190 beds: several 1-, 2- and 3-bed rooms, mainly 4–8-bed, plus 2x9-bed and 1x12-bed options.
Family rooms: Yes. **Rent-a-Hostel:** No.
Classroom: No. **Education packages:** No.
Facilities: Reception, restaurant, TV lounge, showers, luggage room, laundry and meeting room. **Daytime access:** All areas.
Meals: Breakfast, picnic lunch, evening meal.
Reception open: 24hrs.
Getting there: At Blackfriars Underground, turn right onto Queen Victoria Street and take second left into St Andrews Hill. Carter Lane is at the top and the hostel is on the right.
Parking: NCP Queen Victoria Street.
Nearest other hostels: Oxford Street 2 miles, Rotherhithe 3, Earl's Court 5.
Public transport: LONDON TRANSPORT: Frequent services. UNDERGROUND: Blackfriars 0.25 miles (Circle and District), St Paul's (Central Line) 0.25, City Thameslink 0.25, Liverpool Street 1.
NATIONAL EXPRESS Victoria Coach Station 3.25 miles.

● EARL'S COURT ☆☆

38 Bolton Gardens, London SW5 0AQ;
earlscourt@yha.org.uk
Tel: 0870 770 5804 Fax: 0870 770 5805

In the heart of a young, international area full of shops, cafés, restaurants and bars, this hostel buzzes with action. Five minutes' walk from Earl's Court and Olympia exhibition centres, it's also handy for access to Heathrow Airport. Visit the Kensington Museums, including the Science Museum and the Victoria and Albert Museum and, after a busy day, relax in the small courtyard garden.
Location: OS 176, GR 258783.
Great for... a busy city break.
Accommodation: 159 beds: mainly 6–10-bed rooms, plus some 2-, 3- and 4-bed options.
Family rooms: Yes. **Rent-a-Hostel:** No.
Classroom: No. **Education packages:** No.
Facilities: Reception, TV lounge, dining room, self-catering kitchen, showers, luggage store, laundry room, cycle store and garden.
Daytime access: All areas.
Meals: Packed continental breakfast available at an additional cost.
Reception open: 24hrs.

The Natural History Museum near YHA Holland House.

Getting there: Leave Earl's Court Underground station by Earl's Court Road exit. Turn right outside station and take fifth street on left (Bolton Gardens).
Parking: On Warwick Road (0.75 miles).
Nearest other hostels: Holland House 1 mile, Oxford Street 3, City of London 5.
Public transport: LONDON TRANSPORT: Frequent services (tel: 020 7222 1234). UNDERGROUND: Earl's Court (District and Piccadilly). RAIL: Kensington Olympia 1 mile.
NATIONAL EXPRESS Earl's Court Underground 0.25 miles.

HOSTEL MANAGERS CHOOSE...

LONDON'S BEST FREE ATTRACTIONS

Wren's churches YHA City of London: "Within a 20-minute walk of the hostel you'll find 23 Wren-designed churches, built after the Great Fire of 1666. A monument to the fire on London Bridge has great views from the observation gallery."

Museum of London YHA City of London: "A 15-minute walk from the hostel, it charts the history of the capital through the ages."

Speaker's Corner, Hyde Park YHA Rotherhithe: "A great place to watch people ranting and raving. Best on a Sunday afternoon."

The Old Bailey YHA Rotherhithe: "Arrive early to get a seat in the public gallery at the Central Criminal Court. No under-14s, cameras, video equipment or mobile phones are allowed."

Changing of the guard YHA Rotherhithe: "Daily at Buckingham Palace at 11am, mid-April to end of July, and on alternate days at 11.30am the rest of the year. When it gets busy in summer, I tell people to try the changing of the Mounted Guard in Whitehall instead."

HMS Belfast YHA Rotherhithe: "A moored Second World War cruiser free to under-16s."

● FAMILY ● CITY ● GROUP ● TRADITIONAL ● CAMPING BARN ● COASTAL ● RURAL

Oasis: YHA Hampstead Heath has its own enclosed garden.

●● HAMPSTEAD HEATH ☆☆☆

4 Wellgarth Road, Golders Green, London
NW11 7HR; hampstead@yha.org.uk
Tel: 0870 770 5846 Fax: 0870 770 5847

Enjoy a night in this busy hostel which has an enclosed garden and is a short stroll from the heath, where woods and grassland create a quiet oasis of countryside. Climb Parliament Hill for a lofty view of London or visit nearby Golders Hill park (the children will love the goats). Just don't forget that the hustle and bustle of central London is just a 20-minute tube ride away.

Location: OS 176, GR 258973.
Great for... groups who don't want to stay in the centre of London.
You need to know... breakfast is included in the overnight fee.
Accommodation: 199 beds: some 2- and 3-bed rooms, mostly 4–6-bed rooms, plus 1x7- and 1x8-bed options. Also one ground floor room specifically designed for people with disabilities.
Family rooms: Yes. **Rent-a-Hostel:** No.
Classroom: No. **Education packages:** Yes.
Facilities: Lounges with TV and video games, reception, showers, luggage room and laundry facilities. Hot and cold drinks machine, self-catering kitchen, garden and pergola area.
Daytime access: All areas.
Meals: Breakfast, picnic lunch, evening meal.
Reception open: 24hrs.
Getting there: From the bus station, turn left onto North End Road. Take first left (Wellgarth Road) and entrance is past car park on right.
Parking: Small car park. Restrictions apply on street between 11.00hrs and 12.00hrs, Mon–Fri.
Nearest other hostels: St Pancras 2 miles, City of London 4, Holland House 5, Oxford Street 7.

Public transport: LONDON TRANSPORT: Frequent services.
BUS: 268/210 first stop, night bus N13/N5, 13/82 City–Golders Green.
UNDERGROUND: Golders Green 0.5 miles, Hampstead Heath 1.5.
[NATIONAL EXPRESS] Golders Green Bus station 0.5 miles.

●● HOLLAND HOUSE ☆☆☆

Holland Walk, Kensington, London W8 7QU;
hollandhouse@yha.org.uk
Tel: 0870 770 5866 Fax: 0870 770 5867

Feel the history in the heart of elegant Holland Park. One wing of the hostel is a former Jacobean mansion, built in 1607 for Sir Walter Cope, Chancellor of the Exchequer for James I. In the 19th century, Lady Holland had a salon here, attended by such famous names as Sheridan, Sir Walter Scott, Lord Byron, Wordsworth and Dickens. It now offers large, comfortable rooms that overlook the park and is adjacent to the open air theatre. Just off Kensington High Street, the Royal Albert Hall, Kensington Palace and the main museums are all within walking distance.

Location: OS 176, GR 249797.
Great for... visiting the museums.
You need to know... breakfast is included in the overnight fee; use the side gate entrance when park gates are locked at night.
Accommodation: 201 beds: a few 6–8-bed rooms, mostly 12–20-bed rooms.
Family rooms: No. **Rent-a-Hostel:** No.
Classroom: Yes. **Education packages:** Yes.
Facilities: Reception, lounge, TV room, games room, self-catering kitchen, showers, luggage store, lockers, internet and email access, laundry facilities and grounds. **Daytime access:** All areas.
Meals: Breakfast, lunch menu, evening meal.
Reception open: 24hrs.
Getting there: Turn left out of High Street Kensington Station, head down High Street to Holland Park entrance. The hostel is at the top of walkway inside park. If arriving after park gate is closed (16.00hrs in winter, 20.00hrs in summer), please turn right off High Street Kensington into Phillimore Gardens then left into Duchess of Bedfordshire where signs point you to side entrance. Ring bell.

The Royal Albert Hall, near YHA Holland House.

● FAMILY ● CITY ● GROUP ● TRADITIONAL ● CAMPING BARN ● COASTAL ● RURAL

Parking: NCP, 15 minutes' walk. Drop off/pick up at corner of Duchess of Bedford Walk and Phillimore Gdns. No parking at hostel.
Nearest other hostels: Earl's Court 1 mile, City of London 5, Oxford Street 3.
Public transport: LONDON TRANSPORT: Frequent services. UNDERGROUND: Holland Park (Central Line) 0.25 miles, High Street Kensington (Circle and District Lines) 0.25. RAIL: Kensington Olympia 0.5 miles.
NATIONALEXPRESS» Hammersmith Bridge Road 1 mile.

● OXFORD STREET ☆☆
14 Noel Street, London W1F 8GJ;
oxfordst@yha.org.uk
Tel: 0870 770 5984 Fax: 0870 770 5985

Oxford Street is where the action is. In the middle of Soho, you can shop 'til you drop in Britain's most famous shopping street. There are pubs and clubs aplenty and the hostel is within walking distance of many theatres. If you're looking for a quiet break, don't choose this busy, vibrant hostel!
Location: OS 176, GR 294812.
Great for... shoppers, clubbers and theatre goers.
You need to know... it's self-catering accommodation only.
Accommodation: 75 beds: all 2-, 3- and 4-bed rooms.
Family rooms: No. **Rent-a-Hostel:** No.
Classroom: No. **Education packages:** No.
Facilities: Lounge with TV, self-catering kitchen, laundry facilities,

HOSTEL MANAGERS CHOOSE...
THE BEST PARKS

Regent's Park "London's largest park, and one of its most beautiful. The most spectacular areas are Cumberland Terrace and Chester Terrace, which boasts the longest unbroken façade."

Green Park "Although the least grand of the central London parks, I like Green Park. It offers a welcome respite from the noise of the city (and those shopping trips!). Relax in the shade of its tree-lined avenues."

St James's Park "Referred to as the Queen's Front Garden (a step up from most people's front gardens!), this is the oldest of the royal parks, dating from the 16th century. Children will love it here, especially the lake full of pelicans."

Hyde Park "See the sunken garden, the Orangery where you can take tea, and the free-to-enter Serpentine Art Gallery. Kids will enjoy puppet shows in summer, playgrounds and a boating lake."

Kensington Gardens "This is an elegant place for a quiet stroll with tree-lined avenues and distant views of Kensington Palace. It's at its best in summer, when the flowerbeds are full."
(All recommended by YHA Rotherhithe)

lockers and showers. **Daytime access:** All areas.
Meals: Packed breakfast and self-catering only.
Reception open: 24hrs.
Getting there: Leave Oxford Circus Station by Exit 8. Turn left into Argyle Street, at end turn left into Great Marlborough Street and go straight ahead until intersection with Poland Street. There Great Marlborough Street changes into Noel Street and the hostel is next to a mural on the wall.
Parking: No.
Nearest other hostels: St Pancras 1.5 miles, City of London 2, Earl's Court 3, Holland House 3.
Public transport: LONDON TRANSPORT: Frequent services. UNDERGROUND: Oxford Circus, Tottenham Court Rd (Central Line) both 0.25 miles. RAIL: Charing Cross 0.75 miles, Euston 1, Kings Cross 1, Waterloo 1.
NATIONALEXPRESS» Marylebone, Baker Street, Gloucester Place, all 0.5 miles.

Lunch at Covent Garden, near YHA Oxford Street.

●● ROTHERHITHE ☆☆
20 Salter Road, London SE16 5PR;
rotherhithe@yha.org.uk
Tel: 0870 770 6010 Fax: 0870 770 6011

Anyone with children will know how tiring a city visit can be for both parents and youngsters. This modern, purpose-built hostel in the newly developed Docklands area of London, on the south bank of the River Thames, offers an answer. It's a comfortable base with private bathrooms and plenty of child-friendly facilities – travel cots and high chairs are available for hire and there is a free children's library and toy box on site, along with over 30 board games. With close public transport stops offering easy access to Greenwich Meridian Observatory and other South Bank attractions, it makes for a stress-free city break.
Location: OS 176, GR 357804.
Great for... families with young children.
You need to know... with 320 beds, it's a busy hostel popular with groups; breakfast is included in the overnight fee.
Accommodation: 320 beds: some 2-, 4- and 6-bed rooms, plus 3x10-bed rooms, all en-suite.

FAMILY   CITY ● GROUP ● TRADITIONAL ● CAMPING BARN ○ COASTAL ○ RURAL

Family rooms: Yes. **Rent-a-Hostel:** No.
Classroom: Yes. **Education packages:** No.
Facilities: Reception, TV lounge, self-catering kitchen, laundry room, cycle store/workshop, licensed bar with pool table, showers, conference rooms, library, café/bar, luggage store.
Daytime access: All areas.
Meals: Breakfast, picnic lunch, evening meal.
Reception open: 24hrs.
Getting there: From Rotherhithe Underground, turn left out of only exit, walk 600 metres and hostel is on left. From Canada Water station, exit beside Canada Water (keep water on right) and follow canal (left of Decathalon) to Salter Rd then cross pedestrian crossing and turn right. Hostel is on your left after 50 metres. From London Bridge Underground, exit and cross road opposite to London Dungeon and catch 381 bus to hostel. From Waterloo station, exit onto York Road and catch 381 bus to the hostel.
Parking: On-street parking. Coaches free (500 metres).
Nearest other hostels: City of London 3 miles, Oxford Street 5, Earl's Court 6.
Public transport: BUS: 381 (Waterloo St–Peckham), N381 (Trafalgar Square–Peckham), 225 (Lewisham–Bermondsey), 395 (Limehouse–Canada Water). UNDERGROUND: Rotherhithe (East London Line) 300 metres, Canada Water (Jubilee Line) 600 metres. RAIL: London Bridge 1.5 miles, Waterloo 3.
[NATIONALEXPRESS] Victoria Coach Station 5 miles.

●● ST PANCRAS ☆☆☆

79-81 Euston Road, London NW1 2QS;
stpancras@yha.org.uk
Tel: 0870 770 6044 Fax: 0870 770 6045

If you're just stopping for a night mid-trip, then St Pancras is the most convenient hostel in London. Opposite St Pancras station and a short walk from Euston and Kings Cross, it's well situated in terms of access to transport links. If you're looking to stay longer, then lively Camden Town is only a 10-minute walk away. Premium rooms are available, offering en-suite, TV and tea/coffee making facilities.
Location: OS 176, GR 300828.
Great for... a comfortable night mid-trip or long-term stay for exploring London.
You need to know... there's no parking; breakfast is included in the overnight price; no groups (individuals and families only).
Accommodation: 152 beds: 10x2-, 1x3-, 18x4-, 3x5-bed rooms, plus 7x6-bed rooms, mostly en-suite.
Family rooms: Yes. **Rent-a-Hostel:** No.
Classroom: No. **Education packages:** No.
Facilities: Lounge with TV and games area, self-catering kitchen, dining room, cycle store, luggage store, lockers and laundry facilities. **Daytime access:** All areas.
Meals: Breakfast, picnic lunch and evening meal available.
Reception open: 24hrs.
Getting there: From King's Cross/St Pancras stations, turn right onto Euston Road, cross Judd Street and hostel is second building on left-hand side. From Euston station turn left onto Euston Road and the hostel is opposite the British Library.
Parking: 24-hour NCP car park 15-minute walk away.

Nearest other hostels: City of London 1 mile, Oxford Street 1.5, Hampstead Heath 2.
Public transport: BUS: Frequent from surrounding areas. UNDERGROUND: King's Cross, Euston. RAIL: King's Cross and St Pancras only minutes away on foot, Euston 0.25 miles.
[NATIONALEXPRESS] Victoria coach station 3.5 miles.

Find unique bargains at lively Camden Market, near YHA St Pancras.

Go! *Find your hostel*

Use these street maps to locate the 21 hostels we have identified as particularly difficult to find.

Bath

From London Road, follow signs to University and American Museum. From the south-west, follow A36 to roundabout on Pulteney Road.

www.britainonview.com

Beverley Friary

Follow signs to Minster and Friary. Turn down Friar's Lane next to Minster and follow to end of lane to car park.

Brighton

From Patcham village Co-op, follow Old London Road round to left past Post Office to London Road. Hostel is opposite Black Lion pub. By road, hostel is 3 miles north of Brighton city centre on London Road (A23) adjacent to A23/A27 junction.

Bristol

From London or South Wales, exit M4 at J19, then take M32. From Birmingham or South West, exit M5 at J18, then A4.

Broadstairs

From town centre and beach, head uphill along High Street, under railway bridge and left at traffic lights. The hostel is the first building after the row of shops.

For more information visit www.yha.org.uk

Hostel directions

Cambridge

From city centre, follow signs to the railway station. Take last left turning (at hostel sign) before the railway station.

Canterbury

Follow signs for Dover. The hostel is on the A2050, 1.5 miles from the centre.

Chester

The hostel is southwest of city centre on A5104 (signposted to Saltney), 350 metres from traffic lights on right.

Exeter

From M5, J30, follow signs for city centre. Turn right at Countess Wear roundabout, then first left into School Lane. From A379, follow signs for Topsham, turn left at Countess Wear roundabout then left into School Lane. From centre follow signs for Topsham.

Lincoln

On foot from the train station turn right onto St Mary's Street. Continue to Oxford Street. Go under flyover and up steps on the right. Go along Canwick Road and over traffic lights. When the cemetery is on your left, South Park is on your right.

Liverpool

From Lime Street station follow signs for Albert Dock. Turn left onto main dock road (called Wapping). Hostel is on left after Baltic Fleet pub. From James Street station turn right then left onto Wapping, past Albert Dock on right – hostel is on left after Baltic Fleet pub.

Manchester

From bus station and Piccadilly train station, follow signs for Castlefield/ Museum of Science and Industry (MSI); or take Metrolink to the G-Mex station. By car, follow signs for Castlefield/MSI. Hostel is opposite MSI, behind Castlefield Hotel.

Newcastle

From the metro (underground) by foot, it's a 5-minute walk on left side of Jesmond Road East (A1058). By car, access the A1058 (Jesmond Road) from central motorway (A167M), which is left from the northwest or right from the south.

Ninebanks

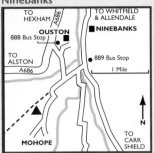

Signposted from A686 south of Whitfield. Hostel is at Mohope, signposted from Ninebanks hamlet.

Oxford

From the station turn right and go under bridge. Hostel is on the right immediately behind the railway station.

Portsmouth

From Cosham police station, take Medina Road, then seventh turning on the right, Old Wymering Lane. The hostel is opposite the church entrance.

Salisbury

Motorists, follow A36 signposts. Follow brown signs on A36 by Salisbury college roundabout. On foot, walk east from tourist information centre following black footpath signs, leading into Milford Street and up hill.

Scarborough

From Scarborough, follow signs to North Bay attractions, then A165 to Whitby. Hostel is 2 miles north of town centre (there is a very sharp turn immediately after bridge – drive past and turn in the layby).

Stratford-upon-Avon

From Stratford-upon-Avon, at Clopton Bridge take Wellesbourne Road. Hostel is 1.5 miles on left. From M40, exit J15 and take A429 south, follow signs to Charlecote Park. Turn right onto the B4086 and hostel is 1.5 miles on right.

Windsor

From M4, J6, take first turning to Windsor. Take exit for Windsor/Maidenhead and at roundabout take third exit to Maidenhead. At mini roundabout turn right into Mill Lane (no through access on Stovell Road).

York

From the Minster, take A19 to Clifton Green, turning left at Old Grey Mare pub into Water End. Hostel is on the right. From ring road, take A19 towards the city, turning right into Water End at the second set of traffic lights.

To make a booking visit www.yha.org.uk

Youth Hostels Index

Hostel Listings

176

Hostel Listings

Camping Barn Listings

Terms and Conditions

Individuals and families
For bookings up to the value of £100, you will be asked to make full payment within seven days of booking for your stay.

For bookings in excess of £100, you will be asked to pay a minimum £100 deposit. The balance of your stay will then be due before or on arrival.

For Youth Hostels in London, or other areas where there is a particularly high demand for accommodation, you will be asked to pay in full for your stay regardless of cost.

Reservations made less than seven days in advance, without payment, will be held until 18.00hrs unless an alternative time has been agreed.

Cancellation
Please let the Youth Hostel know as soon as you can if you have to cancel your visit – even if it is at the last minute someone else may be able to use the accommodation.

In mountainous and remote areas it is vital that you contact the Youth Hostel if you decide not to take up your reservation, otherwise the police or mountain rescue teams may be called out to look for you.

Refunds
Individual and family members of YHA (England and Wales) and other associations within the International Youth Hostel Federation (IYHF) who have booked accommodation and meals are covered by YHA's cancellation refund package.

Under this scheme YHA will refund members in respect of loss of charges paid to YHA for accommodation and meals not taken up where the member is forced to cancel or curtail his or her journey, providing three days' notice of cancellation has been given to the Youth Hostel concerned.

Every claim is subject to an administration fee of £5.

We recommend, for your own peace of mind, you hold a suitable travel insurance policy, including cancellation insurance when you travel.

To apply for a refund, complete an application form available from Youth Hostels or call YHA Customer Services on 0870 770 8868. The form together with all supporting documentation (please include appropriate copies of booking forms, invoices and receipts as well as any relevant medical certificates) should be sent to YHA National Accounts, PO Box 30, Trevelyan House, Dimple Road, Matlock, Derbyshire, DE4 3JX.

Groups
For those making group bookings a cancellation refund package is available. This is strongly recommended and available for a nominal charge. See the reverse of the YHA Group Booking Form for full details, available from Youth Hostels or contact our Group Reservations Department on 0870 770 6117.

Activity holidays, walking holidays, camping barns and Rent-a-hostel
Terms and conditions for each of these services or products are different. Details are contained on the relevant booking forms which will be supplied to you when making an enquiry or booking.

For more information visit www.yha.org.uk